HEALTH & SAFETY IN PRACTICE

Safety Technology

Jeremy Stranks

MSc, FCIEH, FIOSH, RSP

PITMAN
PUBLISHING

London · Hong Kong · Johannesburg · Melbourne ·
Singapore · Washington DC

PITMAN PUBLISHING
128 Long Acre, London WC2E 9AN
Tel: +44 (0)171 447 2000
Fax: +44 (0)171 240 5771

A Division of Pearson Professional Limited

First published in Great Britain 1996

© Jeremy Stranks 1996

British Library Cataloguing in Publication Data
A CIP catalogue record for this book can be obtained from the British Library.

ISBN 0 273 62223 4

10 9 8 7 6 5 4 3 2 1

Typeset by Northern Phototypesetting Co Ltd, Bolton
Printed and bound in Great Britain by Bell & Bain Ltd, Glasgow

The Publishers' policy is to use paper manufactured from sustainable forests.

£17)

Safety
Technology

Contents

Preface

Safety technology covers a wide range of topics, each of which is a separate area of study in its own right. Inevitably the subject is tied up in protective legislation going back over the last century and, to a great extent, has been regulated by statutes and regulations.

As a result of recent European-driven legislation, much of the older legislation has gone, resulting in a totally new approach to the subject based on sound health and safety management systems, risk assessment and the need for organisations to develop and implement internally-set objectives and standards for, for instance, fire prevention and control, the acquisition of work equipment and hazardous processes.

Aspects of safety technology feature in many courses, including those run under the auspices of the National Examination Board in Occupational Safety and Health (NEBOSH). However, many people, such as designers, engineers, architects, planners, building contractors and production managers, now need to be more aware of the safety technology aspects of their disciplines with a view to reducing the risks to all those who may be affected by their designs, decisions and work activities.

This fifth 'Guide to Health and Safety in Practice', whilst directed at candidates studying for NEBOSH examinations, has also been written with these other groups in mind.

Jeremy Stranks
1996

List of abbreviations

ac	Alternating current
ACOP	Approved Code of Practice
BATNEEC	Best available techniques not entailing excessive costs
BPEO	Best practicable environmental option
BS	British Standard
CHIP	Chemicals (Hazard Information and Packaging for Supply) Regulations 1994
CHP	Combined Health and Power
CIMAH	Control of Industrial Major Accidents Hazards Regulations 1984
cl	Clause
CONDAM	Construction (Design and Management) Regulations 1994
CONIAC	Construction Industry Advisory Committee
COSHH	Control of Substances Hazardous to Health Regulations 1994
dc	Direct current
EPA	Environmental Protection Act 1990
FA	Factories Act 1961
FPA	Fire Precautions Act 1971
FSSPSA	Fire Safety and Safety of Places of Sport Act 1987
GMO	Genetically modified organism
HFL	Highly flammable liquid
HMIP	Her Majesty's Inspectorate of Pollution
HMSO	Her Majesty's Stationery Office
HSC	Health and Safety Commission
HSE	Health and Safety Executive
HSWA	Health and Safety at Work etc. Act 1974
IEE	Institution of Electrical Engineers
IPC	Integrated Pollution Control
LEV	Local exhaust ventilation
LPG	Liquefied petroleum gas
MEL	Maximum exposure limit
MHOR	Manual Handling Operations Regulations 1992
MHSWR	Management of Health and Safety at Work Regulations 1992
NPA	National Parks Authority
NRA	National Rivers Authority
OES	Occupational exposure standard
PPE	Personal protective equipment
PSTGCR	Pressure Systems and Transportable Gas Containers Regulations 1989

PUWER	Provisions and Use of Work Equipment Regulations 1992
RIDDOR	Reporting of Injuries, Diseases and Dangerous Occurrences Regulations 1985
RPE	Respiratory protective equipment
RSA	Radioactive Substances Act 1960
SI	Statutory Instrument
SSGA	Safety of Sports Grounds Act 1975
SWG	Standard wire gauge
SWL	Safe working load
TGC	Transportable gas container
WHSWR	Workplace (Health, Safety and Welfare) Regulations 1992
WRA	Waste Regulation Authority

Integrity of materials

Failures of materials, singly, and when integrated as part of a structure or a machine, have been both the direct and indirect causes of a number of disaster situations resulting in fatal and serious injuries, damage to property, machinery and services. Such incidents create substantial direct and indirect losses to an organisation, its employees and members of the public affected by the incident. A typical example was the crane accident at Brent Cross, Hendon in June 1964, the circumstances of which will be considered later in this chapter.

STRENGTHS OF MATERIALS

All solid materials, such as steel, timber, bricks, concrete and plastics, are subject to forces or loading which may take a number of forms. The effect of these forces may result in some form of deformation of the material, such as bending, cracking, distortion and compression. Materials are also subject to expansion and contraction which can affect their strength. When a change in a solid material occurs as a result of an external force, that material is said to be under **stress** due to the tendency of the material to resist that external force.

STRESS

Where, for instance, a metal bar is subjected to a pulling force along its axis, as in Figure 1.1, it is under tensile stress or **tension**. At any cross section (X–X) this stress will be uniformly spread over the cross-sectional area as shown by the arrows.

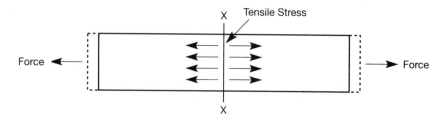

FIG 1.1   Distribution of stress over a section

The amount of stress acting at each unit is the **intensity of stress**, f, and the **total stress** at the section is the intensity of stress multiplied by the area over which it acts, that is, the cross-sectional area, A. The total stress is equal to the total applied force, W. Thus:

$$W = f \times A, \quad A = \frac{W}{f} \quad \text{and } f = \frac{W}{A}$$

$$\text{stress} = \frac{\text{load}}{\text{cross-sectional area}} \quad \text{newtons/sq. metre}$$

The same principle applies in the case of a material subjected to a force causing **compression**. The material is under compressive stress.

In each case, when the force is continued in its application, the material will fail. In the first case, the bar will stretch and ultimately fail by rupturing. In the second case, the material will shorten and eventually fail by crushing. The minimum applied force necessary to cause failure of the material is the **ultimate load**, and the intensity of stress at the point of failure is the **ultimate stress**. Tension and compression are classed as simple stresses.

Shear stress is another form of stress to which materials can be subjected. This occurs when forces act either in opposite directions or towards each other, but not in the same line of action. The physical effect of this action is a sliding effect, one part passing over another part.

$$\text{shear stress} = \frac{\text{applied force}}{\text{cross section of area in shear}}$$

Compound stresses

These are stresses other than tension and compression and direct shear. The most common compound stresses are, **torsional stress**, which is produced by twisting and is a form of shear stress, and **transverse stress**, which arises as a result of bending.

Torsional stress

This can arise in certain types of machinery. An example could be a steel shaft free to rotate in bearings and carrying a heavy flywheel or similar load. The whole is rotated by a turning force applied to the shaft. In overcoming the inertia of the flywheel the turning force tends to twist the shaft. Where the force is applied suddenly, the shaft could fracture by twisting before the flywheel has commenced motion.

Transverse stress

Transverse stress is created when a material is subjected to forces which cause it to bend. This may arise in a structure through overloading, whereby the supporting beams deflect downwards. The upper face of the supporting beam becomes concave and the under face, convex. The concave face of the beam has become shorter, whereas the convex face has increased in length.

Transverse stress is thus a combination of tension and compression produced at the same time by the action of forces on a body.

STRAIN

When a steel bar is subjected to tensile stress, it stretches. Similarly, when a wood block is compressed, it reduces in size. In both cases, the material has gone through some form of elongation or shortening per unit length. Strain is therefore a ratio of the extension/compression to the original length. Thus:

$$\text{strain} = \frac{\text{elongation (or shortening)}}{\text{original length}} \qquad \text{no units}$$

Strain may be expressed as a change in length per unit length of a material. Similarly, **shear strain** is expressed by the amount of deformation in a one part of a body, compared with another part that has not moved.

$$\text{shear strain} = \frac{\text{deformation}}{\text{distance between the deformed layer and static layer}} \qquad \text{no units}$$

ELASTICITY OF MATERIALS

Elasticity is the property of a material which permits strain to disappear on the removal of stress. With most materials, the strain resulting from stress, up to a certain point, disappears when the stress is released, the material returning to its exact original length. If a greater load is applied and a higher stress produced, the body does not quite return to its former length. It finishes longer, in the case of tension, than originally; in other words, the strain does not disappear. This is a permanent strain called **permanent set**, and the stress at which material begins to 'flow', that is, when the body would just fail to regain its original length, is called the **elastic limit**.

Elastic limit

All materials have a certain elastic limit. **Ductile materials**, such as wrought iron and mild steel are elastic only up to a point half way to breaking point. They then become plastic and, in effect, flow, for some time before fractures takes place. The total increase in length is around 20–25 per cent. Timber has this plastic stage when under compression but not under tension. Other substances are said to be **brittle**. For instance, glass is one of the most elastic materials, its elasticity being perfect almost to the point of fracture. Its elongation is minimal due to this brittle property. Similarly cast iron, brick, concrete and stone are brittle, not being perfectly elastic at any level of stress.

Hooke's Law and Young's Modulus of Elasticity

Hooke's Law states that within the elastic limit of a material, stress is proportional to strain.

For any material the relationship between stress and strain can be expressed as:

stress = strain x a constant

The constant is different for different materials and is the force required to stretch a bar of the material of unit sectional area to twice its original length, assuming the material to be perfectly elastic, that is, assuming this amount of strain to be possible within its elastic limit. This constant is known as **Young's Modulus** or the **Modulus of Elasticity**, symbol E. Thus:

$$E = \frac{stress}{strain}$$

$$stress = E \times strain$$

$$strain = \frac{stress}{E}$$

The value of Young's Modulus varies, for the same material, with the type of stress, but for tension and compression its values are approximately identical.

Ultimate tensile stress (ultimate tensile strength)

This is the stress produced in a test piece by the maximum applied force.

$$\textbf{ultimate tensile strength} = \frac{\textbf{maximum applied force}}{\textbf{original cross-sectional area}} \text{ newtons/sq.metre}$$

Tensile test

There are three stages of the tensile test, which is the ultimate test for determining ductility on a purely axial basis, namely the **elastic region**, the **plastic region** and fracture or **ductile failure**. In this test a standard 2" gauge steel test piece is used (see Figure 1.2).

Stress in a tensile test is plotted as a nominal stress of the original area. The material behaves in an elastic manner until, at approximately 280 MNm, the **Yield Stress** is reached. Up to this point the atoms will return to their original position. After Yield Stress is reached, the material goes through a **plastic stage**, where the material will not return to its original shape. This plastic stage consists of the movement of atoms away from their original positions and not returning to same, roughly at angles of 45° from the applied load. At certain points during the plastic process, there will be **dislocations** caused by the absence of atoms at several points. All the dislocations cluster on the grain boundaries causing, in effect, the material to **work harden** and increase in strength. The top of the curve formed will be the **Ultimate Tensile Stress**. **Necking** is caused at the point where the failure takes place followed by fracture. The final failure is a **ductile failure** associated with shear stresses, which cause the material to shear due to a series of minor failures roughly at 45°, the planes sliding across each other.

1

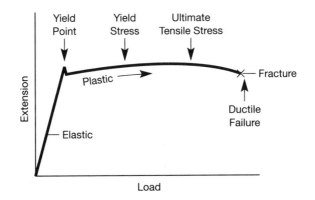

FIG 1.2   The relationship between load and extension of a steel test piece

Ductility is based on a percentage elongation, percentage reduction in cross-sectional area, ultimate tensile stress and yield stress, the last two being the most important.

Proof stress

This is the amount of stress produced by a certain amount of permanent extension.

Factor of safety

In the design of safe structures, using materials such as steel, concrete, timber, brickwork and plastics, the principal objective is to ensure a safe structure designed to meet the service conditions to which it will be exposed. Materials must not, therefore, be stressed to the point of failure or to a point close to same. On this basis it is necessary to adopt working or safe stresses, corresponding to working or safe loads. These are the stresses and loads worked to in the design of structural work, such as a bridge. They are based on the ultimate stresses and loads by adopting a suitable fraction of the known ultimate values. This fraction is the **factor of safety**. Thus:

$$\text{factor of safety} = \frac{\text{ultimate stress}}{\text{working stress}}$$

The factor of safety for different materials varies immensely. Much will depend upon a material's established reliability, the higher the factor of safety, the lower the reliability of the material. For instance, mild steel, because of its established reliability, would have a lower factor of safety than, for instance, certain types of timber. Timber, by virtue of its structure and its potential for cracking, shrinkage, rotting and poor resistance to weather conditions, has limited load bearing properties. Much will depend upon the nature of the timber, for instance, whether a hardwood or a softwood.

Again, certain materials are better adapted to resist tension than compression and vice versa. Concrete, for instance, will withstand extensive compressive stresses, but is weak under tension. Steel is better under tension than compression.

Design stress

A structural member should never be subjected to a stress that could cause it to fail under an identified working load. Similarly, it should never be so stressed to the extent that it becomes plastic, which causes added stress to other parts of a structure which may incorporate that member. Calculation of design stress is, therefore, an important feature of the design of structures, such as bridges, multi-storey buildings and lifting appliances. The design stress must be well within the elastic limit which would indicate the need for a safety factor to be incorporated in any design calculation. Thus:

$$\text{design stress} = \frac{\text{ultimate tensile strength}}{\text{factor of safety}}$$

Depending on the significance of a particular member, the factor of safety may vary from four to 10.

BENDING MOMENTS

These are defined as the sum of the moments along a beam of all the vertical forces acting to one side of a point about that point. In situations where a beam is supported at one end, as with a cantilever, or at both ends, it will always bend about the supports.

The Principle of Moments

A **moment** is a turning effect created by a force around a point. The Principle of Moments states that when a body is in equilibrium under the action of any number of forces acting in a plane, the sum of the moments of those forces about any point in the plane is zero. The 'sum' is the algebraic sum, moments rotating in a clockwise direction being positive, and those rotating in an anti-clockwise direction, negative.

Calculation of Bending Moments

1. Cantilevers

In the cantilever shown in Figure 1.3, the bending moment about point A is the product of the force applied multiplied by the distance from the load to point A.

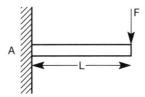

FIG 1.3   Bending moments in a cantilever

Thus the moment about A, **M(A) = F x L**

2. Beams supported at both ends

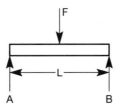

FIG 1.4 Bending moments in a beam supported at both ends

In the supported beam shown in Figure 1.4, the bending moment at B for the left-hand side of the beam is:

$$M(B) = R(A) \times \frac{L}{2}$$

However, the reactions R(A) and R(C) are equal as F is supported at the centre of the beam. Thus:

R(A) = half F

Therefore: $M(B) = \frac{F}{2} \times \frac{L}{2} = \frac{FL}{4}$

FRACTURE MECHANICS

Metals and other materials may fail for a number of reasons. All materials contain various forms of defect, in particular, cracks. These defects may not necessarily be so significant as to cause failure, however.

Fracture mechanics is a branch of engineering science concerned with the study of material failures and factors which determine the probability of catastrophic failure of various structural components. The results of these studies provide information which can be incorporated in the design of a wide range of structures, lifting appliances and machinery. As such, fracture mechanics is an important feature of the study of machinery reliability and in the specification of machinery and plant with a view to preventing future failure.

The purpose or objectives of fracture mechanics are:

- to ensure effective design against brittle fracture, taking account of defects in materials
- to predict fatigue crack growth and
- to predict stress corrosion growth.

All these are directly related in the assessment of the strength of a component as to its mechanical properties, size and shape. Particular attention is paid to assessing the significance of defects in terms of the potential for brittle fracture and metal fatigue. (See **Machinery Reliability** below.)

MACHINERY RELIABILITY

The relative reliability of machinery is directly connected with the forces involved, such as the varying loads and pressures to which the machinery is subjected during normal service conditions and the strength of materials as constructed or fabricated. Failures of machinery and structures are commonly associated with failure of individual components or assemblies of components, that is individual members constructed of various metals, such as high and low carbon steels, mild steel, aluminium, copper, brass, etc.

Metal failure can result from a number of causes. These include ductile failure, brittle fracture, creep, the effects of high temperature, metal fatigue, corrosion and wear.

Ductile failure

This form of failure occurs when a metal is stretched to the point where the yield stress has been exceeded over a large area. Fundamentally, the metal reaches the plastic stage and failure by **ductile fracture** takes place. A classic example is where a crane is overloaded, particularly through 'snatching' a load which was not directly below the jib of the crane. (In extreme cases, this could result in the crane overturning.)

Brittle fracture

This form of failure is commonly the cause of pressure vessel explosions. In a steam boiler, it can occur very suddenly resulting in a rapid energy release from the boiler. Brittle fracture can also occur in lifting appliances, such as cranes, whereby a load comes crashing to the ground without any warning. There are a number of causes of brittle fracture.

Brittle materials

Some materials, such as cast iron, are inherently brittle. Other materials may become brittle as a result of exposure to heat, perhaps from welding activities. It is quite common for structures to collapse as a result of brittle fracture around welded parts.

Low temperature

The effects of very low temperatures can bring about a change in the structure of materials whereby they become embrittled. Pressure vessels are particularly susceptible to brittle fracture at low temperatures.

Impact or shock loading

Where a material is subject to impacts or sudden loading this produces a high rate of stress formation within the metal's structure. In some cases, this stress will be dissipated into the surrounding structure. However, where such dissipation does not take place, brittle fracture can occur.

Fabrication of structures

In certain cases, when structures are being fabricated, for instance in the welding of sections or tightening up of connections, tensile stresses can actually be built into the structure. These stresses are actually added to the structure and, unless they can be dissipated throughout the structure, brittle fracture can occur.

Notches and material defects

Brittle failure is more likely when a notch or defect is present, due to the introduction of areas of high stresses.

Wear

Wear, namely the actual wearing out of component features of machinery, is an important aspect of machinery reliability and safety. Wear is essentially a deterioration in surface finish. It can arise through actual material removal or destruction of the surface finish with use. It also results from deterioration of a surface coating or finish and can promote corrosion of, particularly, metals. Wear may be produced in a variety of ways:

- **Scuffing** – whereby moving parts of a structure rub together due, perhaps, to inadequate lubrication or the absence of lubrication.
- **Pitting** – a form of surface fatigue failure arises from the formation of minute pits or indentations in the surface and occurs as a result of the removal of small surface particles due to rubbing. These particles can increase in hardness due to the process of **work hardening,** and can cause further wear as a result of abrasion.
- **Abrasion** – arises as a result of foreign particles being deposited between moving surfaces which are harder than the main moving surfaces. Particles causing abrasion can include particles shed from surfaces, and extraneous materials such as sand and earth.
- **Fretting** – occurs in pin-jointed, press fitted components, where there should be no motion, but where there is small relative motion between joints and parts. Fretting destroys the surface finish which promotes metal fatigue and corrosion.

Factors influencing wear include the material's surface hardness, loads involved (overloading promotes wear), sliding velocity, surface finish, lubrication and foreign body contamination. Abrasive wear is the prime consideration here.

Corrosion

Corrosion of metals can take place as a direct result of chemical attack and through oxidation at high temperatures. The sources of chemical attack can be various forms of atmospheric pollution, particularly sulphur dioxide from industrial and domestic fuel-burning installations or, in certain cases, direct contact with chemical substances, such as acids and alkalis. Chemical attack results in a chemical conversion process. The metal is converted into a compound, resulting in a weakened structure. Corrosion is the result of direct chemical attack or electrochemical attack on metals, going from an anodic (positive) region to a cathodic (negative) region. In serious situations, pipework or surfaces can fail as a result of chemical corrosion, due to thinning of the material. There are a number of specific forms of corrosion:

- **Pitting** – can occur on surfaces resulting in small pits and flaws being formed where the surface has fallen out in minute parts. This can cause eventual fatigue failure.

- **Oxidation** – the exposure of a surface to oxygen and the subsequent chemical reaction, is accelerated at high temperatures. As with chemical corrosion, the surface of a material will start to deteriorate and break up if no action is taken. A number of treatments are available to prevent or reduce the rate of oxidation of surfaces.

- **Intergranular attack** – occurs in alloys where there is a combination of metals and/or carbon, and where the materials in the boundaries of the grains tend to be different from that in the centre. If the material at the boundary is liable to corrosion, the net effect is that a crack develops around the edges of the grains, leaving the grain boundaries porous. **Dezincification** is a particular form of intergranular attack in brass, where the zinc becomes corroded leaving a mass of copper on its own.

- **High temperature corrosion** – can be caused where the products of a chemical reaction, for instance, between metal and steam or products of combustion, leave a scale or film on a surface under high temperature conditions. When cooled, the scale becomes brittle and flakes off. Fresh attacks reduce the wall thickness (**passivation**). The parent material has very poor corrosive resistance, but when the film starts to build up, the corrosion resistance is improved due to the scale formation.

- **Stress corrosion** – is a common cause of failure. Failures due to stress corrosion cracking or corrosion fatigue take place at stresses well below the normal tensile limit of the metal involved. With **stress corrosion**, fracture results from the combined influence of corrosion with tensile stress. However, with **corrosion fatigue**, rapidly reversing stresses under corrosive conditions lead to failure.

Stress corrosion failures fall into two categories, namely those taking place in the presence of stresses introduced into the metal during a deformation process and remaining locked up, and those stresses imposed by external forces applied during assembly of equipment or during its operation. Locked up stresses can be relieved by a low temperature annealing process which results in more even distribution of stress within the metal without reducing its strength.

Caustic cracking, a form of stress corrosion, consists of a stress-produced crack produced in boilers. It commences with an attack on steel at high temperatures by a local concentration of sodium hydroxide, and occurring in leaking boiler seams afterwards. The crack undergoes a continuous process of being brittle initially and then passing to ductile failure. Feedwater control is extremely important in these cases.

Anti-corrosion methods include the use of corrosion-resistant materials, such as stainless steel and aluminium, organic and inorganic coatings, metallic coatings and the use of corrosion inhibitors in boiler feedwater.

Creep

This is a progressive deformation with time at constant stress. The deformation is irreversible. It is principally associated with static structures and high temperatures. For example, creep can occur when metals such as steel are used at high temperatures under uninterrupted stresses as with steam boiler parts and turbine blades. Under these conditions, they yield very slowly, so that over a period of time they stretch and may ultimately fracture. Creep can also take place at low temperatures, particularly in soft metals with a low melting point. This can occur with lead sheeting on pitched roofs, whereby the lead at the top thins and that at the bottom thickens out as a result of the metal creeping downwards due to gravity.

When stress is applied to a metal under creep conditions, four distinct stages can be identified:

- an initial instantaneous small strain, called **micro-creep**
- a period during which strain or flow occurs at a decelerating rate
- a prolonged period during which further deformation is small and steady and
- an acceleration of the creep rate whereby the material elongates rapidly and ultimately fractures.

Creep can be a causative factor in a number of failure situations. Failure is associated with:

- excessive deformation
- load shedding, where one component becomes longer and ceases to take the load, the load, in fact, passing to another member and
- rupture or final fracture.

Creep is controlled by the use of materials which do not display typical creep properties, the use of appropriate factors of safety at the design stage of installations and the operation of planned maintenance and inspection systems directed at identifying early evidence of creep.

Metal fatigue

Where metals are subject to continuing and fluctuating stresses, as with machinery and structural components, metal fatigue failure can result. This form of fatigue is common where metals are subject to mechanical vibration, whereby fluctuating stresses caused by this vibration result in the formation of cracks which can penetrate the full extent of the metal. Metal fatigue is one of the primary failure mechanisms of cranes and pressure vessels.

Metal parts subjected to fatigue stresses in service fail prematurely under repetitions of stress lower than those established as safe by experiment. The basic mechanism of metal fatigue involves the presence of defects, micro-cracks or finish defects, such as tool marks, notches, etc. One of the likely causes is the influence of an abrupt change in section. In a similar manner, scratches, dents and similar minor damage present become a slowly advancing crack. The actual mechanism involves some degree of plastic deformation although loads tend to be less than the actual yield point.

Factors which promote metal fatigue include the shape and surface finish of the component, defects and notches, the dynamic (fluctuating) stresses and residual tensile stresses.

1

THE EXPANSION OF SOLIDS AND LIQUIDS

When matter is heated it expands and when cooled, it contracts. If these changes in the structure of matter are resisted, large forces are created. The molecules of solids and liquids are in constant vibration. When heated, they vibrate faster and force each other apart, with the resulting expansion. Where allowance is not made, particularly for expansion of materials in either form, hazardous situations, such as pressure vessel failures or explosions, can arise.

SPECIFICATION TO PREVENT FAILURE

It is essential that the factors identified in earlier parts of this chapter are considered in any specification directed at preventing various forms of failure. Such specification is an important feature of quality systems as outlined in BS 5750: Quality Systems.

QUALITY ASSURANCE (BS 5750)

Inevitably quality assurance and health and safety management are directly linked. Many of the objectives of the quality assurance manager are similar in concept to those of the health and safety practitioner. BS 5750:1987 is the

British Standard for Quality Systems, which is split into a number of parts. Fundamentally, BS 5750 is a framework of some 18 points around which a management system is designed to assure that the standard of service desired is being provided consistently. Managers can, by operating a quality assurance system, help to prevent errors in their organisation, some of which lead to accidents, and provide for a far greater probability of doing things right first time.

BS 4778:1987 'Quality Vocabulary' defines **quality** as *'the totality of features and characteristics of a product or service that bear on its ability to satisfy stated or implied needs'*. **Quality assurance**, on the other hand, is defined as *'all those planned and systematic actions necessary to provide adequate confidence that a product or service will satisfy given requirements of quality'*. Quality assurance should not be confused with quality control, however. The former is a much wider philosophy which endeavours to integrate quality with the manufacturing or service process, whereas **quality control** is a series of operational techniques and activities used to fulfil and verify the requirements for quality, for example, inspection and examination systems.

Principal features of a quality system

Management responsibility

The management commitment to quality is identified in a written quality policy which, as with a statement of health and safety policy, should incorporate the responsibilities and levels of authority of staff. Management must provide appropriate personnel and resources to verify the service is being delivered as required. A manager should be appointed as quality officer, whose principal function is that of monitoring operation of the system and ensuring compliance with the British Standard. To ensure that the quality system meets the requirements of the Standard, a management review meeting should be held periodically.

Quality system

Management must identify and clarify all the activities of the organisation that have a bearing on the customer and, where appropriate or required by the Standard, document the system of operation. They must ensure that the planned system is operated and the documentation must be maintained to ensure it is up to date.

Contract review

This is a procedure whereby contracts are reviewed with the customer to ensure that, as a supplier, the organisation is providing what the customer expects and has agreed.

Document control

The documentation system should ensure that:

- all personnel use only current issues of key documentation
- personnel have ready access to relevant documentation
- out of date documentation is disposed of promptly and
- changes and modifications are introduced to the documentation only after the approval of an authorised officer.

Purchasing

The purchasing function must be controlled and managed to ensure:

- what is ordered is what is required
- goods and services are provided by reputable suppliers
- goods and services meet specified requirements and
- purchases are verified.

Purchaser supplied product

Where the customer supplies all or part of the product or service, there must be procedures to ensure the organisation fulfils its responsibilities to the customer.

Product identification and traceability

Identification of product or service location can be by a documented signage scheme. The supplier should ensure that traceability of personnel is built into the system, through duty rotas and other systems.

Process control

This is the principal part of the system, namely controlling those processes that are involved in the delivery of the service. This involves:

- identifying all those factors which go into a standard of service
- ensuring staff have access to documented work instructions and
- post-service inspection to ensure goods and services meet the standard after delivery or use.

Inspection and testing

Goods received on site should be inspected and verified as conforming to the purchase specification. Periodic inspections should also be directed at ensuring products and services meet specified requirements. Final inspection should ensure defective products or services are not delivered to the customer.

Inspection of measuring and test equipment

Specific measurement and test equipment, such as pressure gauges, must be calibrated at frequencies laid down in the manufacturers' instructions.

Inspection and test status

The supplier must identify, by labels for equipment or inspection records for facilities, the condition of the service. This can range from calibration labels to records identifying standards of cleanliness and housekeeping.

Control of non-conforming product

Faults, which indicate non-conformance with the quality specification, must be identified, isolated and reported.

Corrective action

This implies rectification of the problem of non-conformance. Corrective action takes two forms:

- routine corrective action whereby a verbal or written request solves the problem and
- non-routine or repetitive non-conformance which may necessitate a formal corrective action meeting to address the issue with key staff.

Handling, storage, packaging and delivery

Documented procedures must be maintained for correct handling, storage, packaging and delivery.

Quality records

The supplier must retain documents that verify the delivery of service, satisfactory or otherwise. Such documents, for example, inspection records, must be clearly identified in the system, collected and stored in an approved location for specified retention periods.

Internal quality audits

The purpose of quality auditing is to verify whether the quality system is being followed as written and whether the system itself meets the requirements of the customer.

Training

Any comprehensive and documented training systems should meet the requirements of the customer. The supplier should identify training needs, formulate a training plan, maintain comprehensive employee training records and have a mechanism for perceived training requirements.

Statistical techniques

The system for statistical analysis should be capable of monitoring service delivery, for example, usage figures, accident reports, ill-health reports, individual costs of non-conformances.

Documentation of quality systems

Documentation can be split into four specific aspects.

Quality manual

This is a general statement of how the organisation intends to meet the various requirements of the Standard.

Operational procedures

These are the fulcrum of the system identifying the standard of operation and individual responsibilities.

Work instructions

These relate to the requirements of the procedures and detail specific aspects of task performance.

Internal documents

These documents can include a wide range of records, forms, labels, etc all of which are necessary for the successful implementation of the system.

BS 5750 and health and safety

Much of what is advocated in quality systems forms an integral feature of health and safety management. Both systems are concerned with the assessment of reliability, the specification of systems and ensuring compliance with the systems once established. In addition, the systems for monitoring performance, through various forms of audit, investigation and trouble-shooting techniques, are similar. Health and safety management must, therefore, be seen as an integral feature of the quality system.

NON-DESTRUCTIVE TESTING TECHNIQUES

These techniques supplement destructive testing techniques, such as tensile, compressive and shear tests on components and materials, whereby no damage is caused as a result of testing. The purposes of non-destructive tests are:

- to establish the proportions, dimensions and fitness for manufacture of components and
- for checking the durability or deterioration of structures.

Scope of non-destructive testing

Inspection of surfaces

A number of methods are used for the inspection of the surfaces of components, machinery and equipment. These include:

- **visual** examinations
- **optical** examination using a small binocular microscope
- **mechanical** examination, taking account of factors such as surface finish measurements and the degree of surface roughness
- **ultrasonic** techniques which entail transmitting waves of certain frequencies to observe reflections which indicate flaws and defects
- **magnetic** techniques, whereby the component is magnetised and iron filings sprinkled on the surface; variations in the magnetic fields produced indicate flaws
- **electrical resistivity** tests, based on the fact that the resistance between two wires can indicate flaws in the surface; this is based on the time taken for the current to pass around the flaw or crack being greater than that if no flaw or crack existed and
- the use of **dye penetrants**, whereby the crack is coated with oil containing a dye, followed by visual observation to ascertain the oil entering and leaving the crack under examination.

Detection of internal flaws

Various **radiographic techniques** are operated using gamma-rays, neutrons and X-rays. These tests are concerned with detecting the thickness of the metal and the degree of fusion of welds on pipes and internal surfaces. These techniques feature in the traditional radiography of pipe lines. **Ultrasonic techniques** are also used for locating variations in the thickness of materials.

REPORT OF THE INVESTIGATION OF THE CRANE ACCIDENT AT BRENT CROSS, HENDON

20TH JUNE 1964 (MINISTER OF LABOUR CMND.2768:1965)

On the morning of Saturday, 20th June 1964 the jib of a mobile crane operating alongside the North Circular Road at Brent Cross collapsed and its load fell upon a passing motor coach. Seven passengers were killed and 32 injured. The mobile crane was a 15-ton Coles Crane manufactured by Steels Engineering Products Ltd., subsequently known as British Crane & Excavator Corporation Ltd. (BCEC) which used it thereafter. The jib was of welded tubular steel construction; it consisted of a heel section 15 feet in length, a head section also 15 feet in length, and other sections which could be inserted between the two basic sections to produce lengths varying up to a maximum of 80 feet.

On 1st November 1962 regulations under the Road Traffic Act were introduced which imposed severe restrictions upon the movements along a road of a vehicle having a forward projection exceeding six feet. To overcome the consequent inconvenience to mobile crane owners, certain manufacturers commenced to build basic jibs with a hinge or 'gate' incorporated in the head section and permitting this section to fold back alongside the heel section when in transit, thus reducing the forward overhang within the six feet limit. Cleveland Bridge did not obtain such a new jib for this crane but did purchase from BCEC a separate 'gate section' which could be inserted in the existing jib and served the same purpose. BCEC had designed this gate section to meet the requirements of Pickfords Ltd., and had supplied the prototype to that company. The gate supplied to Cleveland Bridge was the second and only other gate manufactured from this design before the accident.

The design of the gate played an important part in the findings of the investigation. Each half of the gate was intended to be bolted to the plates at which the main booms of each section of the jib terminated, and the top and bottom halves of the gate were joined by four pins passing through lugs. With one pair of pins removed the gate could be folded as a hinge. Each pin passed through three lugs, two outer ones attached to the lower portion and the centre one attached to the top portion. The two outer lugs were roughly triangular in shape. The centre lug was thicker and rectangular in shape. The reason for its shape was that it was not only designed to provide a point of attachment for the pin but was also intended, when the gate was closed, to come into contact with the end plate of the lower portion.

According to Mr Innes', the design engineer, statement 'the purpose of the square lug was to transmit the principal loading on this hinge which within the limits I have set were compressive loads, to take these compressive loads direct through from the upper part of the hinge section to the lower part of the hinge section without a major part of it going through the pin'. In other words, by bedding down with its flat side against the end plates, the compressive forces in the jib members would be transmitted in a straight line through the gate. If it did not initially bed down, these forces would be transmitted via the pin, and as this was offset five inches from the line of the main booms, what was described as a 'scissors action' would be set up until stopped by the lug bedding down. This scissors action would create bending stresses in the adjacent jib members.

The causes of the accident

1 The tubes immediately above the gate section buckled and the king post being lifted crashed over the bridge on to a coach on the road below.
2 The crane was standing on a 1:30 slope.
3 The crane jib was of tubular construction, with the round sections crimped in to the bases, thereby reducing the strength.
4 The gate section was incorporated 10 or 11 years after manufacture of the crane to comply with new regulations.
5 Failure was due to bending stresses created by the presence of the gate and, in particular, the lugs. Bending stresses increase progressively along the length of a jib, whereas the forces should have been transmitted directly through the base of the middle lug. If there is any clearance between the lug and that point, it should 'bottom down'. As designed, the system depended upon the lug bedding down and on high precision assembly, which did not take place.
6 The basic fault was in the manufacture of the gate, which involved two thicknesses of lugs and two different shapes. By a series of errors the gate lacked the stop intended by the designers to transmit compression forces.
7 The parts list for the gate was not adequately differentiated in relation to the working drawings.
8 The bending stresses increased from 2 tons/sq.in. to 20 tons/sq.in as a result of the incorrect design of the lugs.
9 The crane had installed the king post on the southern side beforehand. The 6.5 tons load which was lifted was very close to the safe working load (SWL) of 7 tons.
10 The location of the crane was awkward, which could have affected the structural stability of the crane.
11 Extra side forces were incurred when the load was lifted due to the location of the centre of gravity, which promoted buckling of the tubes on the side of the jib.
12 This was largely a ductile failure which takes a period of time.

Conclusions of the report

The official report concluded that the accident was a result of series of coincidences, namely:

● the making of the wrong lugs by BCEC

- the making of four substitute lugs of the wrong shape by Steel Process Plants
- the failure of inspection to remedy the error
- the failure to notify the designer's limitations on use to the user
- the failure of Cleveland Bridge to detect the error by tests
- the underestimate of the weight of the load and
- the defect in the safe load indicator.

All these came together to produce the result, an unusual accident.

An examination of the report indicates that this accident involved virtually every element of structural and component reliability and failure. These include:

- basic design faults – the design of the gate was not a neat design in that it relied on close tolerances to available stresses
- defects in fabrication – the lugs of the gate were not manufactured to the drawing
- errors in inspection by the contractors
- the controversy as to whether the crane complied with the British Standard, and the fact that the British Standard changed, which affected the safety factor and the SWL, for example, the SWL went from 7 tons to 0.8 tons or 5 tons depending upon the particular British Standard
- gross failure to comply with the Construction (Lifting Operations) Regulations 1961
- the failure of the SWL indicator
- the role of the insurance company inspector
- the role of Her Majesty's Factories Inspectorate who inspected the site some weeks beforehand and drew the attention of the company to their failure to inspect
- the system for calculation of residual and main stresses and
- the controversy over the cause of failure of the jib, which was based on a study of the broken parts.

PLANNED MAINTENANCE PROGRAMMES

An important feature of health and safety management is the operation of planned preventive maintenance programmes for all items of work equipment, the structural items of the workplace and, in some cases, for vehicles, in particular fork-lift trucks.

Planned maintenance programmes incorporate written schedules which should cover the following features:

- the item of work equipment, structure, vehicle, etc to be maintained by reference to a plant, structural or vehicle maintenance register
- the maintenance procedure, including specific methods of maintenance, the materials and equipment to be used and, for equipment, the criteria for testing following the maintenance operation
- the frequency of maintenance, eg at the end of each production run, daily, weekly, every 1000 miles, etc.
- identification of the person with specific responsibility for ensuring the written maintenance procedure has been correctly applied and
- details of hazards and the specific precautions to be taken by maintenance staff.

Regular monitoring to ensure correct implementation of the programme should be undertaken by a senior manager, eg engineering director, chief engineer, with corrective action being taken where necessary.

Planned maintenance programmes are dealt with in BS 3811:1974. A number of definitions in this British Standard must be considered.

- **Maintenance:** A combination of any actions carried out to retain an item in, or restore it to, an acceptable condition.
- **Planned maintenance:** Maintenance organised and carried out with forethought, control and the use of records to a predetermined plan.
- **Corrective maintenance:** Maintenance carried out to restore (including adjustment and repair) an item which has ceased to meet an acceptable condition.
- **Emergency maintenance:** Maintenance which it is necessary to put in hand immediately to avoid serious consequences.
- **Reliability:** The ability of an item to perform a required function under the stated conditions for a stated period of time. This may be expressed as a probability.
- **Maintainability:** A function of the rapidity and ease with which maintenance operations can be performed to help prevent malfunctions or to correct them if they occur.
- **Maintenance programme:** A list allocating maintenance to a specific period.

Common problem areas in maintenance management

Figure 1.5 shows a classification which incorporates most maintenance problems.

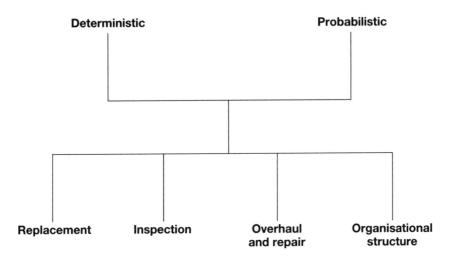

Deterministic   Probabilistic

Replacement   Inspection   Overhaul   Organisational
                          and repair   structure

FIG   1.5

1

Deterministic problems

Deterministic problems are ones where no uncertainty is associated with the timing or consequence of the maintenance action. For example, an item of equipment may not be subject to failure but its operating cost may increase with its utilisation. To reduce this cost, some form of maintenance work can be done, such as replacement or overhaul. After the maintenance, the future trend in operating cost is known. Such a deterministic situation is shown below.

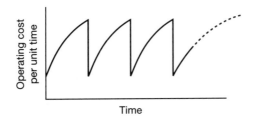

Time

FIG 1.6   Deterministic problems (maintenance)

Probabilistic problems

With probabilistic problems, the timing and outcome of the maintenance may depend upon chance. In the simplest situations, the equipment may be described as being 'good' or 'failed'. From a frequency distribution of the time elapsed between maintenance actions and failure, it is possible to determine the variations in the probability of failure with elapsed time.

Replacement problems

These are concerned with determining the best time at which an item, such as a component or a complex machine, should be replaced. The basic purpose behind an inspection is to determine the condition of equipment. The terms **overhaul** and **repair** are reserved for maintenance actions that improve the condition of an item, but do not necessarily return it to a 'good as new' condition. Generally, **overhaul** is interpreted as a preventive maintenance action while a **repair** is reserved for maintenance of an item which has reached a defined failed state. Organisational structure problems in maintenance are thus concerned with determining what facilities, in terms of manpower and equipment, should be available with which to perform the maintenance.

Inspection of equipment

The basic purpose behind an inspection is to determine the condition of the equipment. The major decisions required are:

- the depth or thoroughness of an inspection
- the indicators to be used to describe the equipment conditions, such as bearing wear, product quality and
- the timing/frequency of such inspections.

MAINTENANCE WORK

Principal hazards

The principal hazards associated with maintenance operations can be classified thus:

- **Mechanical** – machinery traps, entanglement, contact, ejection; reciprocating traps, shearing traps, in-running nips; uncovenanted strokes; unexpected start-up.
- **Electrical** – electrocution, shock, burns.
- **Pressure** – unexpected pressure releases, explosion.
- **Physical** – extremes of temperature, noise, vibration, dust and fume.
- **Chemical** – gases, fogs, mists, fumes, etc prejudicial to health.
- **Structural** – obstructions, floor openings.
- **Access** – work at heights, confined spaces.

Precautions

A number of both general and specific precautions are necessary for these types of activity, in particular:

- the operation of safe systems of work, in certain cases permit to work systems
- designation of competent persons for certain high risk operations
- the use of method statements, particularly where contractors may be involved in maintenance operations
- enforcement of company contractors' regulations where contractors are involved
- designation of controlled areas
- access control
- the provision of information, instruction and training
- signs, marking and labelling and
- appropriate personal protective equipment.

The operation of a planned maintenance programme is vital.

①

STATUTORY EXAMINATION FREQUENCIES FOR PRINCIPAL TYPES OF PLANT

One month

Local exhaust ventilation plant (blasting of metal castings).

Six months

Chains, ropes or lifting tackle; power driven lifts (passenger and goods); power presses/press brakes (automatic, interlocking or photo-electric guards) electric motors and wiring (mines and quarries); local exhaust ventilation plant (grinding of metals, asbestos); builders' hoists; fork-lift trucks (if fitted with ropes or chains); order pickers; motor vehicle lifting tables; powered access equipment; permanently installed suspended access equipment; escalators.

Twelve months

Manual driven lifts (passenger and goods); power presses/press brakes (fixed guards); electrical installations in cinemas; cranes (Docks, Shipbuilding and Ship Repairing Regulations); electrical installations associated with petrol pumps.

Fourteen months

Steam boilers; economisers; superheaters; bakers' ovens; self-fired vessels; cranes and other lifting machines; excavators; local exhaust ventilation plant (general).

Twenty-six months

Steam receivers; air receivers.

2

Work equipment safety

Injuries associated with machinery and various forms of work equipment are common. Such injuries include amputations of limbs and parts of limbs, crushing injuries, entanglement of limbs, clothing and hair in moving parts of machinery, injuries associated with items being emitted from machines and various contact injuries, such as burns, where people come into contact with hot surfaces of machinery and plant.

PRINCIPLES OF MACHINERY SAFETY

As with many areas of occupational health and safety, the risk of a machinery-related accident is associated with:

- **The objective danger** which is a measure of the severity of the injury which could be sustained through contact with a machinery component, such as a circular saw blade or a drill.
- **The subjective perception of risk** of the individual to identify various forms of danger and his ability to avoid that danger.

Any accident prevention strategy must, therefore, be directed to reducing the objective danger from machinery through the use of well-designed machinery guarding systems and various forms of safety device aimed at preventing the operator or other persons from coming anywhere near the danger points or areas of a machine. This should be supported by the provision of information, instruction, training and supervision directed at increasing people's perceptions of risk.

Current legal requirements are incorporated in the FA, HSWA, MHSWR, PUWER and various regulations and ACOPs. HSE Guidance Notes, particularly those in the Plant and Machinery series of Guidance Notes, together with BS 5304: 'Safeguarding of Machinery', provide excellent guidance on this matter.

BS 5304 defines a 'machine' as *an apparatus for applying power having fixed and moving parts, each with definite functions*. Machines have:

- **operational parts**, which perform the primary output function of the machine, for instance, the manufacture of a product or a component and
- **non-operational or functional parts**, which convey power or motion to the operational parts, for instance, drives to motors.

The functional parts comprise the prime mover and transmission machinery, which are defined in the FA, section 176(1) as follows:

Prime mover means any engine, motor or other appliance which provides mechanical energy derived from steam, water, wind, electricity, the combustion of fuel or other source.

Transmission machinery means every shaft, wheel, pulley, drum, system of fast and loose pulleys, coupling, clutch, driving belt or other device by which the motion of a prime mover is transmitted to or received by any machine or appliance.

Risk assessment

Under the MHSWR and PUWER, employers are required to assess the risks associated with work equipment and to either eliminate or control such risks.

Risk assessment is very much concerned with the suitability of the work equipment and any specific risks arising from same. This should take into account:

- its initial integrity, namely the design and constructional features of the machine and the form and distribution of harm
- the place where it will be used
- the purpose for which it will be used
- the actual persons at risk – operator, supervisor, third parties – and general circumstances of operation and
- specific events which could lead to injury.

MACHINERY HAZARDS

Many machines, including new machines, incorporate hazards in their basic design. BS 5304 classifies these hazards as follows:

1 Traps

Traps can take a number of forms:

- **reciprocating trap** – these may have an up and down motion eg presses; at the point where the injury occurs, the limb is stationary
- **shearing trap** – these have a guillotine effect and
- **in-running nips** – these are to be found on rollers, conveyors and gears.

Figures 2.1 to 2.3 show examples of the various forms of trap.

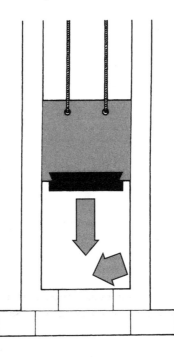

FIG 2.1 Vertical reciprocating motion of a power press
(Source BS 5304: 'Safeguarding of Machinery')

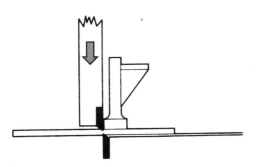

FIG 2.2 Shearing trap created by a guillotine

FIG 2.3 In-running nips
(Source BS 5304)

2 Entanglement

The risk of entanglement of hair, clothing and limbs in, for instance, revolving shafts, line shafts, chucks and drills. Figure 2.4 shows typical entanglement risks.

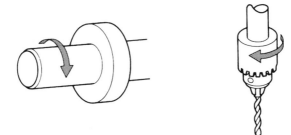

FIG 2.4 Entanglement risks
(Source BS 5304)

3 Ejection

The emission or throwing off of particles from a machine eg abrasive wheels, disintegration of swarf on a lathe.

2

4 Contact

Contact with a machine at a particular point can cause injury eg heat, temperature extremes, sharp projections, as in plastic moulding machines, circular saws. Figure 2.5 shows an example of contact risks.

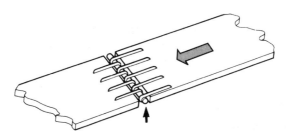

FIG 2.5 Contact risks
(Source BS 5304)

General circumstances involving operators and others

The tasks that people undertake can be a source of danger eg job loading and removal, tool changing, waste removal, operation of process, routine and emergency maintenance, gauging, breakdown situations and trying out.

Another source of danger can be associated with unauthorised presence and/or use.

Specific events leading to injury

Events leading to machinery-related injuries vary considerably. Typical events include:

- unexpected start-up or movement due, perhaps, to an electrical fault
- reaching into a feed device which is inadequately fenced
- uncovenanted stroke by a machine and
- machine failure.

THE 17 DANGEROUS PARTS OF MACHINERY

Certain parts, or combinations of parts are classified by the HSE as dangerous should workers operate unsafely or should an unsafe action develop in respect of their motion. Such parts **must** be securely fenced. The 17 dangerous parts are listed below with examples.

1 **Revolving shafts, spindles, mandrels and bars,** eg line and counter shafts, machine shafts; drill spindles; chucks and drills, etc; boring bars; stock bars; traverse shafts.

2 **In-running nips between pairs of rotating parts,** eg gear wheels; friction wheels; calendar bowls; mangle rolls; metal manufacturing rolls; rubber washing, breaking and mixing rolls; dough brakes; printing machines; paper-making machines.

3 **In-running nips of the belt and pulley type,** eg belts and pulleys, plain, flanged (ie V-belts) or grooved; chain and sprocket gears; conveyor belts and pulleys; metal coiling and the like.

4 **Projections on revolving parts,** eg key heads; set screws; cotter pins; coupling belts.

5 **Discontinuous rotating parts,** eg open arm pulleys; fan blades; spoked gear wheels and spoked flywheels.

6 **Revolving beaters, spiked cylinders and revolving drums,** eg scutchers; rag flock teasers; cotton openers; carding engines; laundry washing machines.

7 **Revolving mixer arms in casings,** eg dough mixers; rubber solution mixers.

8 **Revolving worms and spirals in casings,** eg meat mincers; rubber extruders; spiral conveyors.

9 **Revolving high-speed cages in casings,** eg hydro-extractors; centrifuges.

10 **Abrasive wheels,** eg manufactured wheels; natural sandstone.

11 **Revolving cutting tools,** eg circular saws; milling cutters; circular shears; wood slicers; routers; chaff cutters; woodworking machines such as spindle moulders, planing machines and tenoning machines.

12 **Reciprocating tools and dies,** eg power presses, drop stamps; relief stamps; hydraulic and pneumatic presses; blending presses; hand presses; revolution presses.

13 **Reciprocating knives and saws,** eg guillotines for metals, rubber and paper; trimmers; corner cutters; perforators.

14 **Closing nips between platen motions,** eg letterpress platen printing machines; paper and cardboard platen machine cutters; some power presses; foundry moulding machines.

15 **Projecting belt fasteners and fast-running belts,** eg bolt and nut fasteners; wire pin fasteners and the like; woodworking machinery and the like; woodworking machinery belts; centrifuge belts; textile machinery side belts.

16 **Nips between connecting rods or links, and rotating wheels, cranks or discs,** eg side motion of certain flat-bed printing machines; jacquard motions on looms.

17 **Traps arising from the traversing carriages of self-acting machines,** eg metal planing machines.

SAFEGUARDING OF MACHINERY

BS 5304 defines a **safeguard** as 'a guard or device to protect persons from danger'. In the Standard, **danger** is defined thus: '*When applied to machinery in motion, it is a situation in which there is a reasonably foreseeable risk of injury from the mechanical hazards referred to in clause 6*' (These mechanical hazards are itemised under **Machinery Hazards** earlier in this chapter.) It should be noted that the law defines machinery as **dangerous** when '*it is a possible cause of injury to anybody acting in a way in which a human being may be reasonably expected to act in circumstances which may reasonably expected to occur*'. (**Walker v Bletchley Flettons Ltd [1973] 1 AER 170**)

Machinery guards

Fixed guard

This is '*a guard which has no moving parts associated with it, or dependent on the mechanism of any machinery, and which, when in position, prevents access to a danger point or area'.* (BS 5304)

This form of guard is designed to prevent all access to the dangerous parts and is principally used to cover non-operational parts. Many fixed guards are sold castings, sheet metal (minimum 18 SWG – 1.22 mm), perforated or expanded metal (minimum 17 SWG), 'Weldmesh' (minimum 14 SWG), safety glass panels or polycarbonate panels. Wood as a guard material is not recommended, except where there may be a risk of electric shock.

Figure 2.6 shows examples of fixed guards.

Interlocking guard

This is *'a guard which has a movable part so connected with the machinery controls that:*

(a) *the part(s) of the machinery causing danger cannot be set in motion until the guard is closed*

(b) *the power is switched off and the motion braked before the guard can be opened sufficiently to allow access to the dangerous parts and*

(c) *access to the danger point or area is denied while the danger exists'.* (BS 5304)

An interlocking guard is, fundamentally, a moving guard which, in the closed position, prevents all access to the dangerous parts. The control gear for starting up cannot be operated until the guard is fully closed, and the guard cannot be opened until the dangerous parts are at rest.

For a true interlock system, everything must be at rest before the guard or gate can be opened. Some interlocks control only the power supply, and others, the power supply and the movement. In order to achieve the same level of safety as with fixed guards, the reliability and maintenance of interlocking guards are significant. Whatever the form, the system should fail to safety (**fail-safe**).

Note: The term 'failure to safety' is commonly used in machinery guarding. It implies that *'any failure in, or interruption of, power supply will result in the prompt stopping or, where appropriate, stopping and reversal of the movement of the dangerous parts before injury can occur, or the safeguard remaining in position to prevent access to the danger point or area'.* (BS 5304)

Methods of interlocking include:

Mechanical interlocking

Mechanical interlocking incorporates two specific elements: first, the operation or actuation of a device, which may be a hydraulic or pneumatic valve, and second, as a result of the operation of the device, the movement of a particular component, generally a guard.

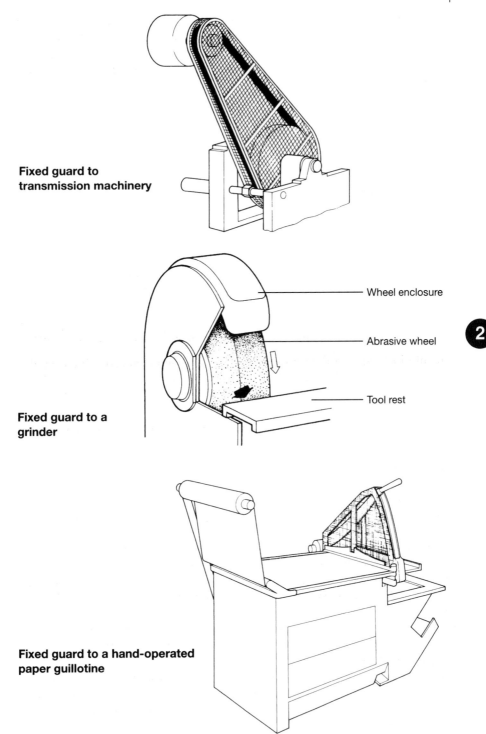

Fixed guard to transmission machinery

Fixed guard to a grinder

Wheel enclosure

Abrasive wheel

Tool rest

Fixed guard to a hand-operated paper guillotine

FIG 2.6 Fixed guards

In the example of mechanical interlocking, shown in Figure 2.7, the guard slides horizontally to close. When the guard is open the control lever is held down, that is, 'safe'. Only after the guard has been closed can the control lever be raised so as to initiate the machine sequence. The lever then holds the guard in the closed position.

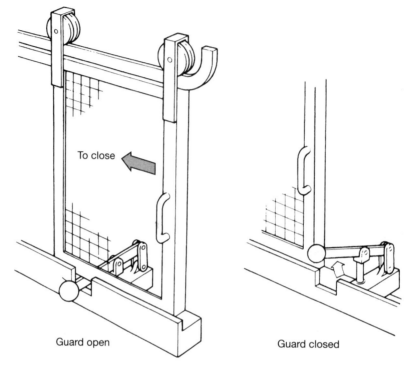

To close

Guard open

Guard closed

FIG 2.7   Mechanical interlocking

Electrical interlocking

BS 5304 identifies four methods of electrical interlocking of guards as follows.

Control interlocking

This incorporates an actuating switch operated by the guard, interposed electromechanical relays and/or solid state switching devices, if any, the electromagnetic contactor (or solid state equivalent eg thyristor), and/or a pneumatic or hydraulic solenoid valve controlling power to the drive. Failure of any of these elements or of the wiring interconnecting them can all be failures to danger. All elements of the system should therefore be designed to give the maximum degree of reliability.

The range of switching methods used for associating guard movement with an on/off electrical control signal includes cam or track operated limit switches, captive key switches, trapped key control of electrical switches, magnetic switches and diode links [cl.44].

Specific aspects of these switching methods are shown in BS 5304.

Power interlocking

This is achieved by direct mechanical control of a switch in series with the main power supply to the drive of the machinery. The direct mechanical control may be by links, etc by captive key or by trapped key.

Power interlocking is inherently superior to control interlocking, and is thus acceptable for high risk situations, because the mechanical link between the guard and the switch ensures that the guard cannot be opened if, for any reason, the switch contacts stick in the 'on' position. However, because direct power interlocking involves the stopping of the drive motor(s), it should only be applied to machinery where the requirement to open the guard is infrequent, or the motor is of low power. (See further BS 5304.)

Control interlocking with back-up

In high risk situations, where frequent access to the danger area is required, control interlocking is acceptable if combined with a back-up power drive interlock incorporated in the cyclic control element, for example direct pneumatic or hydraulic actuation of the ram etc. of air-operated or electromagnetic clutch. The basic requirement of back-up power drive interlocking is that the air or hydraulic pressure to the drive cylinder or clutch has to be exhausted or dumped automatically in the event of control interlock failure. (See further BS 5304.)

2

Dual circuit interlocking

Where direct mechanical linkage between the guard gate and the back-up exhaust or dump valve is not practicable, electrical actuation of the back-up is acceptable. It is essential that the normal control interlock and back-up circuits are kept wholly separate from each other, except for connection to the supply, to minimise the possibility of common faults. The control and back-up limit switches should be arranged in opposite modes, the control being negative and the back-up positive. (See further BS 5304.)

Automatic guard

This is *'a guard which is associated with, and dependent upon, the mechanism of the machinery and operates so as to remove physically from the danger area any part of a person exposed to danger'*. (BS 5304)

These guards incorporate a device so fitted in relation to the dangerous parts that the operator is automatically prevented from contacting same eg heavy power presses, press brakes, paper-cutting guillotines. The guard is independent of the operator and closes automatically when the machine cycle commences. Trip devices are generally fitted on power press guards where trapping points occur as the two parts of the guard meet.

The function of an automatic guard is to remove the operator from the dangerous parts of the machine by means of a moving barrier or arm. There is some degree of risk in that the operator can be injured by the moving barrier, and this type of guard is only suitable for large slow-moving barriers as on presses. These guards operate on a side-to-side, sweep-away or push-out motion.

Automatic guards have a number of disadvantages:

- risk of injury to the operator as a result of the sweep-away motion
- the linkages to the motion must be rigidly connected as they can become loose through constant use
- when the linkages become worn the guard is often racing the tools to maintain safe operation (and can lose!) and
- they need extensive careful maintenance and frequent inspection.

One variation of the automatic guard is the **self-adjusting automatic guard**. This is defined as '*a guard which prevents accidental access of a person to a danger point or area but allows the access of a workpiece which itself acts as part of the guard, the guard automatically returning to its closed position when the operation is completed*'. This form of guarding is particularly appropriate to portable electric circular saws, as shown in Figure 2.8.

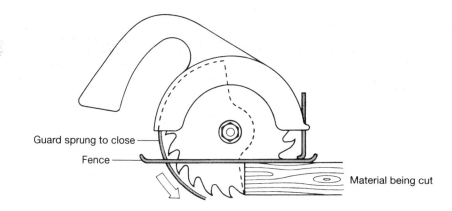

Guard sprung to close

Fence

Material being cut

FIG 2.8   Self-adjusting guard to a portable circular saw

Distance guard

This is '*a guard which does not completely enclose a danger point or area but which places it out of normal reach*'. (BS 5304)

A fixed grill or rail positioned at sufficient distance so that access to the moving parts cannot be gained except by a deliberate unsafe act.

An example of a distance guard is shown in Figure 2.9.

Adjustable guard

This is '*a guard incorporating an adjustable element which, once adjusted, remains in that position during a particular operation*'. (BS 5304)

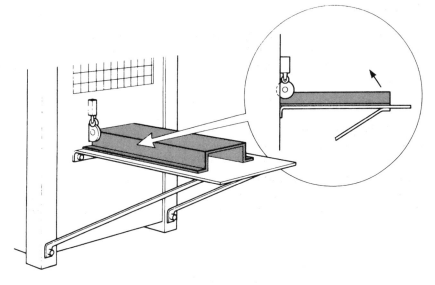

FIG 2.9   Tunnel guard for a metal cutting machine

Such a guard is the least reliable form of guard in that it requires the operator to adjust same prior to operation of the machine. Adjustable guards feature in woodworking machinery in particular eg circular saws and band saws.

An example of an adjustable guard is shown in Figure 2.10.

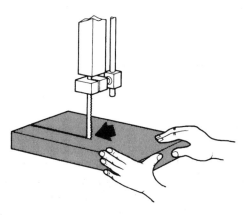

FIG 2.10   Adjustable guard to a band saw blade

Types of safety devices

A safety device is a *'protective appliance, other than a guard, which eliminates or reduces danger before access to a danger point or area can be achieved'*. Most safety devices operate on a trip system.

Trip devices

This is a means whereby any approach by a person beyond the safe limit of working machinery causes the device to actuate and stop the machinery or reverse its motion, thus preventing or minimising injury at the danger point. (BS 5304)

There are various forms of trip device:

Mechanical trip device

This device incorporates a barrier which is contacted by part of the body as it approaches the danger area. Contact with the barrier operates the device which brings the machine to rest.

An example of a mechanical trip device is shown in Figure 2.11, namely a safety trip bar for horizontal two-roll mills used in the rubber industry.

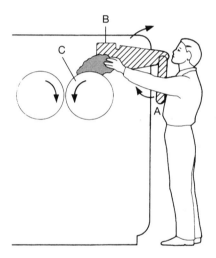

FIG 2.11   Safety trip bar on a horizontal two-roll mill
(Source BS 5304)

Movement of the trip bar A towards the front roll switches off the drive to the rolls by means of limit switch B and applies a brake. The position of the trip bar is important. Its height above the floor and its horizontal distance from the in-running nip should be such that the operator cannot reach beyond the safety limit C which is dependent upon the efficiency of the brake, making allowance for brake wear. After the trip bar A has been tripped the brake should arrest the motion of the rolls before a hand can be drawn into the nip.

Photo-electric trip device

This device provides a curtain of light which can be arranged in either a horizontal (A) or vertical (B) configuration as shown in Figure 2.12. Interruption of the curtain while the dangerous parts of the machinery are moving results in a signal being given for the machine to stop. The speed of stopping should be such as to ensure that the dangerous parts have come to rest before they can be reached by the operator.

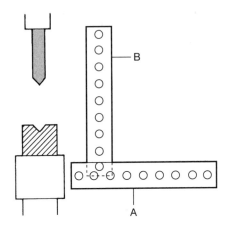

FIG 2.12   Photo-electric trip device
(Source BS 5304)

Access to the danger area from any direction not protected by the device should be prevented by effective fixed or interlocking guards.

Photo-electric trip devices are particularly suitable for guarding power presses, hydraulic presses and guillotines and trimmers.

Pressure sensitive mat

This device operates by means of a number of suitably spaced electrical or fluid switches/valves contained within a mat connected to a control unit and covering the approaches to the danger area. Pressure on the mat operates one or more of these switches. Electrical pressure-sensitive mats are connected into machine control circuits and their use should therefore be restricted to normal risk situations. A pressure-sensitive mat may be appropriate in circumstances where the use of a fixed guard is impracticable, and is particularly suitable for use as an emergency stopping device, as a means of protecting a person who may be inside machinery, or as a secondary safety device to augment a conventional guard.

Ultrasonic devices

With these devices inaudible high frequency sound senses the presence of an object or person in the danger area. Ultrasonics are not affected by strong light or dirt, but sound attenuates over a distance so the width of protection is limited. The variation in sensitivity with distance can create difficulties in ensuring the effectiveness of the device, however, and BS 5304 recommends that such devices should be restricted to the guarding of machinery at which normal interlocking is appropriate.

Two-hand control device

This is a device which requires both hands to operate the machinery controls, thus affording a measure of protection from danger only to the machinery operator and not other persons. The provision of two-hand controls shown at the clicking press in Figure 2.13, used in the manufacture of footwear, ensures that the operator has both hands in a safe position while the press head descends. To protect against accidental operation, the buttons should be shrouded. (See inset.)

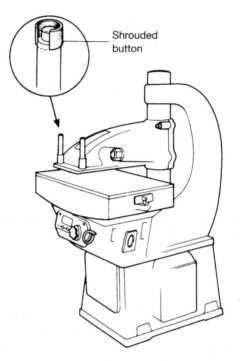

Shrouded button

FIG 2.13   Two-hand control on a clicking press
(Source BS 5304)

A two-hand control device should be designed in accordance with the following requirements outlined in BS 5304:

● The hand controls should be so placed, separated and protected as to prevent spanning with one hand only, being operated with one hand and another part of the body, or being bridged by a tool.

● It should not be possible to start the machinery unless the controls are operated within approximately one second of each other. This prevents the operator from locking one control in the start position so allowing him to operate the machinery by means of the other control leaving one hand free.

● Movement of the dangerous parts should be arrested immediately or, where appropriate, arrested and reversed if one or both controls are released while there is yet danger from the movement of these parts. This should ensure that both hands of the operator are clear of the danger area during the whole of the dangerous movement.

- It should not be possible to initiate a subsequent cycle until both controls have first been returned to their original position. This prevents the possibility of one control being locked in the start position.

Overrun device

This is a device which, used in conjunction with a guard, is designed to prevent access to machinery parts which are moving by their own inertia after the power supply has been interrupted, so as to prevent danger. (BS 5304) Where a machine is liable to overrun after the power supply has been switched off it is necessary to ensure that the guard cannot be opened until the motion has ceased. This can be achieved by one of three means:

- A **rotation sensing device**, which ensures that after the power has been cut off the guard remains locked closed until the device has sensed that rotation of the dangerous parts has ceased. These are used with high speed mixers and centrifuges.

- A **timing device**, which ensures that after the power has been cut off the guard remains locked closed until the dangerous parts have come to rest.

- A **brake**, which is interlocked with the guard and the machine controls so that the act of cutting off the power to the dangerous parts or opening the guard applies the brake. A brake is virtually instantaneous in action.

Mechanical restraint device

This is a device which applies mechanical restraint to a dangerous part of machinery which has been set in motion owing to failure of the machinery controls or other parts of the machinery, so as to prevent danger. (BS 5304)

Mechanical restraint devices are commonly found on pressure die-casting machines and plastics injection-moulding machines. With these hydraulically or pneumatically-operated machines a trap is created between a fixed and a moving platen to which access is required usually once in every cycle. With horizontally moving platens, a simple method of applying mechanical restraint is to provide a scotch in the form of a strut which falls into place between the platens as soon as they are fully open. A device of this kind gives adequate protection provided the guard remains locked closed until the platens are fully open.

THE DESIGN OF SAFETY MECHANISMS

The detailed design of the mechanism controls the safety of the operator. Any consideration of safety mechanisms should include the following objectives and requirements.

Reliability

Given the conditions a component is subjected to over a period of time, it must perform in a reliable way. Warning systems must also be reliable to the extent that they operate for the purposes for which they were designed, and should be reliable when exposed to oil, vibration, shock, water, etc.

Precise operation

The mechanism should operate positively e.g. precise linkage between rams and guards. The transmission angle on linkages must be minimal and control over wear on linkages is essential.

Protection against operator abuse and misuse

Abuse is associated with the operator trying to open the guard before it is due to open, causing wear, and as a result of harsh treatment. Misuse, on the other hand, is a calculated attempt to defeat the safety mechanism. Mechanisms must, therefore, be designed to prevent both abuse and misuse.

Fail-safe

When the component fails, it must do so in such a way that the machine stops and the guards stay closed, and not vice versa. This cannot always be achieved.

Correct method of assembly

Correct assembly of the safety mechanism is vital.

THE ERGONOMICS OF MACHINERY GUARDING

One definition of 'ergonomics' is *'the study or the man-machine interface'*. A more general definition is *'the scientific study of work'* or *'the science of work'*. **Anthropometry** is a branch of ergonomics concerned with the study and measurement of body dimensions, the orderly treatment of resulting data and the application of those data in the design of workspace layouts and equipment. The fact that this is not done creates many problems, best demonstrated by research at the Cranfield Institute of Technology, which created 'Cranfield Man'.

Using a horizontal lathe, researchers examined the positions of controls and compared the locations of these controls with the physical dimensions of the average operator. Table 2.1 shows the wide differences between the two.

Table 2.1 **Physical dimensions of an average operator compared with those of 'Cranfield Man'**

Average operator	Dimension	Operator who would suit these controls
1.75m	Height	1.35m
0.48m	Shoulder width	0.61m
1.83m	Arm span	2.44m
1.07m	Elbow height	0.76m

The ideal operator would be 1.35m tall with a 2.44m arm span (see Figure 2.14).

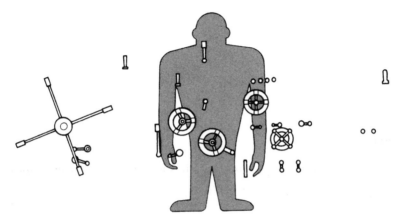

FIG 2.14 **'Cranfield Man' – 1.35m tall with a 2.44m arm span**

Clearly, no effort had been made to design the machine even remotely within the bodily limitations of the average operator. More recently, however, greater attention has been paid to this aspect, particularly in the design of machinery. This can be seen in the approved design of controls and displays on motor vehicles, cranes, aircraft, computer terminals and processing machinery, the objective being to reduce the potential for operator fatigue and error, which can result in lower productivity and can contribute to accidents.

The results of ergonomic study, and particularly data relating to human measurements, have an important influence upon the design of machinery guarding systems. For instance an operator may need to reach upwards, over, around or along, and into or through the machinery guarding.

Reach generally is limited by the arms and, in the case of openings, by fingers and hands also. The distance a person can reach determines the minimum height of certain kinds of guards, or the minimum distance of barriers from machines they are intended to fence.

Reach over a barrier is interrupted by the body at the point of contact with a barrier. Where the barrier is low, the body can be bent and therefore the extent of reach is longer than the arm. If the barrier is above shoulder height, interruption is at the elbow or, when higher still, at the wrist or fingers. A person's arm reaching over a barrier can describe a curve. It is this curve or 'reach curve' which determines at what distances from the barrier dangerous parts of machinery at varying heights are safe by position.

Reach around a barrier depends upon the distance that the side of the barrier extends from the body position. The ability to reach around barriers is determined by the distance of the elbow joint and wrist joint from the reach curve.

Reach through or into a barrier is related, fundamentally, to the size of the average finger. The distance between the guard and the danger point needs to be no greater than the reasonable maximum length of the longest finger plus a clearance allowance. Much will depend upon the size of the opening in the guard, however. If all four fingers can be admitted through the one opening, the size and shape of the opening will be an important factor in determining the extent of the reach possible. In some cases, reach will be limited by the root of the thumb, and in others by the thickness of the hand, the wrist or the arm. In a case where reach is restricted by the root of the thumb, the distance necessary is the reasonable maximum length of a hand from finger tip to root of thumb, plus clearance.

MACHINERY RELIABILITY (CRITERIA FOR ASSESSMENT – MACHINERY GUARDS AND SAFETY DEVICES)

Design considerations

Regulation 11 of the PUWER lays down a hierarchy of measures with regard to dangerous parts of machinery. (See pp. 56–7). The following principles must also be considered:

1 Whenever practicable, dangerous parts should be eliminated or effectively enclosed in the initial design of the machinery. If they cannot be eliminated, then suitable safeguards should be incorporated as part of the design. If this is impossible, provision should be made for safeguards to be easily incorporated at a later stage.

2 Provision should be made to facilitate the fitting of alternative types of safeguards on machinery where it is known that this will be necessary because the work to be done on it will vary.

3 Where a movable guard, cover, etc is used a safeguard, it should be interlocked with the drive, of whatever kind, to the parts being safeguarded; maintenance operations may require complete isolation of the machinery from the power supply.

4 The guard must be securely attached to the machine in such a way that it can only be removed by a tool.

5 Lubrication and routine maintenance facilities should be incorporated remote from the danger area.

6 Suitable supplementary lighting should be provided at operating points; a light fitting which is portable or which relies on manual action for directional adjustment should preferably be supplied at extra-low voltage, ie not normally exceeding 50 V between conductors and not exceeding 30 V a.c. or 50 V d.c. between any conductor and earth.

7 Every mechanism and control forming part of a safeguard should, so far as is practicable, be of fail-safe design.

Construction of safeguards

1 All safeguards should be of sound design and adequate strength.

2 Guards may be made of metal, timber laminated or toughened glass, suitable plastics or a combination of these, as may be appropriate to the conditions; the use of shatter-resistant materials may be an advantage.

3 The size of openings between the interstices of wire mesh guards should be properly considered in relation to finger and hand access.

2

4 Whatever safeguard is selected, it should not itself present a hazard such as trapping or shear points, splinters, rough or sharp edges, or other sources likely to cause injury. In the case of food processing machinery, the safeguard should not constitute a source of contamination of the product.

5 Where an opening in a fixed guard is necessary for the feeding of material by hand, it should not allow the operator access to the dangerous parts. Where it is necessary to provide such an opening, it should be at a sufficient distance from a danger point. Figure 2.15 provides a guide to show the relationship between the guard opening and the distance of the guard from the danger point which, if followed in the design, should prevent unsafe access.

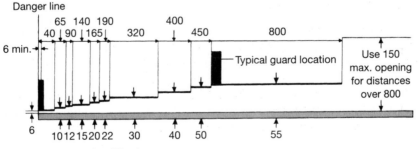

All measurements in millimetres

FIG 2.15   Prevention of unsafe access to a danger point
(Source BS 5304)

6 The guard must be securely attached to the machine and must require the use of a tool to remove it.

THE USE OF MICROPROCESSORS AND ROBOTIC-CONTROLLED MACHINERY

A recent development in the safeguarding of machinery has been the introduction of microprocessors and microcomputers. One microchip can now replace a whole series of electromechanical switches, relays and circuits, which implies less wear, less noise and reduced maintenance costs.

Microprocessors operate according to specific programmes (or 'software') which are conveyed to the microprocessor unit through a manually operated keyboard or keypad, prerecording on magnetic tape or floppy disc or by 'hard wiring' or 'burning on' one or more of the microchips in the microprocessor unit. Whilst this is a relatively new departure in machinery safety, the integrity and reliability of software systems are critical if accidents are to be prevented. HSE (1981) Occasional Paper **Microprocessors in Industry: Implications in the Use of Programmable Electronic Systems** provides further information on this subject.

Robots in industry

Robots fall into three categories, namely fixed sequence robots, variable sequence robots and playback robots.

Fixed sequence robots

These are capable of performing successive steps of a given operation in a predetermined sequence, condition and position. The present information is normally programmed into the robot and cannot easily be changed.

Variable sequence robots

Essentially these are similar to fixed sequence robots except that set information can be more readily changed. The original design of the mechanical system is more complex than that of a fixed sequence robot. It must be capable of fulfilling a variety of movements to accommodate different sets of instructions or programmes. The advent of the microprocessor, with its reduction in size and corresponding increase in capacity ratios, has greatly influenced the performance of this type of robot.

Playback robots

This robot has a memory, but has to be taught the sequence, positions and operations required by a human operator. When required, this information is recalled and the operations are repetitively carried out automatically from memory. Two systems operate with playback robots, namely point-to-point and continuous path.

With **point-to-point robots** (see Figure 2.16), the operator has a control unit to operate the robot. The robot is thus moved to its START position which is then stored in the robot memory. The movements, positions, actions are then carried out in sequence, each step being recorded as an instruction in the memory until the final STOP position is reached. From then on the human operator should no longer be needed and the robot will repeat its taught programme continuously, for instance, spot welding on a vehicle assembly line.

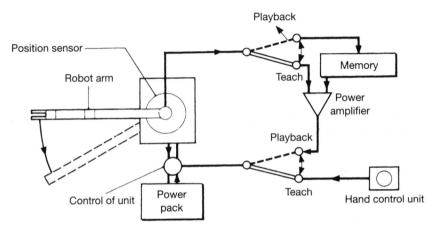

FIG 2.16 Block diagram of point-to-point playback robot system

The **continuous path system** requires a more sophisticated and skilful 'teacher', so that the robot can continuously record all the movements initiated by the human operator. Equally, it will record and repeat all the faults made by the operator. This technique produces a smooth movement following a continuous path, for example, paint spraying.

Industrial robot applications

The main industrial robot applications are in handling, assembly work, hot forging, spot welding and finishing. Handling or **pick-and-place robots** are used for handling heavier loads, ie above 15 kilograms. The handling of billets in hot forging and the unloading of die-casting machines are typical examples which can demonstrate significant increases in production whilst releasing the worker from hazardous or tedious tasks. The robot can do much to reduce danger to workers by replacing them in potentially hazardous situations. However, the robot itself can introduce dangers into the work situation through impact injuries from the moving parts of the robot, trapping the worker against a fixed part, ejection of the object or material being handled against the worker, and traps within the body of the robot when its 'metal clothes' are removed for maintenance. The robot is, of course, a machine and the hazards it presents when operating may be viewed as similar to those presented by dangerous moving parts of any other machine. It is during maintenance, adjustment, programming and fault-finding operations that the robot can be at its most dangerous. The requirements of PUWER apply to robots as do the recommendations in BS 5304. Thus where the machine is in operation, these legal requirements must be applied. In many cases, the provision of fixed perimeter guards, with interlocked access gates to the robot enclosure, must be considered. The access gates to the enclosure should be interlocked in such a way that, when they are opened, power is cut off from all the machinery until they are closed again. An emergency stop to the mains supply of all the machinery should be situated on the robot control box outside the fencing.

In situations where workers require access for maintenance, lubrication, fault-finding or programming, (the last two cases requiring the robot to be 'live'), then a specific procedure or safe system of work is vital. In this case, the safe system of work to be used for reprogramming a robot should ensure that:

- the programmer is highly skilled and trained

- he enters the work area on his own, ensuring that any equipment used by the robot is correctly located and the gate closed so that no one else can enter

- he carries with him a mobile emergency stop device that is connected to a relay box from the mains supply, within the perimeter of the fencing, after ensuring that the emergency stop device is functional and

- the robot is designed and set to run at 'creep' speed only during this operation.

THE SAFETY OF HAND TOOLS

The definition of **work equipment** under PUWER includes hand tools. The abuse and misuse of hand tools frequently result in injuries, many of which are of a serious nature, eg amputations of fingers, blinding, severing of arteries as a result of deep cuts, and account for approximately 10 per cent of all lost-time injuries.

Regulation 6 of PUWER places a strict duty on employers to ensure that work equipment is **maintained in efficient state, in efficient working order and in good repair**. This duty is particularly appropriate in the case of hand tools, and implies the need for frequent inspection of hand tools to ensure this duty is complied with. Furthermore, the correct use of hand tools should be ensured through training and regular supervision of users. Hand tools used by contractors and their employees should also be subject to regular examination.

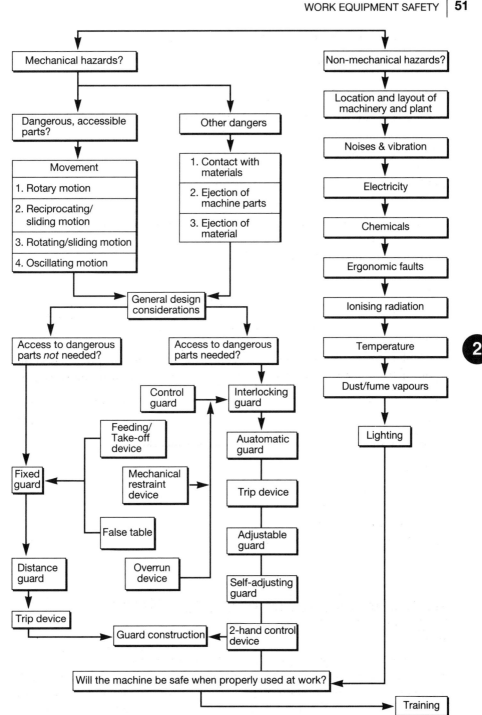

FIG 2.17   Is the machine safe for use at work?

Hand tool inspections

A number of points should be considered when examining hand tools.

Chisels

'Mushroomed' chisel heads are a frequent cause of blinding and eye injuries and any mushrooming should be removed through grinding. Chisel heads should be kept free from dirt, oil and grease.

Hammers

The shaft should be in sound condition and soundly fixed to the head. Where the shaft is split, loose to the head, broken or damaged, it should be replaced. Chipped, rounded or badly worn hammer heads should not be used, and heads should be kept free of oil and grease.

Files

A file should never be used without a handle, and the handle should be in sound condition. Evidence of chips and other signs of damage indicate a file could be dangerous.

Spanners

Open-ended spanners which are splayed or box spanners with splits should be discarded. Adjustable spanners and monkey wrenches should be examined regularly for evidence of free play and splaying of the jaws.

Screwdrivers

Handles and tips should be in sound condition and worn-ended screwdrivers should never be used. A screwdriver should never be used as a chisel and when using a screwdriver, the work should be clamped or secured, never held in the hand. Employees must be trained to use the correct size screwdriver at all times.

PROVISION AND USE OF WORK EQUIPMENT REGULATIONS 1992 (PUWER)

These regulations implement the European Council Directive of 30th November 1989 'concerning the minimum safety and health requirements for the use of work equipment by workers at work', generally known as the 'Machinery Safety' Directive 89/655/EEC. Regulations 1 to 10 came into force on 1st January 1993. Regulations 11 to 24, 27 and Schedule 2 do not come into force until 1st January 1997 for work equipment first provided before 1st January 1993 ('existing equipment').

They revoke much of the old legislation – 17 codes of regulations, seven sections of the Factories Act 1961, one section of the Offices, Shops and Railway Premises Act 1963 and two sections of the Mines and Quarries Act 1954.

These comprehensive regulations are intended to:

- implement the Machinery Safety Directive
- simplify and clarify existing laws on the provision and use of work equipment by the reform of older legislation and
- form a coherent single set of key health and safety requirements concerning the provision and use of work equipment.

The regulations are supported by guidance prepared by the HSE and HSC containing practical advice on implementation of the regulations.

Generally, the regulations are framed in a simple and straightforward way. They cover the more general requirements relating to the selection, suitability and maintenance of work equipment, together with procedures for dealing with specific risks and the giving of information, instruction and training. The more specific risks associated with dangerous parts, machinery failure, temperature and operating conditions, and the procedures and precautions necessary to avert these risks are also dealt with.

The majority of the requirements are of an absolute nature implying no form of defence is available to an employer, self-employed person or manufacturer, designer, supplier, importer or installer of work equipment when charged with an offence under the regulations.

Regulation 2 – interpretation

'**Work equipment**' includes any machinery, appliance, apparatus or tool and any assembly of components which, in order to achieve a common end, are arranged and controlled so that they function as a whole.

'**Use**' in relation to work equipment means any activity involving work equipment including starting, stopping, programming, setting, transporting, repairing, modifying, maintaining, servicing and cleaning, and related expressions shall be construed accordingly.

Regulation 4 – application of requirements under these regulations

1 The requirements imposed by these regulations on an employer shall apply in respect of work equipment provided for or used by any of his employees at work.

2 The requirements imposed by these regulations on an employer shall also apply:

(a) to a self-employed person in respect of work equipment he uses at work
(b) to any person who has control, to any extent, of non-domestic premises made available to persons as a place of work, in respect of work equipment used in such premises by such persons and to the extent of his control
(c) to any person to whom the provisions of the Factories Act 1961 apply by virtue of section 17(5) of that Act as if he were the occupier of a factory, in respect of work equipment used in the premises deemed to be a factory by that section.

3 Any reference in para 2(b) to a person having control of any premises or matter is a reference to the person having control of the premises or matter in connection with the carrying on by him of a trade, business or other undertaking (whether for profit or not).

Regulation 5 – suitability of work equipment

1 Every employer shall ensure that work equipment is so constructed or adapted as to be suitable for the purpose for which it is used or provided.

2 In selecting work equipment, every employer shall have regard to the working conditions and to the risks to health and safety of persons which exist in the premises or undertaking in which that work equipment is to be used and any additional risk posed by the use of that work equipment.

3 Every employer shall ensure that work equipment is used only for operations for which, and under conditions for which, it is suitable.

4 In this regulation 'suitable' means suitable in any respect which it is reasonably foreseeable will affect the health or safety of any person.

Regulation 6 – maintenance

1 Every employer shall ensure that work equipment is **maintained** in **an efficient state, in efficient working order and in good repair.**

2 Every employer shall ensure that where any machinery has a maintenance log, the log is kept up to date.

Regulation 7 – specific risks

1 Where the use of work equipment is likely to involve a specific risk to health or safety, every employer shall ensure that:
(a) the use of that work equipment is restricted to those persons given the task of using it and

(b) repairs, modifications, maintenance or servicing of that work equipment is restricted to those persons who have been specifically designated to perform operations of that description (whether or not also authorised to perform other operations).

2 The employer shall ensure that the persons designated for the purposes of the above paragraph have received adequate training related to any operations in respect of which they have been so designated.

Regulation 8 – information and instructions

1 Every employer shall ensure that all persons who use work equipment have available to them adequate health and safety information and, where appropriate, written instructions pertaining to the use of that work equipment.

2 Every employer shall ensure that any of his employees who supervises or manages the use of work equipment has available to him adequate health and safety information and, where appropriate, written instructions pertaining to the use of that work equipment.

3 Without prejudice to the generality of paras (1) and (2), the information and instructions required by either of these paragraphs shall include information and, where appropriate, written instructions on:
(a) the conditions in which and the methods by which the work equipment may be used
(b) foreseeable abnormal situations and the action to be taken if such a situation were to occur and
(c) any conclusions to be drawn from experience in using the work equipment.

4 Information and instruction required by this regulation shall be readily comprehensible to those concerned.

Regulation 9 – training

1 Every employer shall ensure that all persons who use work equipment have received adequate training for the purpose of health and safety, including training in the methods which may be adopted when using the work equipment, any risks which such use may entail and the precautions to be taken.

2 Every employer shall ensure that any of his employees who supervises or manages the use of work equipment has received adequate training for purposes of health and safety, including training in the methods which may be adopted when using the work equipment, any risks which such use may entail and precautions to be taken.

Regulation 10 – conformity with EU requirements

1 Every employer shall ensure that any item of work equipment provided for use in the premises or undertaking of the employer complies with any enactment (whether in an Act or instrument) which implements in the UK any of the relevant EU directives listed in Schedule 1 which is applicable to that item of work equipment.

2 Where it is shown that an item of work equipment complies with an enactment (whether an Act or instrument) to which it is subject by virtue of para 1, the requirements of regulations 11 to 24 shall apply in respect of that item of work equipment only to the extent that the relevant EU directive implemented by that enactment is not applicable to that item of work equipment.

Regulation 11 – dangerous parts of machinery

1 Every employer shall ensure that measures are taken in accordance with para 2 which are effective:
   (a) to prevent access to any dangerous part of machinery to any rotating stock-bar or
   (b) to stop the movement of any dangerous part of machinery or rotating stock-bar before any part of a person enters a danger zone.

2 The measures required by para 1 shall consist of:
   (a) the provision of fixed guards enclosing every dangerous part or rotating stock-bar where and to the extent that it is practicable to do so, but where or to the extent that it is not, then
   (b) the provision of other guards or protection devices where and to the extent that it is practicable to do so, but where or to the extent that it is not, then
   (c) the provision of jigs, holders, push-sticks or similar protection appliances used in conjunction with the machinery where and to the extent that it is practicable to do so, but where or to the extent it is not, then
   (d) the provision of information, instruction, training and supervision.

3 All guards and protection devices provided under sub-paras (a) or (b) of para 2 shall:
   (a) be suitable for the purpose of which they are provided
   (b) be of good construction, sound material and adequate strength
   (c) be maintained in an efficient state, in efficient working order and in good repair
   (d) not give rise to any increased risk to health or safety
   (e) not be easily bypassed or disabled
   (f) be situated at sufficient distance from the danger zone
   (g) not unduly restrict the view of the operating cycle of the machinery, where such a view is necessary

(h) be so constructed or adapted that they allow operations necessary to fit or replace parts and for maintenance work, restricting access so that it is allowed only to the area where the work is to be carried out and, if possible, without having to dismantle the guard or protection device.

4 All protection appliances provided under sub-para (c) or para 2 shall comply with sub-paras (a) to (d) and (g) of para 3.

5 In this regulation **danger zone** means any zone in or around machinery in which a person is exposed to a risk to health or safety from contact with a dangerous part of machinery or a rotating stock-bar; **stock-bar** means any part of a stock bar which projects beyond the head-stock of a lathe.

Regulation 12 – protection against specified hazards

1 Every employer shall take measures to ensure that the exposure of a person using work equipment to any risk to his health or safety from any hazard specified in para 3 is either prevented, or, where that is not reasonably practicable, adequately controlled.

2 The measures required by para 1 shall:
   (a) be measures other than the provision of personal protective equipment or of information, instruction, training and supervision, so far as is reasonably practicable and
   (b) include, where appropriate, measures to minimise the effects of the hazard as well as to reduce the likelihood of the hazard occurring.

3 The hazards referred to in para 1 are:
   (a) any article or substance falling or being ejected from work equipment
   (b) rupture or disintegration of parts of work equipment
   (c) work equipment catching fire or overheating
   (d) the unintended or premature discharge of any article or of any gas, dust, liquid, vapour or other substance which, in each case, is produced, used or stored in the work equipment
   (e) the unintended or premature explosion of the work equipment or any article or substance produced, used or stored in it.

4 For the purposes of this regulation, **adequate** means adequate having regard only to the nature of the hazard and the nature and degree of exposure to the risk, and **adequately** shall be construed accordingly.

Regulation 13 – high or very low temperature

Every employer shall ensure that work equipment, parts of work equipment and any article or substance produced, used or stored in work equipment which, in each case, is at a high or very low temperature shall have protection where appropriate so as to prevent injury to any person by burn, scald or sear.

Regulation 14 – controls for starting or making a significant change in operating conditions

1 Every employer shall ensure that, where appropriate, work equipment is provided with one or more controls for the purposes of:
   (a) starting the work equipment (including re-starting after a stoppage for any reason) or
   (b) controlling any change in the speed, pressure or other operating conditions of the work equipment where such conditions after the change result in risk to health and safety which is greater than or of a different nature from such risks before the change.

2 Subject to para 3, every employer shall ensure that where a control is required by para 1, it shall not be possible to perform any operation mentioned in sub-para (a) or (b) of that paragraph except by a **deliberate action** on such control.

3 Para 1 shall not apply to re-starting or changing operating conditions as a result of the normal operating cycle of an automatic device.

Regulation 15 – stop controls

1 Every employer shall ensure that, where appropriate, work equipment is provided with one or more readily accessible controls the operation of which will bring the work equipment to a safe condition in a safe manner.

2 Any control required by para 1 shall bring the work equipment to a complete stop where necessary for reasons of health and safety.

3 Any control required by para 1 shall, if necessary for reasons of health and safety, switch off all sources of energy after stopping the functioning of the work equipment.

4 Any control required by para 1 shall operate in priority to any control which starts or changes the operating conditions of the work equipment.

Regulation 16 – emergency stop controls

1 Every employer shall ensure that, where appropriate, work equipment is provided with one or more emergency stop controls unless it is not necessary by reason of the nature of the hazards and the time taken for the work equipment to come to a complete stop as a result of the action of any control provided by virtue of regulation 15(1).

2 Any control required by para 1 shall operate in priority to any control required by regulation 15(1).

Regulation 17 – controls

1 Every employer shall ensure that all controls for work equipment shall be clearly visible and identifiable, including by appropriate marking where necessary.

2 Except where necessary, the employer shall ensure that no control for work equipment is in a position where any person operating the control is exposed to risk to his health or safety.

3 Every employer shall ensure where appropriate:
   (a) that, so far as is reasonably practicable, the operator of any control is able to ensure from the position of that control that no person is in a place where he would be exposed to any risk to his health or safety as a result of the operation of that control, but where or to the extent that it is not reasonably practicable.
   (b) that, so far as is reasonably practicable, systems of work are effective to ensure that, when work equipment is about to start, no person is in a place where he would be exposed to a risk to his health or safety as a result of the work equipment starting, but where neither of these is reasonably practicable
   (c) that an audible, visual or other suitable warning is given by virtue of regulation 24 whenever work equipment is about to start.

Regulation 18 – control systems

1 Every employer shall ensure, so far as is reasonably practicable, that all control systems of work equipment are safe.

2 Without prejudice to the generality of para 1, a control system shall not be safe unless:
   (a) its operation does not create an increased risk to health or safety
   (b) it ensures, so far as is reasonably practicable, that any fault in or damage to any part of the control system or the loss of supply of any source of energy used by the work equipment cannot result in additional or increased risk to health or safety
   (c) it does not impede the operation of any control required by regulation 15 or 16.

Regulation 19 – isolation from sources of energy

1 Every employer shall ensure that where appropriate work equipment is provided with suitable means to isolate it from all its sources of energy.

2 Without prejudice to the generality of para 1, the means mentioned in that paragraph shall not be suitable unless they are clearly identifiable and readily accessible.

3 Every employer shall take appropriate measures to ensure that reconnection of any energy source to work equipment does not expose any person using the work equipment to any risk to his health or safety.

Regulation 20 – stability

Every employer shall ensure that work equipment or any part of work equipment is stabilised by clamping or otherwise where necessary for purposes of health or safety.

Regulation 21 – lighting

Every employer shall ensure that suitable and sufficient lighting, which takes account of the operations to be carried out, is provided at any place where a person uses work equipment.

Regulation 22 – maintenance operations

Every employer shall take appropriate measures to ensure that work equipment is so constructed or adapted that, so far as is reasonably practicable, maintenance operations which involve a risk to health or safety can be carried out while the work equipment is shut down or, in other cases:

(a) maintenance operations can be carried out without exposing the person carrying them out to a risk to his health or safety or

(b) appropriate measures can be taken for the protection of any person carrying out maintenance operations which involve a risk to his health or safety.

Regulation 23 – markings

Every employer shall ensure that work equipment is marked in a clearly visible manner with any marking appropriate for reasons of health and safety.

Regulation 24 – warnings

1 Every employer shall ensure that work equipment incorporates any warnings or warning devices which are appropriate for the reasons of health and safety.

2 Without prejudice to the generality of para 1, warnings given by warning devices on work equipment shall not be appropriate unless they are unambiguous, easily perceived and easily understood.

Comments

These regulations incorporate important provisions of both a general and specific nature. It must be appreciated that the term 'work equipment' covers just about every form of machine, appliance and hand tool used by people at work. The implications for employers are systems-related, namely:

- the assessment of risks at the selection stage of new work equipment in terms of:
  - the actual construction of the equipment
  - the intended use of the equipment
  - its suitability for use in the workplace and
  - the conditions under which it is used
- on-going safety assessment of existing work equipment
- the implementation of formally-documented planned maintenance systems
- designation of certain trained persons to undertake identified high risk activities, such as maintenance or fault-finding without guards in position.
- the provision of information, instruction and training for staff using any form of work equipment and
- the development, documentation and implementation of management procedures aimed at ensuring safe use of work equipment in all work situations.

SECOND-HAND, HIRED AND LEASED WORK EQUIPMENT

Second-hand equipment

In situations where existing work equipment is sold by one company to another and brought into use by the second company, it becomes 'new equipment' and must meet the requirements for such equipment, even though it is second-hand. This means that the purchasing company will need to ascertain that the equipment meets the specific hardware provisions of regulations 11 to 24 before putting it into use.

Hired and leased equipment

Such equipment is treated in the same way as second-hand equipment, namely that it is classed as 'new equipment' at the hire/lease stage. On this basis, organisations hiring or leasing an item of work equipment will need to check that it meets the requirements of regulations 11 to 24 before putting it into use.

SUPPLY OF MACHINERY (SAFETY) REGULATIONS 1992

These regulations came into operation on 1st January 1993, and apply to:

- all types of machinery not specifically covered by legislation implementing other EU directives
- all machinery which is powered and has moving parts
- assemblies of several machines
- parts that modify the function of machines and
- components that can operate on their own.

They do not apply to:

- manually powered machinery
- machinery for transporting people or goods on the road
- machinery for lifting people
- machinery where the main hazard is electrical or specific hazards dealt with by other directives
- machinery for export outside the EU; or
- second-hand machinery, other than that imported from outside the EU.

The regulations require the suppliers of most machinery to certify that machinery satisfies the relevant essential safety requirements (ESRs) set out in Schedule 3 to the regulations and be prepared, on request, to justify this certification.

Dangerous machinery

In the case of the more dangerous classes of machinery, such as saws, presses and underground equipment, the requirements are more onerous.

Suppliers must send to an approved test house a technical file detailing how the machine complies with European harmonised standards, or if it does not, a sample of the machine itself for type approval.

The regulations also prescribe that the supplier must provide operating instructions in a European Community language that the operator can understand, and installation and maintenance instructions in a language, agreed with the purchasers, that the installers will understand.

The CE mark must be affixed by the supplier to demonstrate that the machine complies with the requirements of the directive or of any other directive prescribing the CE mark.

Enforcement

The regulations are enforced by trading standards officers for domestic use and HSE inspectors for machinery intended for use in the workplace and elsewhere.

2

Hazardous processes

Industry operates many hazardous processes. These processes may involve the use or manufacture of hazardous chemicals and the operation of plant at high or low temperatures and/or pressures. The potential for major disaster situations and pollution incidents must, therefore, be considered. The question of the transport of hazardous substances must further be taken into account.

Legislation dealing with these matters is covered in a number of regulations, in particular, the Chemicals (Hazard Information and Packaging for Supply) (CHIP) Regulations 1994, the Control of Industrial Major Accident Hazards (CIMAH) Regulations 1984 and 1988, the Dangerous Substances (Conveyance by Road in Road Tankers and Tank Containers) Regulations 1981, the Control of Substances Hazardous to Health (COSHH) Regulations 1994, the Notification of New Substances Regulations 1993 and the Pressure Systems and Transportable Gas Containers Regulations 1989.

Safety in plant design and construction, operation and maintenance is of crucial significance. In the majority of cases, this will require high standards of expertise in the design of installations, some form of risk assessment, including consideration of the risks to the local population, formally-established waste storage and disposal procedures, planned preventive maintenance systems and the use of well-trained and supervised operators.

This chapter deals with the legal requirements and operational procedures necessary to ensure safe operation of hazardous processes.

CONTROL OF SUBSTANCES HAZARDOUS TO HEALTH REGULATIONS 1994 (COSHH 2)

The COSHH Regulations apply to every form of workplace and every type of work activity involving the use of substances which may be hazardous to health to people at work. The regulations are supported by a number of Approved Codes of Practice (ACOPs), including 'Control of substances hazardous to health', 'Control of carcinogenic substances' and 'Control of biological agents'. Because of the relative significance of these regulations to all who use or come into contact with substances hazardous to health at work, the full extent of the duties under the regulations are covered below.

Introduction to the COSHH Regulations

The regulations and the various ACOPs set out a strategy for safety with substances hazardous to health covering more than 40,000 chemicals and materials, together with hazardous substances generated by industrial processes.

The strategy established in the COSHH Regulations covers four main areas:

- acquisition and dissemination of information and knowledge about hazardous substances
- the assessment of risks to health associated with the use, handling, storage, etc of such substances at work
- elimination or control of health risks by the use of appropriate engineering applications, operating procedures and personal protection
- monitoring the effectiveness of the measures taken.

It should be appreciated that the majority of the duties imposed on employers and others are of an absolute or strict nature. The 1994 regulations revoke in full the 1988 regulations.

THE COSHH REGULATIONS 1994

Application of regulations 6 to 12

1 Regulations 6 to 12 shall have effect with a view to protecting persons against risks to their health, whether immediate or delayed, arising from exposure to substances hazardous to health **except**:
   (a) lead – so far as the Lead at Work Regulations 1980 apply and asbestos – so far as the Control of Asbestos at Work Regulations 1987 apply
   (b) where the substance is hazardous solely by virtue of its radioactive, explosive or flammable properties, or solely because it is at a high or low temperature or a high pressure
   (c) where the risk to health is a risk to the health of a person to whom the substance is administered in the course of his medical treatment
   (e) below ground in any mine within the meaning of sec. 180 of the Mines and Quarries Act 1954.

2 In para 1(c) **medical treatment** means medical or dental examination or treatment which is conducted by, or under the direction of, a registered medical practitioner or registered dentist and includes any such examination, treatment or administration of any substance conducted for the purpose of research.

3 Nothing in these regulations shall prejudice any requirement imposed by or under any enactment relating to public health or the protection of the environment.

Regulation 2 – definitions

The following definitions in regulation 2 are of significance.

Approved supply list has the meaning assigned to it in regulation 4(1) of the Chemicals (Hazard Information and Packaging for supply) (CHIP) Regulations 1994.

Biological agent means any micro-organism, cell, culture, or human endoparasite, including any which have been genetically modified, which may cause any infection, allergy, toxicity or otherwise create a hazard to human health.

Carcinogen means:

- any substance or preparation which if classified in accordance with the classification provided by regulation 5 of the CHIP 2 Regulations 1994 would be in the category 6 danger, carcinogenic (category 1) or carcinogenic (category 2) whether or not the substance or preparation would be required to be classified under those regulations or
- any substance or preparation:
  - listed in Schedule 8 and
  - any substance or preparation arising from a process specified in Schedule 8 which is a substance hazardous to health.

Fumigation means any operation in which a substance is released into the atmosphere so as to form a gas to control or kill pests or other undesirable organisms; and **fumigate** and **fumigant** shall be construed accordingly.

Maximum exposure limit for a substance hazardous to health means the maximum exposure limit for that substance set out in Schedule 1 in relation to the reference period specified therein when calculated by a method approved by the HSC.

Micro-organism includes any microbiological entity, cellular or non-cellular, which is capable of replication or of transferring genetic material.

Occupational exposure standard for a substance hazardous to health means the standard approved by the HSC for that substance in relation to the specified reference period when calculated by a method approved by the HSC.

Substance means any natural or artificial substance whether in solid or liquid form or in the form of a gas or vapour (including micro-organisms).

Substance hazardous to health means any substance (including any preparation) which is:

(a) a substance listed in Part I of the approved supply list as dangerous for supply within the meaning of the CHIP 2 Regulations 1994 and for which an indication of danger specified for the substance in Part V of that list is very toxic, toxic, harmful, corrosive or irritant

(b) a substance specified in Schedule 1 (which lists substances assigned maximum exposure limits) or for which the HSC has approved an occupational exposure standard. (See current HSE Guidance Note EH 40 'Occupational Exposure Limits')

(c) a biological agent

(d) dust of any kind when present at a substantial concentration in air and

(e) a substance, not being a substance mentioned in sub-paragraphs (a) to (d) above, which creates a hazard to the health of any person which is comparable with the hazards created by substances mentioned in those sub-paragraphs.

Regulation 6 – assessment of health risks created by work involving substances hazardous to health

1 An employer shall not carry on any work which is liable to expose any employees to any substance hazardous to health unless he has made a **suitable and sufficient assessment** of the risks created by that work to the health of those employees and of the steps that need to be taken to meet the requirements of the regulations.

2 This assessment shall be reviewed forthwith if:
   (a) there is reason to suspect that the assessment is no longer valid or
   (b) there has been a significant change in the work to which the assessment relates.
   Where as a result of the review, changes in the assessment are required, those changes shall be made.

Note: A 'suitable and sufficient' assessment

The General ACOP indicates that a suitable and sufficient assessment should include:

- an assessment of the risks to health
- the steps which need to be taken to achieve adequate control of exposure, in accordance with regulation 7 and
- identification of other action necessary to comply with regulations 8–12.

An assessment of the risks created by any work should involve:

- a consideration of:
  - which substances or types of substances (including micro-organisms) employees are liable to be exposed to (taking into account the consequences of possible failure of any control measures provided to meet the requirements of regulation 7)
  - what effects those substances can have on the body

- where the substances are likely to be present and in what form
- the ways in which and the extent to which any groups of employees or other persons could potentially be exposed, taking into account the nature of the work and process, and any reasonably foreseeable deterioration in, or failure of, any control measure provided for the purpose of regulation 7

● an estimate of exposure, taking into account engineering measures and systems of work currently employed for controlling potential exposure

● where valid standards exist, representing adequate control, comparison of the estimate with those standards.

Detailed guidance on COSHH assessment is provided in the HSE publication 'A step by step guide to COSHH assessment' (HMSO).

Regulation 7 – prevention or control of exposure to substances hazardous to health

1 Every employer shall ensure that the exposure of his employees to substances hazardous to health is either prevented or, where this is not reasonably practicable, adequately controlled.

2 So far as is reasonably practicable, the prevention or adequate control of exposure of employees to substances hazardous to health, except to a carcinogen or biological agent, shall be secured by measures other than the provision of personal protective equipment.

3 Without prejudice to the generality of (1), where the assessment made under regulation 6 shows that it is not reasonably practicable to prevent exposure to a **carcinogen** by using an alternative substance or process, the employer shall employ **all** the following measures, namely:
   (a) the total **enclosure** of the process and handling systems unless this is not reasonably practicable
   (b) the use of plant, processes and systems of work which **minimise** the generation of, or **suppress and contain**, spills, leaks, dust, fumes and vapours of carcinogens
   (c) the **limitation** of the quantities of a carcinogen at the place of work
   (d) the keeping of the number of persons exposed to a **minimum**
   (e) the prohibition of **eating, drinking and smoking** in areas that may be contaminated by carcinogens
   (f) the provision of **hygiene measures** including adequate washing facilities and regular cleaning of walls and surfaces
   (g) the **designation** of those areas and installations which may be contaminated by carcinogens, and the use of suitable and sufficient **warning signs** and
   (h) the **safe storage, handling and disposal** of carcinogens and the use of closed and clearly labelled **containers**.

4 Where the measures taken in accordance with paras 2 or 3, as the case may be, do not prevent, or provide adequate control of, exposure to substances hazardous to health to which those paragraphs apply, then, **in addition** to taking those measures, the employer shall provide those employees with suitable **personal protective equipment** as will adequately control their exposure to those substances.

5 Any personal protective equipment provided by an employer shall comply with any enactment which implements in the UK any provision on design or manufacture with respect to health or safety in any relevant EU directive listed in Schedule 1 to the Personal Protective Equipment at Work Regulations 1992 which is applicable to that item of personal protective equipment.

6 Where there is exposure to a substance for which a maximum exposure limit (MEL) is specified in Schedule 1, the control of exposure shall, so far as the inhalation of that substance is concerned, only be treated as being adequate if the level of exposure is reduced so far as is reasonably practicable and in any case below the MEL.

7 Without prejudice to the generality of para 1, where there is exposure to a substance for which an occupational exposure standard (OES) has been approved, the control of exposure shall, so far as the inhalation of the substance is concerned, only be treated as adequate if:
(a) the OES is not exceeded or
(b) where the OES is exceeded, the employer identifies the reasons for the standard being exceeded and takes appropriate action to remedy the situation as soon as is reasonably practicable.

8 Where **respiratory protective equipment** is provided in pursuance of this regulation, then it shall:
(a) be suitable for the purpose and
(b) comply with para 5 or, where no requirement is imposed by virtue of that paragraph, be of a type approved or shall conform to a standard approved, in either case, by the HSE.

9 In the event of a failure of a control measure which might result in the escape of **carcinogens** into the workplace, the employer shall ensure that:
(a) only those persons who are responsible for the carrying out of repairs and other necessary work are permitted in the affected area and they are provided with suitable respiratory protective equipment and protective clothing and
(b) employees and other persons who may be affected are informed of the failure forthwith.

10 Schedule 9 of these regulations shall have effect in relation to biological agents.

11 In this regulation **adequate** means adequate having regard only to the nature of the substance and the nature and degree of exposure to substances hazardous to health and **adequately** shall be construed accordingly.

Regulation 8 – use of control measures, etc

1 Every **employer** who provides any control measure, PPE or other thing or facility pursuant to these regulations shall take all reasonable steps to ensure that it is properly used or applied as the case may be.

2 Every **employee** shall make full and proper use of any control measure, PPE or other thing or facility provided pursuant to these regulations and shall take all reasonable steps to ensure it is returned after use to any accommodation provided for it and, if he discovers any defect therein, he shall report it forthwith to his employer.

Regulation 9 – maintenance, examination and test of control measures, etc

1 Any employer who provides any control measure to meet the requirements of regulation 7 shall ensure that it is maintained **in efficient state, in efficient working order and in good repair** and, in the case of personal protective equipment, in a clean condition.

2 Where engineering controls are provided to meet the requirements of regulation 7, the employer shall ensure that thorough examinations and tests of those engineering controls are carried out:
   (a) in the case of local exhaust ventilation (LEV) plant, at least once every 14 months, or for LEV plant used in conjunction with a process specified in column 1 of Schedule 3, at not more than the interval specified in the corresponding entry in column 2 of that Schedule and
   (b) in any other case, at suitable intervals.

3 Where respiratory protective equipment (RPE) (other than disposable RPE) is provided to meet the requirements of regulation 7, the employer shall ensure that at suitable intervals thorough examinations and, where appropriate, tests of that equipment are carried out.

4 Every employer shall keep a suitable record of examinations and tests carried out in accordance with the paras 2 and 3, and of any repairs carried out as a result of those examinations and tests, and that record or a suitable summary thereof, shall be kept available for at least five years from the date on which it was made.

Regulation 10 – monitoring exposure at the workplace

1 In any case in which:
   (a) it is a requisite for ensuring the maintenance of adequate control of the exposure of employees to substances hazardous to health or
   (b) it is otherwise requisite for protecting the health of employees
      the employer shall ensure that the exposure of employees to substances hazardous to health is monitored in accordance with a suitable procedure.

2 Where a substance or process is specified in column 1 of Schedule 4, monitoring shall be carried out at the frequency specified in the corresponding entry in column 2 of that Schedule.

3 The employer shall keep a record of any monitoring carried out for the purpose of the regulation and that that record or a suitable summary thereof shall be kept available:
   (a) where the record is representative of the personal exposure of identifiable employees, for at least 40 years
   (b) in any other case, for at least five years.

Regulation 11 – health surveillance

1 Where it is appropriate for the protection of the health of his employees who are, or are liable to be exposed to a substance hazardous to health, the employer shall ensure that such employees are under suitable health surveillance.

2 Health surveillance shall be treated as being appropriate where:
   (a) the employee is exposed to one of the substances specified in column 1 of Schedule 5 and is engaged in a process specified in column 2 of that Schedule, unless that exposure is not significant or
   (b) the exposure of the employee to a substance hazardous to health is such that an identifiable disease or adverse health effect may be related to the exposure, there is a reasonable likelihood that the disease or effect may occur under the particular conditions of his work and there are valid techniques for detecting indications of the disease or that effect.

3 The employer shall ensure that a health record, containing particulars approved by the HSE, in respect of each of his employees to whom para 1 relates is made and maintained and that that record is kept in a suitable form for at least 40 years from the date of the last entry made in it.

4 Where an employer who holds records in accordance with para 3 ceases to trade, he shall forthwith notify the HSE in writing and offer those records to the HSE.

Paras 5–11 deal with the following matters:

5 Medical surveillance where employees are exposed to substances specified in Schedule 5.

6 Prohibition by an employment medical adviser on engagement in work of employees considered to be at risk.

7 Continuance of health surveillance for employees after exposure has ceased.

8 Access by employees to their health records.

9 Duty on employees to present themselves for health surveillance.

10 Access to inspect a workplace or any record kept by employment medical advisers or appointed doctors.

11 Review by an aggrieved employee or employer of medical suspension by an employment medical adviser or appointed doctor.

12 In this paragraph:

Appointed doctor means a registered medical practitioner who is appointed for the time being in writing by the HSE for the purposes of this regulation.

Employment medical adviser means an employment medical adviser appointed under section 56 of the 1974 Act.

Health surveillance includes biological monitoring.

Regulation 12 – information, instruction and training for persons who may be exposed to substances hazardous to health

1 An employer who undertakes work which may expose any of his employees to substances hazardous to health shall provide that employee with such information, instruction and training as is suitable and sufficient for him to know:
(a) the risks to health created by such exposure and
(b) the precautions which should be taken.

2 Without prejudice to the generality of para 1, the information provided under that paragraph shall include:
(a) information on the results of any monitoring of exposure at the workplace in accordance with regulation 10 and, in particular, in the case of substance hazardous to health specified in Schedule 1, the employee or his representatives shall be informed forthwith if the results of such monitoring shows that the MEL has been exceeded and
(b) information on the collective results of any health surveillance undertaken in a form calculated to prevent it from being identified as relating to a particular person.

3 Every employer shall ensure that any person (whether or not his employee)

who carries out work in connection with the employer's duties under these regulations has the necessary information, instruction and training.

Regulation 13 – provisions relating to certain fumigations

1   This regulation shall apply to fumigations in which the fumigant used or intended to be used is **hydrogen cyanide, ethylene oxide, phosphine or methyl bromide**, except that this regulation shall not apply to fumigations using the fumigant specified in column 1 of Schedule 6 when the nature of the fumigation is that specified in the corresponding entry in column 2 of that Schedule.

2   An employer shall not undertake any fumigation to which this regulation applies unless he has:
   (a) notified the persons specified in Part I of Schedule 7 of his intention to undertake the fumigation and
   (b) provided to those persons the information specified in Part II of that Schedule at least 24 hours in advance, or such shorter time in advance, as the person required to be notified may agree.

3   An employer who undertakes a fumigation to which this regulation applies shall ensure that, before the fumigant is released, suitable warning notices have been affixed at all points of reasonable access to the premises or to those parts of the premises in which the fumigation is to be carried out and that after the fumigation has been completed, and the premises are safe to enter, the warning notices are removed.

Regulation 16 – defence under the regulations

In any proceedings for an offence consisting of a contravention of these regulations it shall be a defence for any person to prove that he took **all reasonable precautions** and exercised **all due diligence** to avoid the commission of that offence.

Note: To rely on this defence, the employer must establish that, on the balance of probabilities, he has taken **all** precautions that were reasonable and exercised **all** due to diligence to ensure that these precautions were implemented in order to avoid such a contravention. It is unlikely that an employer could rely on a regulation 16 defence if:

- precautions were available which had not been taken or
- that he had not provided sufficient information, instruction and training, together with adequate supervision, to ensure that the precautions were effective.

Thus a stated policy on the use of substances hazardous to health, company code of practice or other form of instructions to staff is insufficient without evidence of such staff being provided with the appropriate information, instruction, training and supervision.

Schedules to the COSHH Regulations

1 List of substances assigned maximum exposure limits.

2 Prohibition of certain substances hazardous to health for certain purposes.

3 Frequency of through examination and test of local exhaust ventilation plant used in certain processes.

4 Specific substances and processes for which monitoring is required.

5 Medical surveillance.

6 Fumigations excepted from regulation 13.

7 Notification of certain fumigations.

8 Other substances and processes to which the definition of 'carcinogen' relates.

9 Special provision relating to biological agents.

The COSHH package

Control of Substances Hazardous to Health Regulations 1994 (SI 1994 No. 3246) HMSO, London.

Approved Codes of Practice:

Control of Substances Hazardous to Health
Control of Carcinogenic Substances
Control of Biological Agents
Control of Vinyl Chloride at Work
Control of Substances Hazardous to Health in the Production of Pottery.

CLASSIFICATION OF HAZARDOUS SUBSTANCES (SUPPLY REQUIREMENTS)

Hazardous substances are classified according to Schedule 1 of the Chemicals (Hazard Information and Packaging for Supply) (CHIP 2) Regulations 1994 as follows.

PART I   CATEGORIES OF DANGER

Column 1 *Category of danger*	Column 2 *Property (See Note 1)*	Column 3 *Symbol–letter*
PHYSICO-CHEMICAL PROPERTIES		
Explosive	Solid, liquid, pasty or gelatinous substances and preparations which may react exothermically without atmospheric oxygen thereby quickly evolving gases, and which under defined test conditions detonate, quickly deflagrate or upon heating explode when partially confined.	E
Oxidising	Substances and preparations which give rise to a exothermic reaction in contact with other sub-stances, particularly flammable substances.	0
Extremely flammable	Liquid substances and preparations having an extremely low flash point and a low boiling point, and gaseous substances and preparations which are flammable in contact with air at ambient temperature and pressure.	F+
Highly flammable	The following substances and preparations: ● substances and preparations which may become hot and finally catch fire in contact with air at ambient temperature without any application of energy ● solid substances and preparations which may readily catch fire after brief contact with a source of ignition and which continue to burn or to be consumed after removal of the source of ignition ● liquid substances and preparations having a very low flash point ● substances and preparations which, in contact with water or damp air, evolve highly flammable gases in dangerous quantities. (See Note 2)	F
Flammable	Liquid substances and preparations having a low flash point.	None

Column 1 Category of danger	Column 2 Property (See Note 1)	Column 3 Symbol– letter
HEALTH EFFECTS		
Very toxic	Substances and preparations which in **very low quantities** can cause death or acute or chronic damage to health when inhaled, swallowed or absorbed via the skin.	T+
Toxic	Substances and preparations which in **low quantities** can cause death or acute or chronic damage to health when inhaled, swallowed or absorbed via the skin.	T
Harmful	Substances and preparations which may cause death or acute or chronic damage to health when inhaled, swallowed or absorbed via the skin.	
Corrosive	Substances and preparations which may, on contact with living tissues, **destroy** them.	C
Irritant	Non-corrosive substances and preparations which through immediate, prolonged or repeated contact with the skin or mucous membrane, may cause **inflammation**.	Xi
Sensitising	Substances and preparations which, if they are inhaled or if they penetrate the skin, are capable of eliciting a reaction by **hypersensitisation** such that on further exposure to the substance or preparation, characteristic adverse effects are produced.	
Sensitising by inhalation		Xn
Sensitising by skin contact		Xi
Carcinogenic (See Note 3)	Substances and preparations which, if they are inhaled or ingested or if they penetrate the skin, may induce **heritable genetic defects** or increase their incidence.	

Column 1 *Category of danger*	Column 2 *Property (See Note 1)*	Column 3 *Symbol– letter*
category 1 category 2 category 3		T T Xn
Mutagenic **(See Note 3)**	Substances and preparations which, if they are inhaled or ingested or if they penetrate the skin, may induce **heritable generic defects** or increase their incidence.	
category 1 category 2 category 3		T T Xn
Toxic for reproduction **(See Note 3)**	Substances and preparations which, if they are inhaled or ingested or if they penetrate the skin, may produce or increase the incidence of **non-heritable adverse effects** in the progeny and/or an impairment of male or female reproductive functions or capacity.	
category 1 category 2 category 3		T T Xn
Dangerous for the environment **(See Note 4)**	Substances which, were they to enter into the environment, would present or might present an immediate or delayed danger for one or more components of the environment	N

③

Notes:

1 As further described in the **approved classification and labelling guide.**

2 Preparations packed in **aerosol dispensers** shall be classified as **flammable** in accordance with the additional criteria set out in Part II of this Schedule.

3 The categories are specified in the **approved classification and labelling guide.**

4 (a) In certain cases specified in the **approved supply list** and in the **approved classification and labelling guide as dangerous for the environment** do not require to be labelled with the symbol for this category of danger.

  (b) This category of danger does not apply to preparations.

THE PHYSICAL STATE OF HAZARDOUS SUBSTANCES

In the evaluation of the risks associated with hazardous substances and any air monitoring to be undertaken, it is necessary to consider the actual form taken by that substance. Substances carried in air are **aerosols**.

Forms of aerosol

Features of the various forms of aerosol are outlined below.

Dusts

Dust is an aerosol composed of solid inanimate particles. Dusts are solid airborne particles, often created by operations such as grinding, crushing, milling, sanding and demolition. Two of the principal dusts encountered in industry are asbestos and silica.

Dusts may be:

- *fibrogenic* – they cause fibrotic changes to lung tissue, eg silica, cement dust, coal dust and certain metals
- *toxic* – they eventually poison the body systems, eg arsenic, mercury, beryllium, phosphorus and lead.

Mists

A mist comprises airborne liquid droplets, a finely dispersed liquid suspended in air. Mists are mainly created by spraying, foaming, pickling and electro-plating. Danger arises most frequently from acid mist produced in industrial treatment processes, eg oil mist, chromic acid mist.

Fumes

These are fine solid particulates formed from the gaseous state usually by vaporisation or oxidation of metals, eg lead fume. Fumes usually form an oxide in contact with air. They are created by industrial processes which involve the heating and melting of metals, such as welding, smelting and arc air gouging. A common fume danger is the lead poisoning associated with the inhalation of lead fume.

Gases

These are formless fluids usually produced by chemical processes involving combustion or by the interaction of chemical substances. A gas will normally seek to completely fill the space into which it is liberated. A classic gas encountered in industry is carbon monoxide. Certain gases such as acetylene, hydrogen and methane are particularly flammable.

Vapours

A vapour is the gaseous form of a material normally encountered in a solid or liquid state at normal room temperature and pressure. Typical examples are solvents, such as trichloroethylene, which release vapours when the container is opened. Other liquids produce a vapour on heating, the amount of vapour being directly related to the boiling point of that particular liquid. A vapour contains very minute droplets of the liquid. However, in the case of a **fog**, the liquid droplets are much larger.

Smoke

Smoke is a product of incomplete combustion, mainly of organic materials. It may include fine particles of carbon in the form of ash, soot and grit that are visibly suspended in air.

SAFETY IN PLANT DESIGN, CONSTRUCTION AND OPERATION

To ensure appropriate safety standards in plants operating hazardous processes, a number of factors need consideration with regard to the design and the plant and its actual construction.

Location

The Flixborough and Seveso incidents focused attention on the question of the actual locations of high-risk processing plants. In the first case, the Nypro plant was totally destroyed by a vapour cloud explosion, and 28 people, engaged in various activities on site, were killed. The Seveso incident, on the other hand, was a classic air pollution incident in which an estimated kilogramme of Dioxin, a highly toxic substance, was released over the town, which had significant health effects on the local population.

The actual location of similar plants is now controlled, in particular, by the CIMAH Regulations. Clearly, any new installation operating a potentially hazardous process must be appropriately located, taking into account the risks not only to workers but to members of the public associated with that particular installation. Consideration must also be given to arrangements for the safe disposal of wastes and to the transport of dangerous substances to and from such a location.

At the actual construction stage of the plant there should be continuing liaison with the manufacturers and designers with a view to ensuring correct installation. Commissioning procedures should take account of possible adverse situations which could arise.

Layout

This term refers to the space available for those employees working within a particular room or area, and the situation of plant, equipment, machinery, processes and stored goods in relation to the operative and the work carried out. An efficient layout should meet the requirements of the Workplace (Health, Safety and Welfare) Regulations 1992 in terms of preventing or reducing overcrowding. It should enable the process to be carried out with and orderly and sequential flow of work, ensuring maximum safety and hygiene standards throughout.

Physical segregation of designated high risk areas may be necessary, and the premises should be large enough, allowing easy movement between one part and another.

A well-designed layout will eliminate many of the hazards which are associated with traditionally hazardous processes.

Safety in production activities

A commonly occurring hazard, encountered in many workplaces, is that of large quantities of potentially hazardous materials being stored in totally unsuitable locations. This can include, for example, large numbers of 50 gallon drums of flammable substances stored in production areas and service corridors, or the storage of toxic substances in places such as boiler houses, workshops and amenity areas. This situation is commonly brought about as a result of purchasing practices, which are more concerned with the financial benefits of purchasing in large quantities sooner than the hazards which can arise from such storage.

The need for some form of inventory control is, therefore, essential. Much will depend upon the range of hazardous substances used in a process, but a conscious attempt to limit the quantities stored is the first stage in reducing the risks. Where appropriate, it may be possible to substitute certain hazardous substances with substances which are less hazardous, a basic concept in protecting people at work.

In certain processes, it may be possible to improve reaction rates through more efficient mixing of chemical using, perhaps, high speed mixers. This permits smaller quantities of hazardous substances to be maintained or stored in a reactor or process vessel at any point in time.

Process design may also take into account the question of batch or continuous processing. Quite simply, the potential for overheating of plant which can have adverse effects, such as accelerated reaction rates, is greater in a continuous process than with batch processes. With a batch process cooling can take place in between individual batches of product, thereby eliminating the potential for escalating temperatures encountered with continuous processes. On the other hand, continuous processing avoids many of the risks that can be encountered with large inventories of chemical substances in batch processing operations, such as a runaway chemical reaction. Where there is a need to increase the rate of processing encountered with batch processing, continuous processing using a limited inventory of substances in tubular reactors is relatively safe. Tubular reactors have the safety advantage in that they can be isolated in sections, thereby reducing the outcome of a fault or malfunction in the system.

In process design, a number of other factors should be considered. For instance, pipework and storage tanks should be constructed to withstand pumping against a closed valve. Certain reactions, in particular vapour phase oxidation reactions, operate at temperatures very near the flammable limits of substances. Such reactions should, as far as possible, be eliminated or avoided by the appropriate choice of catalysts which permit the process to operate away from a potentially explosive temperature range. Where plastic-lined tanks are used, they should be steam-heated, as opposed to the use of immersion heaters. Low-level trip devices can be unreliable, with the result that the lining can become exposed to excess heat and a fire can start. This situation arose in the Seveso incident due to the fact that process steam was of a temperature sufficient to initiate a runaway reaction.

Information, instruction and training

Safe operation of plant hinges around effective levels of information, instruction and training for plant operators, together with high standards of supervision. This entails the documentation of written instructions on safe operating procedures and emergency procedures, the provision of information which is comprehensible and relevant to the staff concerned and, in some cases, one-to-one instruction. Training procedures should incorporate a form of written test to ensure competence of operators.

Housekeeping and cleaning procedures

A high standard of cleaning and housekeeping is required in high risk processing operations. Good housekeeping implies 'everything in its place and a place for everything'.

Cleaning schedules or programmes should identify in writing each item and/or area to be cleaned, the specific cleaning procedure and cleaning standards to be achieved, the frequency of cleaning, individual responsibility for ensuring each cleaning task is completed satisfactorily, and any precautions which may be necessary by cleaning staff with regard to, for instance, the safe use and storage of cleaning materials and equipment, the correct use of PPE and procedures for disposal of soiled cleaning items. Cleaning schedules should be subject to regular review.

Planned preventive maintenance

A written planned preventive maintenance schedule should be established and followed at all times. Engineering management should ensure that the maintenance programme is operated according to the schedule and sufficient resources should be made available to ensure the programme is on schedule according to the predetermined frequencies of maintenance of individual plant items and systems.

HAZARDOUS SUBSTANCES – BASIC REQUIREMENTS FOR HANDLING, STORAGE AND DISPOSAL

A wide range of hazardous substances is used in industry and commercial operations. The following basic principles should be considered to ensure safe use of such substances and preparations.

Handling and storage

- Meticulous levels of cleaning and housekeeping should be maintained.
- Smoking, eating or drinking in handling/storage areas should be prohibited.
- Staff should be trained and supervised in sound levels of personal hygiene practice.
- Only minimum quantities should be stored in working areas.
- Containers, including transfer containers, should be completely and accurately labelled.
- Hazardous substances should be carried with care, including the use of purpose-designed carriers for winchesters.
- Staff should be trained in the correct and regular use of personal protective equipment, ie full-face protection, apron, gauntlets.
- Any injuries, particularly skin wounds and eye splashes, should receive prompt treatment.
- Fume cupboards in laboratories should operate with a minimum face velocity of 0.4m/sec with sash opening at 300mm maximum.
- There should be clear identification of responsibilities at all levels of staff, supported by comprehensive information, instruction and training.

Toxic substances

- These should be used in diluted form wherever possible.
- Only limited quantities should be stored in work areas.
- A suitable system for containment of toxic substances should be provided.
- Wherever possible, all handling and dispensing from bulk should be eliminated.

- Working areas should be adequately ventilated.
- Toxic substances should be physically separated from other hazardous substances.
- Appropriate personal protective equipment should be provided and used.

Bulk chemical stores

Any store used for the bulk storage of hazardous chemical substances should, preferably, be a freestanding brick or concrete panel building with a solid floor. It should incorporate the following features:

- Corrosion-resistant finishes to walls, floors and other parts.
- Permanent ventilation at high and low level to provide a minimum ventilation rate of 20 air changes per hour.
- Artificial lighting by sealed bulkhead or fluorescent fittings to a minimum overall illuminance of 300 Lux.
- Floor drainage to an interceptor trap outside the building.
- Water supply and hose available to facilitate washing down and dilution of spillages.
- Sufficient space to allow all chemical substances to be stored in a safe manner with complete physical separation of strong acids and alkalis and by provision of bund walls capable of retaining potential spillages.
- Suitable access for bulk delivery should be provided.
- Dispensing facilities with appropriate personal protective equipment should be readily available.
- An emergency shower and eye wash, together with fire appliances should be located in close proximity to, but not inside, the store.
- Cautionary notices in accordance with the Safety Signs Regulations 1980 should be prominently displayed.

Containers

All containers

- These should be of suitable material and strength.
- These should be marked to indicate the contents and incorporate a hazard warning symbol.

Suppliers' containers

- Such containers should be marked with the information required under the CHIP Regulations.
- All staff should receive regular information, instruction and training in the correct use of containers and be advised to read such information.

Portable transfer containers

- These should incorporate a tight fitting lid or closure.
- They should be suitable for carrying.

GENERAL INSTRUCTIONS FOR OPERATORS
Never use:

- **Unmarked, unsuitable or makeshift containers.**
- **Containers normally used for some innocuous material, food or drink.**

Disposal

Disposal arrangements will depend upon whether a major or minor spillage has taken place.

Major spillages

Certain major spillage situations are classed as 'dangerous occurrences' under the Reporting of Injuries, Diseases and Dangerous Occurrences Regulations 1985, eg:

- the sudden uncontrolled release of one tonne or more of a highly flammable liquid from a plant
- an uncontrolled release or escape of a specified dangerous substance from a road tanker or tank container.

   In such circumstances:

- notify the police and HSE immediately and
- report the occurrence in writing on Form 2508 within seven days.

Minor spillages

The principal control objectives are:

- to contain the spillage and
- to remove or treat in order to render harmless.

Containment may be by the use of earth, sand, sawdust or prescribed neutralising absorbent materials.

   Treatment will depend on the risk involved. If dangerous to remove once contained, treat with the neutralising compound specified in the manufacturer's data sheet. Dilution with water may be a simple alternative in certain cases.

Disposal of waste materials

These should be removed to labelled and lidded refuse containers and contained inside heavy duty sealed plastic bags if appropriate.

It may be necessary to consult with the enforcing authority to ensure compliance with the Environmental Protection Act 1987. This legislation imposes heavy penalties for the unlawful disposal/dumping of chemical wastes.

HIGHLY FLAMMABLE LIQUIDS AND LIQUEFIED PETROLEUM GASES REGULATIONS 1972

These regulations lay down requirements for the following matters in relation to highly flammable liquids, etc used in a factory, ie:

- manner of storage
- marking of storage accommodation and vessels
- precautions to be observed for the prevention of fire and explosion
- provision of fire-fighting apparatus and
- securing means of escape in the event of fire.

'**Highly flammable liquids**' include both liquefied flammable gas, although not aqueous ammonia, and liquefied petroleum gases and therefore includes any liquid, liquid solution, emulsion or suspension which:

- gives off a flammable vapour at a temperature less than 32 °C when tested in the manner set out in Schedule 1 to the regulations (closed cup flash-point determination method) and
- supports combustion when tested in a manner set out in schedule 2 (combustibility test).

'**Liquefied flammable gas**' is any substance which would be a flammable gas at a temperature of 20 °C and a pressure of 760mm of mercury, but which is in a liquid form as a result of the application of pressure or refrigeration or both.

'**Liquefied petroleum gas**' covers both commercial butane and commercial propane, and any mixture of them.

Application of the regulations

The regulations apply to factories and impose duties on the occupier of the premises or, in some cases, the owner of the substances.

Storage of highly flammable liquids – general

When not in use or being conveyed, all highly flammable liquids (HFLs) should be stored in a safe manner. All HFLs should be stored in one of the following ways:

- in suitable fixed storage tanks in a safe position or
- in suitable closed vessels kept in a safe position in the open air and, where necessary, protected against direct sunlight or
- in suitable closed vessels kept in a store room which either is in a safe position or is of fire-resisting structure or
- in the case of a workroom where the aggregate quantity of HFL stored does not exceed 50 litres, in suitable closed vessels kept in a suitably placed cupboard or bin which is a fire-resisting structure.

Other storage precautions

Bund walls
Storage tanks should be provided with a bund wall enclosure which is capable of containing 110 per cent of the capacity of the largest tank within the bund.

Ground beneath vessels
The ground beneath storage vessels should be impervious to liquid and be so sloped that any minor spillage will not remain beneath the vessels, but will run away to the sides of the enclosure.

Bulk storage
Bulk storage tanks should not be located inside buildings or on the roof of a building. Underground tanks should not be sited under the floors of process buildings.

Drum storage
The area to be utilised for drum storage should be surrounded with a sill capable of containing the maximum spillage from the largest drum in store.

Marking of store rooms and containers

Every store room, cupboard, bin, tank and vessel used for storing HFLs should be clearly and boldly marked 'Highly Flammable' or 'Flashpoint below 32 °C' or 'Flashpoint in the range of 22 °C to 32 °C'.

Specific provisions for the storage of liquefied petroleum gas

All liquefied petroleum gas (LPG) must be stored in one of the following ways:

- in suitable underground reservoirs or in suitable fixed storage tanks located in a safe position, either underground or in the open air or
- in suitable movable storage tanks/vessels kept in a safe position in the open air or
- in pipelines or pumps forming part of an enclosed system or
- in suitable cylinders kept in safe positions in the open air or, where this is

not reasonably practicable, in a store room constructed of non-combustible material, having adequate ventilation, being in a safe position, of fire-resisting structure, and being used solely for the storage of LPG and/or acetylene cylinders.

LPG cylinders must be kept in a store until they are required for use, and any expended cylinder must be returned to store as soon as is reasonably practicable. This should ensure that only the minimum amount of LPG is kept in any workplace.

Marking of store rooms and containers

Every tank, cylinder, store room, etc used for the storage of LPG should be clearly and boldly marked 'Highly Flammable – LPG'.

Precautions against spills and leaks (all HFLs)

Where HFLs are to be conveyed within a factory, a totally enclosed piped system should be used, where reasonably practicable. Where not reasonably practicable, a system using closed non-spill containers will be acceptable.

Portable vessels, when emptied, should be removed to a safe place without delay.

Where in any process or operation any HFL is liable to leak or be spilled, all reasonably practicable steps should be taken to ensure that any such HFL should be contained or immediately drained off to a suitable container, or to a safe place, or rendered harmless.

Precautions against escaping vapours

No means likely to ignite vapour from any HFL should be present where a dangerous concentration of vapours from HFL may be present.

Where any HFL is being utilised in the workplace, reasonably practicable steps should be taken so as to minimise the risk of escape of HFL vapours into the general workplace atmosphere. Where such escape cannot be avoided, then the safe dispersal of HFL vapours should be effected, so far as is reasonably practicable.

Relaxation of fire resistance specifications in certain circumstances

In cases where either explosion pressure relief or adequate natural ventilation are required in a fire-resistant structure, a relaxation of the specification of a fire-resistant structure is allowable.

Fire escapes and fire certificates

There must be adequate and safe means of escape in case of fire from every room in which any HFL is manufactured, used or manipulated. This regulation does not apply where there is storage only.

Fire certificates are generally necessary where:

- HFLs are manufactured
- LPG is stored and
- liquefied flammable gas is stored.

Prevention of build up of deposits

Whenever, as a result of any process or, operation involving any HFL, a deposit of any solid waste residue liable to give rise to a risk of fire is liable to occur on any surface:

- steps must be taken to prevent the occurrence of all such deposits, so far as is reasonably practicable and
- where any such deposits occur, effective steps must be taken to remove all such residues, as often as necessary, to prevent danger.

Smoking controls

No person may smoke in any place in which any HFL is present and where the circumstances are such that smoking will give rise to the risk of fire.

Provision of fire-fighting equipment

Appropriate fire-fighting equipment should be made readily available for use in all factories where HFL is manufactured, used or manipulated.

Duties of employees

It is the duty of every employee to comply with them and co-operate in carrying them out.

If an employee discovers any defect in plant, equipment or appliance, it is his duty to report the defect without delay to the occupier, manager or other responsible person.

CONTROL OF INDUSTRIAL MAJOR ACCIDENT HAZARDS (CIMAH) REGULATIONS 1984

These regulations are concerned with the prevention of major incidents which can affect not only employees, but members of the public living in neighbouring areas to a major industrial installation. The CIMAH Regulations implemented the Seveso Directive.

The regulations apply to certain installations which are listed below. Before commencing activities at any of these types of installations, manufacturers must prepare a written report and send a copy to the HSE at least three months before commencing that activity.

Installations, substances used and isolated storage of certain substances

The installations covered by the regulations and listed in schedule 4 to the regulations are those:

- for the production, or treatment, or processing of organic or inorganic chemicals, using, amongst others:
  - alkylation
  - amination by ammonolysis
  - carbonylation
  - condensation
  - dehydrogenation
  - esterification
  - halogenation and manufacture of halogens
  - hydrogenisation
  - hydrolysis
  - oxidation
  - polymerisation
  - sulphonation
  - desulphurisation, manufacture and transformation of sulphur-containing compounds
  - nitration and manufacture of nitrogen-containing compounds
  - manufacture of phosphorus-containing compounds
  - formulation of pesticides and pharmaceutical products
  - distillation
  - extraction
  - solvation and
  - mixing
- for the purpose of distillation, refining or other processing of petroleum or other products
- for the total or partial disposal of solid or liquid substances by incineration or chemical decomposition
- for the production, processing or treatment of energy gases, eg LPG, LNG, SNG
- for the dry distillation of coal or lignite and
- for the production of metals or non-metals by a wet process or through electrical energy.

The regulations also apply:

- to substances listed in Schedule 1 which specifies a range of very toxic, other toxic substances and flammable substances which might be used in such installations and
- in the case of the isolated storage of certain dangerous substances, eg

ammonium nitrate, liquid oxygen and sulphur dioxide, where such a substance is stored and in excess of a quantity specified in Schedule 2.

Regulation 4 – duties of manufacturers

Manufacturers in control of major accident potential industrial activities must:

- identify major accident hazards and
- take steps to:
  - prevent major accident hazards and limit their consequences to persons and the environment and
  - provide those working on site with information, training and equipment, and, if necessary, produce documentation of this.

Regulation 5 – duty to notify major accidents

Where a major accident occurs on site, a manufacturer must notify the HSE of the accident. The HSE must then obtain from the manufacturer the following:

- information relating to:
  - the circumstances of the accident
  - the dangerous substances involved
  - data available for assessing the effects of the accident on man and the environment and
  - emergency measures taken
- the action considered necessary to:
  - alleviate medium or long-term effects of the accident and
  - prevent its recurrence.

Regulation 7 – duty to prepare and update reports

Where industrial activities involving a quantity of **reportable substances** (as listed in Schedule 3) or those involving isolated storage where the quantity to be stored is equal to or greater than the quantity specified, the manufacturer must, before undertaking the activity, prepare a written report containing the information required under regulation 8 and send such a report to the HSE at least three months before commencing that activity.

Under Schedule 6 the following information relating to every **dangerous substance** involved in an activity in a relevant quantity should be supplied by way of a written report to the HSE:

- the name of the dangerous substance or, for a dangerous substance of a general designation, the name corresponding to the chemical formula of the dangerous substance

- a general description of the analytical methods available to the manufacturer for determining the presence of the dangerous substance, or reference to such methods in the scientific literature
- a brief description of the hazards which may be created by the dangerous substance and
- the degree of purity of the dangerous substance and the names of the main impurities and their percentages.

The following information relating to the **installation** should be supplied to the HSE:

- a map of the site and its surrounding area to a scale large enough to show any features that may be significant in the assessment of the hazard or risk associated with the site
- a scale plan of the site showing the locations and quantities of all significant inventories of the dangerous substances
- a description of the processes or storage involving the dangerous substances and an indication of the conditions under which it is normally held
- the maximum number of persons likely to be present on site and
- information about the nature of the land use and the size and distribution of the population in the vicinity of the industrial activity to which the report relates.

Information relating to the **management system** for controlling the industrial activity must further be supplied to the HSE, such information to incorporate:

- the staffing arrangements for controlling the industrial activity with the name of the person responsible for safety on the site and the names of those who are authorised to set emergency procedures in motion and to inform outside authorities
- the arrangements made to ensure that the means provided for the safe operation of the industrial activity properly designed, constructed, tested, operated, inspected and maintained and
- the arrangements for training of persons working on the site.

The following information relating to the **potential major accidents** is also required:

- a description of the potential sources of a major accident and the conditions or events which could be significant in bringing one about
- a diagram of any plant in which the industrial activity is carried on, sufficient to show the features which are significant as regards the potential for a major accident or its prevention or control
- a description of the measures taken to prevent, control or minimise the consequences of any major accident

- information about the emergency procedures laid down for dealing with a major accident occurring at the site
- information about prevailing meteorological conditions in the vicinity of the site and
- an estimate of the number of people on site who may be exposed to the hazards considered in the report.

Regulation 8 – duty to report modifications to industrial activities

Manufacturers must not carry out any modifications to the industrial activity unless a further report to the HSE is made detailing those changes and sent to the HSE at least three months before making same.

Regulations 10 and 11 – duties to prepare safety plans

Manufacturers operating on specified major accident sites must prepare and update an adequate

- on-site emergency plan, detailing how major accidents will be dealt with on site together with the name of the person responsible for safety and the names of those persons authorised to take action and
- an off-site emergency plan.

PROJECT SAFETY ANALYSIS

Project safety analysis is a technique, undertaken as a joint exercise by an engineering manager, architect, plant and equipment supplier and installer, health and safety specialist, liability surveyor and other specialists. It aims to ensure that account is taken of accumulated experience, knowledge of the technology and best practice in the initial design of a project. It should be undertaken at the design stage of all major projects.

A typical form of analysis follows.

PROJECT SAFETY ANALYSIS	
Project Title	*Date of Analysis*

Dangerous substances

1 List all substances which are:
   (a) flammable
   (b) exoplosive
   (c) corrosive
   (d) toxic (state effects) and/or
   (e) have other specific hazards (state hazards).

2 State whether:
   (a) raw material
   (b) intermediate product
   (c) final product or by-product or
   (d) waste material.

3 List the points where such substances are encountered in the process by process description, equipment and cross reference to the operating process manual.

4 List significant physical properties, including:
   (a) incompatibility with other chemicals
   (b) chemical reaction rates
   (c) conditions of instability
   (d) other pertinent properties.

5 Show source of data and list available information sources on critical points.

Process hazards

1 List maximum operating pressures under both normal and abnormal operating conditions.

2 (a) State the form of pressure relief provided.
   (b) State the location of pressure relief provided.
   (c) State the condition of the relief devices.

3 (a) State the date when the relief devices were last tested.
   (b) State whether personnel are exposed to risk or injury on discharge of emergency relief devices.

4 (a) List the maximum permissible operating temperatures and sources of heat.
   (b) Identify the overtemperature controls that are provided for abnormal operating conditions.
   (c) State the protection provided to hot surfaces to protect personnel from burns.

FIG 3.1 Project safety analysis

Project Title	Date of Analysis
5 State the dangers that may be present if process reaction conditions are deviated from in the manner below and the protection procedures necessary. (a) abnormal temperature (b) abnormal reaction times (c) instrument failure (d) adding materials at the wrong stage (e) the materials added (f) material flow stoppage (g) equipment leaks, both out of the process and into the process (h) agitation failure (i) loss of inert gas blanket (j) error in valve or switch operation (k) blocked relief line (l) failure of relief line and (m) material spillage on floor or dispersal to air.	
Waste disposal **1** (a) List gaseous stack effluents and concentrations, together with smoke characteristics. (b) State whether scrubbers, electrostatic or centrifugal removal of stack effluents is needed. **2** State the approved height of the stacks. **3** State the direction of prevailing winds as they relate to exposed areas. **4** (a) State the effluents which are run through waste disposal, from any point in the process, and the method of transfer. (b) State their pH, relative toxicity, flammability and miscibility with water. **5** State whether waste chemicals can react with other waste chemicals in waste disposal systems and create hazards/difficulties. **6** State the procedure for preventing flammable liquids from reaching sewers. **7** List any special hazardous solid waste products, and the procedure for handling same, eg asbestos.	
Ventilation **1** (a) State the frequency of air changes required.	

FIG 3.1 Continued

Project Title	Date of Analysis

(b) State the frequency of checking ventilation equipment on a regular basis and the responsibility for same.

2 (a) State whether exhaust ventilation is required at specific processes.

(b) List the air flow rates to be achieved and the responsibility for checking same.

3 State the risk of the ventilation intakes recirculating contaminants.

Piping systems

1 Confirm that piping systems are adequately supported with permanent hangers.

2 Confirm that pipework is of proper material and scheduled thickness for service.

3 Confirm that pressure tests for critical services and processes are scheduled and on a regular basis.

4 Confirm that any bumping and/or tripping hazards are protected.

5 Confirm that safe access is provided to all valves.

Electrical equipment

1 Confirm that all hazardous locations are classified.

2 Confirm that all electrical equipment complies with the above, including:
   (a) lighting
   (b) wiring and switches
   (c) motors
   (d) instrumentation and
   (e) intercoms, telephones, clocks, etc.

3 Confirm that all earthing meets the required standard.

4 Identify the person responsible for checking the above and frequency of checking.

Access

1 Confirm two routes of access are provided to all occupied parts of buildings.

Working platforms

1 Confirm safety rails with toe boards are provided on all platforms over 1m high and all occupied enclosed portions of roof.

3

▶

Project Title	Date of Analysis

2 Confirm safe means of access is provided to all working platforms.

Fire protection

1 Confirm all fire doors are checked on a regular basis.

2 Confirm exposed steel supporting major items of equipment is fire-proofed.

3 Confirm whether automatic or manually-operated sprinkler protection system is installed.

4 Confirm whether special fire extinguishing equipment is provided.

5 State the number, type and location of fire appliances and the system for ensuring regular servicing of such appliances.

6 Identify the location of fire hydrants and hose reels.

7 Identify the locations of fire alarm boxes and building evacuation alarms.

8 State whether any flammable substances are handled in the open.

9 Specify the amount stored and the location of flammable substances in operating buildings.

10 Specify the amount stored, location and the system for protection of flammable liquids and gases stored outdoors.

Personnel, equipment and facilities

1 Specify the type of protective overclothing provided.

2 Confirm that safety boots/shoes are provided and worn.

3 Confirm that gloves/gauntlets are provided and worn for certain jobs.

4 Confirm that the correct type or eye protection is provided and used where there is a risk of eye injury.

5 Confirm that safety helmets/bump caps are provided for and worn by all operators.

6 Confirm that respirator stations are adequately identified and maintained.

7 State the frequency of overall changing, particularly where there is a risk of heavy soiling.

FIG 3.1 Continued

Project Title	Date of Analysis

8 Confirm that an amenity block of WCs, urinals, wash basins, showers, hot and cold water, and a separate mess room, is provided.

9 Confirm that a first aid facility is provided, together with trained first aiders.

Training

1 Confirm that operating manuals are available and have been provided.

2 Confirm that health and safety components of routine training for operators have been identified.

3 Confirm there is a training schedule, and that staff are adequately trained.

4 Confirm that the effectiveness of training is monitored.

5 Confirm that occupational health practices are adequately covered in training.

6 Confirm that safety rules have been written, published and are enforced.

3

Legal requirements

1 Confirm compliance with Health and Safety at Work, etc Act 1974 with particular reference to:
(a) provision and maintenance of plant and systems of work that are safe and without risks to health
(b) arrangements for the safe use, handling, storage and transport of articles and substances
(c) provision of information, instruction, training and supervision of employees
(d) provision of a safe place of work, with safe means of access to and egress from same
(e) provision and maintenance of a safe working environment
(f) provisions for consultation on health and safety issues and
(g) preparation and presentation of a statement of health and safety policy.

2 Confirm compliance with current regulations, in particular:
Construction (General Provisions) Regulations 1961
Construction (Lifting Operations) Regulations 1961
Construction (Health and Welfare) Regulations 1966
Construction (Working Places) Regulations 1966
Construction (Head Protection) Regulations 1989
Highly Flammable Liquids and Liquefied Petroleum Gases Regulations 1972

▶

Project Title	Date of Analysis

Safety Signs Regulations 1980
Health and Safety (First Aid) Regulations 1981
Building Regulations 1985
Ionising Radiations Regulations 1985
Reporting of Injuries, Diseases and Dangerous
    Occurrences Regulations 1985
Noise at Work Regulations 1989
Electricity at Work Regulations 1989
Pressure Systems and Transportable Gas Containers
    Regulations 1989
Health and Safety (Information for Employees)
    Regulations 1989
Management of Health and Safety at Work Regulations
    1992
Workplace (Health, Safety and Welfare) Regulations 1992
Provision and Use of Work Equipment Regulations 1992
Personal Protective Equipment at Work Regulations 1992
Manual Handling Operations Regulations 1992
Health and Safety (Display Screen Equipment)
    Regulations 1992
Control of Substances Hazardous to Health Regulations
    1994
Construction (Design and Management) Regulations
    1994
 	
3 Confirm risk assessments prepared and available under:
Noise at Work Regulations 1989
Management of Health and Safety at Work Regulations
    1992
Provision and Use of Work Equipment Regulations 1992
Personal Protective Equipment Regulations 1992
Manual Handling Operations Regulations 1992
Health and Safety (Display Screen Equipment)
    Regulations 1992
Control of Substances Hazardous to Health Regulations
    1994
 	
4 Confirm competent persons appointed in compliance
with:
Management of Health and Safety at Work Regulations
    1992
Construction (General Provisions) Regulations 1961
Construction (Lifting Operations) Regulations 1961
Construction (Working Places) Regulations 1966
Construction (Design and Management) Regulations
    1994
Pressure Systems and Transportable Gas Containers
    Regulations 1989
Electricity at Work Regulations 1989	

FIG 3.1 Continued

4

The movement of people and materials

This chapter deals with a wide range of topics involving the movement of people and materials, a common cause of accidents in the workplace.

Factors for consideration include structural safety aspects, in particular, the design and layout of floors, traffic routes, both internally and externally, and general access provisions. Specialised structural aspects, such as teagle openings and elevated work/storage areas, are also considered, along with the requirements for escalators and moving walkways.

The significance of appropriate standards of lighting must be appreciated, along with the use of colour in the workplace. Both of these aspects can contribute as indirect causes of accidents.

Safe mechanical and manual handling operations, together with well-run internal transport systems, are a prerequisite for safe systems of work and the prevention of accidents. Mechanical handling is, of course, a particularly broad area, involving the requirements for the safe use of lifting tackle, cranes, lifts, conveying equipment and mobile handling equipment of various types. Manual handling injuries are the most common type of injury sustained by people at work. Recent legislation, such as the Manual Handling Operations Regulations (MHOR) 1992 and the Workplace (Health, Safety and Welfare) Regulations 1992 (WHSWR) now require much greater attention to these matters than in previous years.

STRUCTURAL SAFETY – PRINCIPAL CONSIDERATIONS

Accidents associated with structural features of workplaces are common. These may include slips, trips and falls on the same level, falls down staircases, contact with fixed structural features and vehicles using traffic routes, falls through teagle openings and from elevated work/storage platforms.

Floors and traffic routes

Specific provisions relating to the safety of floors and traffic routes in work-places are dealt with in regulation 12 of the WHSWR. Floors and the surfaces of traffic routes must be of suitable construction, free from dangerous holes, slopes and uneven and slippery surfaces, and provided with effective means of drainage where necessary. So far as is reasonably practicable, they must be kept free from obstruction and from articles and substances which could cause slips, trips or falls.

Floors should be of sound construction, free from obstruction and sudden changes in level, and of non-slip finish. Where safety levels, production or the storage of goods are materially assisted, storage areas should be clearly marked by the use of yellow or white lines. 'No Go' areas should be cross-hatched with yellow lines. All openings in floors or significant differences in floor level should be fenced. Attention should also be paid to ensuring that floor loading does not produce structural instability.

Where a wet process is carried out, or where frequent floor washing is necessary, the floor should be laid to a fall to a drainage system. Floor channels, incorporating metal gratings or covers, can sometimes be used as an alternative.

Stairs, ladders and catwalks

Suitable and sufficient handrails and, if appropriate, guards must be provided on all traffic routes which are staircases except in circumstances in which a handrail cannot be provided without obstructing the traffic route. In the case of very wide staircases, further handrails may be necessary in addition to those at the sides. If necessary, the space between the handrail and the treads should be filled in, or an intermediate rail fitted.

Fixed vertical ladders and catwalks, including bridges to them, should be securely fixed. Where practicable, back rings should be fitted to vertical ladders from a height of two metres upwards and spaced at one metre intervals. Catwalks and bridges should be adequately fenced by means of one metre high guard rails, 500 millimetre high intermediate rails and toe boards.

External areas, traffic routes and approach roads

Regulation 17 of the WHSWR deals with the organisation and safety features of traffic routes, with the general requirement that every workplace shall be organised in such a way that pedestrians and vehicles can circulate in a safe manner. A **traffic route** is defined as meaning a route for pedestrian traffic, vehicles or both and includes any stairs, staircase, fixed ladder, doorway, gateway, loading bay or ramp.

Traffic routes must be suitable for the persons or vehicles using same, sufficient in number, in suitable positions and of sufficient size.

Particular precautions must be taken to prevent pedestrians or vehicles causing danger to persons near that route, ensure there is sufficient separation of traffic routes for vehicles from doors, gates and pedestrian routes, and where pedestrians and vehicles use the same traffic routes, ensure there is sufficient separation between them. Traffic routes must be suitably indicated where necessary for reasons of health and safety.

To facilitate access to and egress from the workplace by people and vehicles, external areas should have impervious and even surfaces and be adequately drained to a drainage system. The provision of water supply points and hoses, for washing down yards and approaches, is recommended.

Windows, doors, gates and walls, etc

Specific provisions relating to structural items such as windows, doors, gates, walls, skylights and ventilators are incorporated in the WHSWR.

Every window or other transparent or translucent surface in a wall or partition and every transparent or translucent surface in a door, gate or wall shall, where necessary for reasons of health and safety:

- be of safety material or be protected against breakage and
- be appropriately marked or incorporate features so as, in either case, to make it apparent. (Regulation 14)

No window, skylight or ventilator which is capable of being opened shall be likely to be opened, closed or adjusted in a manner which exposes any person performing such operations to a risk to his health or safety. No window, skylight or ventilator shall be in a position to expose any person in the workplace to a risk to his health or safety. (Regulation 15)

All windows and skylights in a workplace shall be of a design or so constructed that they may be cleaned safely. In considering whether a window or skylight is safe, account may be taken of any equipment used in conjunction with the window or skylight or of devices fitted to the building. (Regulation 16)

Doors and gates shall be suitably constructed (including fitted with any necessary safety devices). Specific safety provisions apply to sliding doors/gates, powered doors and doors/gates which are capable of being opened by being pushed from either side. (Regulation 18) Thus:

- any sliding door or gate must be fitted with a device to prevent it coming off its track during use
- any upward opening door or gate must be fitted with a device to prevent it falling back
- any powered door or gate must incorporate suitable and effective features to prevent it causing injury by trapping any person
- where necessary for reasons of health or safety, any powered door or gate must be capable of being operated manually unless it opens automatically if the power fails and any door or gate which is capable of opening by

being pushed from either side must be of such a construction as to provide, when closed, a clear view of the space close to both sides.

Interior walls have a contribution to make to illuminance levels, colour schemes, the maintenance of physical cleanliness, sound insulation and the prevention of fire spread. They should be substantial, durable, smooth, easily cleaned and reflect light.

Ceilings and inner roof surfaces of workrooms should also assist in the maintenance of appropriate illuminance levels, heat insulation, sound insulation and physical cleanliness. Ceiling heights should be a minimum of 2.4 metres.

Escalators and moving walkways

Regulation 19 of the WHSWR makes special provisions for escalators and moving walkways. In both cases, they shall:

- function safely
- be equipped with any necessary safety devices and
- be fitted with one or more emergency stop controls which are easily identifiable and readily accessible.

In all the above cases, further detail is provided in the ACOP accompanying the regulations.

Teagle openings and elevated work/storage platforms

A teagle opening is an opening in the fabric of a building above ground level through which goods can be hoisted into the building. Such openings are a common structural feature of mills, potteries, warehouses and agricultural buildings. Section 24 of the FA 1961 requires that every teagle opening or similar doorway used for hoisting or lowering goods or materials, whether by mechanical power or otherwise, must be securely fenced and provided with a secure handhold at each side. The fencing must be properly maintained and kept in position, except when hoisting or lowering goods or materials. What constitutes 'secure fencing' within the requirements of section 24 is a matter for legal interpretation, but it is quite common to see openings fenced solely by a metal bar or wooden beam set horizontally approximately one metre from the floor (see Figure 4.1). The relative safety of this arrangement, however, relies heavily on operators replacing the bar after loading or unloading operations and there is always the risk of operators falling under or over the bar. Furthermore, the sole provision of handholds at each side of the opening is of limited value in preventing falls from teagle openings and platform edges.

Specific consideration must also be given to the need to place and remove materials on or from elevated work/storage areas or mezzanine platforms, perhaps through the use of a fork-lift truck. In these circumstances, where operators may be operating close to the edge of an elevated platform, the risk of falling is greater than in normal circumstances.

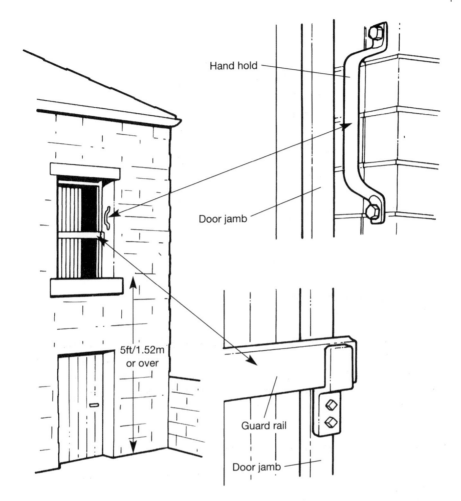

Hand hold

Door jamb

5ft/1.52m
or over

Guard rail

Door jamb

FIG 4.1 Standard method of fencing a teagle opening

Recently a number of safety barriers for high-level openings have been developed, the Ajax safety barrier being the most common (see Figure 4.2). This barrier is designed to give continuous protection to anyone working at a high level loading point or teagle opening. The barrier operates on the basis that when a load has to be placed on a platform or through a teagle opening, the barrier is pivoted laterally through 180 degrees and comes to rest in a similar position some distance back from the edge of the platform or opening. Once the materials have been placed on the platform, the barrier is pivoted upwards and over the load until it rests in its original position at the platform edge so that the load can be removed. The moving part of the barrier is spring-loaded for ease of operation and a simple automatic catch locks the barrier in the closed position.

FIG 4.2   The Ajax safety barrier
Reproduced by courtesy of Weller Engineering Ltd

While the standard application is at loading points on platforms or mezzanine floors, the barrier can also be made to suit difficult installations where it is not practicable to make structural alterations, such as teagle openings, where doors may be involved or the pallet load is too large for a standard type of barrier.

The use of colour in the workplace

Colour is an important factor in the maintenance of a sound working environment, and influences:

● the extent to which the creation of a congenial environment is achieved
● the amount of visual assistance afforded to employees by:
    – general and specific illuminance levels
    – drawing attention to specific parts of the workplace, eg fire escape routes, 'no go' areas and
    – the control of glare
● general safety performance, eg colour coding of safety signs, the use of 'tiger striping' to identify particular hazards.

LIGHTING OF THE WORKPLACE

Two specific health and safety-related aspects are relevant in relation to lighting at work, namely:

- a gradual deterioration in an individual's visual acuity and performance and
- the basis for lighting design and specific applications, as in the case of display screen equipment (visual display units).

In any consideration of lighting, including lighting deficiencies and their control, it is important to distinguish between the quantitative and qualitative aspects of lighting.

Quantitative aspects

The quantity of light flowing from a source such as a light bulb or fluorescent light (luminaire) is the luminous flux or light flow, which is generally termed 'illuminance'. The units of measurement of luminous flux were formerly foot candles or lumens per square foot, but more recently this unit has become the lux, which is the metric unit of measurement. Thus:

Foot candles = lumens per square foot
Lux = lumens per square metre
10.76 lux = 1 lumen per square metre
1 lux = 0.093 lumens per square metre

4

On this basis, a conversion factor of 10 or 11 is used for converting from lumens per square foot to lux, ie 20 lumens per square foot = 200 lux.

The illuminance value in lux is measured using a standard photometer or light meter and is the quantity of light present at a particular point.

Lighting standards are detailed in HSE Guidance Note HS(G)38 '**Lighting at work**'. The guidance note distinguishes between **average illuminances** and **minimum measured illuminances** according to the general activity undertaken and the type of work undertaken and typical work location (see Table 4.1).

Table 4.1 Average illuminances and minimum measured illuminances for different types of work

General activity	Typical locations/ type of work	Average illuminance (lux)	Minimum measured illuminance (lux)
Movement of people, machines and vehicles (See Note 1.)	Lorry parks, corridors, circulation routes	20	5
Movement of people, machines and vehicles in hazardous areas: rough work not requiring any perception of detail (See Note 1.)	Construction site clearance, excavation and soil work, docks, loading bays, bottling and canning plants	50	20
Work requiring limited perception of detail (See Note 2.)	Kitchens, factories, assembling large components, potteries	100	50
Work requiring perception of detail (See Note 2.)	Offices, sheet metal work, bookbinding	200	100
Work requiring fine perception of detail (See Note 2.)	Drawing offices, factories assembling electronic components, textile production	500	200

Note:

1. Only safety has been considered, because no perception of detail is needed and visual fatigue is unlikely. However, where it is necessary to see detail to recognise a hazard or where error in performing the task could put someone else at risk, for safety purposes as well as to avoid visual fatigue, the figure should be increased to that for work requiring perception of detail.
2. The purpose is to avoid visual fatigue: the illuminances will be adequate for safety purposes.

The ratio between working areas and adjacent areas is also featured in the guidance note (see Table 4.2). The guidance note recommends that where there is conflict between the recommended average illuminance shown in Table 4.1 and the maximum ratios of illuminance in Table 4.2, the higher value should be taken as the appropriate average illuminance.

Table 4.2   Maximum ratios of illuminance for adjacent areas

Situations to which recommendation applies	Typical location	Maximum ratio of illuminances Working area		Adjacent area
Where each task is individually lit and the area around the task is lit to a lower illuminance	Local lighting in an office	5	:	1
Where two working areas are adjacent, but one is lit to lower illuminance than the other	Localised lighting in a works store	5	:	1
Where two working areas are lit to different illuminances by a barrier but there is frequent movement between them	A storage area inside a factory and a loading bay outside	10	:	1

4

Qualitative aspects

The concept of average illuminances in the guidance note relates only to the quantity of light, and in the design and assessment of lighting installations consideration must be given to the qualitative aspects.

Factors which contribute to the quality of lighting include the presence or absence of glare in its various forms, the degree of brightness, the distribution of light, diffusion, colour rendition, contrast effects and the system for lighting maintenance.

Glare

This is the effect of light which causes discomfort or impaired vision, and is experienced when parts of the visual field are excessively bright compared with the general surroundings. This usually occurs when the light source is directly in line with the visual task or when light is reflected off a given surface or object. Glare is experienced in three different forms.

Disability glare

Disability glare is the visually disabling effect caused by bright, bare lamps directly in the line of sight. The resulting impaired vision (dazzle) may be hazardous if experienced when working in high risk processes, at heights or when driving. It is seldom experienced in workplaces because most bright lamps, eg filament and mercury vapour, are usually partly surrounded by some form of fitting.

Discomfort glare

Discomfort glare is caused mainly by too much contrast of brightness between an object and its background, and is associated with poor lighting design. It causes visual discomfort without necessarily impairing the ability to see detail, but over a period can cause eye strain, headaches and fatigue. Discomfort glare can be reduced by:

- careful design of shades which screen the lamp
- keeping luminaires as high as practicable and
- maintaining luminaires parallel to the main direction of lighting.

Reflected glare

Reflected glare is the reflection of bright light sources on shiny or wet work surfaces such as glass or plated metal, which can almost entirely conceal the detail in or behind the object which is glinting. Care is necessary in the use of light sources of low brightness and in the arrangement of the geometry of the installation, so that there is no glint at the particular viewing position.

Distribution

The distribution of light, or the way in which light is spread, is important in lighting design. Poor lighting design may result in the formation of shadowed areas which can create dangerous situations particularly at night. For good general lighting, regularly spaced luminaires are used to give evenly distributed illuminance. This evenness of illuminance depends upon the ratio between the height of the luminaire above the working position and the spacing of the fittings.

Colour rendition

This term refers to the appearance of an object under a given light source compared to its colour under a reference illuminant, eg natural light. Colour rendition enables the colour appearance to be correctly perceived. The colour rendering properties of light fitments should not clash with those of natural light, and should be equally effective at night when there is no daylight contribution to the total illumination of the workplace.

Brightness

Brightness, or more correctly, 'luminosity', is essentially a subjective sensation and cannot be measured. It is possible, however, to consider a brightness ratio, which is the ratio of the apparent luminosity between a task object and its surroundings. To achieve the recommended brightness ratio, the reflectance of all surfaces in the workplace should be carefully maintained and consideration given to reflectance values in the design of interiors. Given a task illuminance factor of 1, the effective reflectance values should be:

Ceilings	–	0.6
Walls	–	0.3 to 0.8
Floors	–	0.2 to 0.3

Diffusion

This is the projection of light in many directions with no directional predominance. The directional effects of light are just as important as the quantity of light, however, as the directional flow of light can often determine the density of shadows, which may affect safety. Diffused lighting can soften the output from a particular source and so limit the amount of glare that may be encountered from bare fittings.

Stroboscopic effect

All lamps that operate from an alternating current electricity supply produce oscillations in light output. When the magnitude of the oscillations is great and their frequency is a multiple or sub-multiple of the frequency of movement of machinery, that machinery will appear to be stationary or moving in a different manner. This is called the 'stroboscopic effect'. It is not common with modern lighting systems but where it does occur it can be dangerous, so appropriate action should be taken to avoid it. Possible remedial measures include:

- supplying adjacent rows of light fittings from different phases of the electricity supply
- providing a high frequency supply
- washing out the effect with local lighting which has much less variation in light output, eg tungsten lamp and/or
- use of high frequency control gear is applicable.

Lighting maintenance

A well-organised lighting programme is necessary for permanently good illumination to be achieved. This programme should incorporate regular cleaning and replacement of lamp fittings as a basic consideration, together with regular assessment of illuminance levels with a standard photometer at predetermined points. Furthermore, the actual function of the lighting provided should be reviewed in line with changes that may be made in production, storage or office arrangements. To facilitate safe lamp cleaning and replacement, high-level luminaires should be fitted with raising and lowering gear, so that this work can be undertaken at floor level.

MANUAL HANDLING

More than a third of all industrial injuries result from manual handling activities. Statistics from the last 60 years indicate that in almost every year the number of people injured in this way has increased. As a result, more than 70,000 workers are off work for variable periods of time. This amounts to nearly 30 per cent of all reportable accidents. Even more surprising is the fact that, during this period, there have been greater advances in the technology and engineering aspects of mechanical handling than ever before. Certainly workers today perform fewer manual handling tasks than their grandfathers, and it would be reasonable, therefore, to expect a comparable reduction in injuries associated with manual handling.

Not only manual workers contribute to the handling injuries statistics, however. Those in sedentary occupations are similarly at risk, eg office workers, library staff, catering staff, hospital workers and people working in shops.

The Manual Handling Operations Regulations (MHOR) 1992 came into operation on 1st January 1993. The introduction to the HSE Guidance on the Regulations 'Manual Handling – Guidance on Regulations' (HMSO) indicates that more than a quarter of the accidents reported each year to the enforcing authorities are associated with manual handling – the transporting or supporting of loads by hand or by bodily force. The vast majority of reported manual handling accidents result in over-three-day injury, most commonly a sprain or strain, often of the back.

The guidance classifies the types of injury caused by handling accidents thus – sprains and strains – 65%, superficial injuries – 9%, contusions – 7%, lacerations – 7%, fractures – 5% and other forms of injury – 5%. Sites of bodily injury caused by handling are backs – 45%, fingers/thumbs – 16%, arms – 13%, lower limbs – 9%, rest of torso – 8%, hands – 6% and other sites – 3%.

What comes out of the statistical information on manual handling injuries is the fact that four out of five people will suffer some form of back condition at some time in their lives, the majority of these conditions being associated with work activities.

Manual handling injuries and conditions

Typical injuries and conditions associated with manual handling can be both external and internal. External injuries include cuts, bruises, crush injuries and lacerations to fingers, hands, forearms, ankles and feet. Generally, such injuries are not as serious as the internal forms of injury which include muscle and ligamental tears, hernias (ruptures), prolapsed intervertebral discs and damage to knee, ankle, shoulder and elbow joints. One of the most significant injuries, and the one which results in frequent incapacity and even permanent crippling, is the prolapsed intervertebral disc. The various features of internal handling injuries are discussed below, together with certain conditions resulting from manual handling.

Muscle and ligamental strain

Muscle is the most abundant tissue in the body, and accounts for some two-fifths of the body weight. The specialised component is the muscle fibre, a long slender cell or agglomeration of cells which becomes shorter and thicker in response to a stimulus. These fibres are supported and bound by ordinary connective tissue, and are well supplied with blood vessels and nerves. When muscles are utilised for manual handling purposes, they are subjected to varying degrees of stress. Carrying generally imposes a pronounced static strain on many groups of muscles, especially those of the arms and trunk. This is a particularly unsuitable form of labour for human beings because the blood vessels in the contracted muscles are compressed and the flow of blood, and with it the oxygen and sugar supply, is thereby impeded. As a result, fatigue very soon sets in, with pains in the back muscles, which perform static work only, occurring sooner than in the arm muscles, which perform essentially dynamic work.

Ligaments are fibrous bands occurring between two bones at a joint. They are flexible but inelastic, come into play only at the extremes of movement, and cannot be stretched when they are taut. Ligaments set the limits beyond which no movement is possible in a joint. A joint can be forced beyond its normal range only by tearing a ligament: this is a sprain. Fibrous tissue heals reluctantly, and a severe sprain can be as incapacitating as a fracture. There are many causes of torn ligaments, in particular jerky handling movements which place stress on the joint, uncoordinated team lifting, and dropping a load half-way through a lift, often caused by failing to assess the load prior to lifting.

Hernia

A hernia is a protrusion of an organ from one compartment of the body into another, eg of a loop of intestine into the groin or through the frontal abdominal wall. Both these forms of hernia can result from incorrect handling techniques and particularly from the adoption of bent back stances, which produce compression of the abdomen and lower intestines.

The most common form of hernia or 'rupture' associated with manual handling is the inguinal hernia. The weak point is the small gap in the abdominal muscles where the testis descends to the scrotum. Its vessels pass through the gap, which therefore cannot be sealed. Excessive straining, and even coughing, may cause a bulge at the gap and loop of intestine or other abdominal structure easily slips into it. An inguinal hernia sometimes causes little trouble, but it can, without warning, become strangulated, whereby the loop of intestine is pinched at the entrance to the hernia. Its contents are obstructed and fresh blood no longer reaches the area. Prompt attention is needed to preserve the patient's health, and even his life will be at risk if the condition does not receive swift attention. The defect, in most cases, must be repaired surgically.

'Prolapsed' disc

The spine consists of a number of small interlocking bones or vertebrae (see Figure 4.3). There are seven neck or cervical vertebrae, 12 thoracic vertebrae, five lumbar vertebrae, five sacral vertebrae and four caudal vertebrae. The sacral vertebrae are united, as are the caudal vertebrae, the others being capable of independent but co-ordinating articulating movement. Each vertebra is separated from the next by a pad of gristle-like material (intervertebral disc). These discs act as shock absorbers and help to protect the spine. A prolapsed or 'slipped' disc occurs when one of these intervertebral discs is displaced from its normal position and is no longer performing its function properly. In other cases, there may be squashing or compression of a disc. This results in a painful condition, sometimes leading to partial paralysis, which may be caused when the back is bent while lifting, as a result of falling awkwardly, getting up out of a low chair or even through over-energetic dancing.

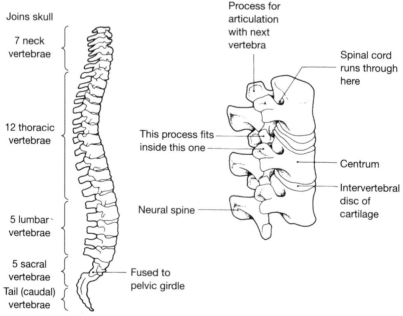

FIG 4.3 The human spine

Rheumatism

Rheumatism is a painful disorder of joints or muscles not directly due to infection or injury. This rather ill-defined group includes rheumatic fever, rheumatoid arthritis, osteoarthritis, gout and 'fibrositis', itself an ill-defined group of disorders in which muscular and/or joint pain are common factors. There is much evidence to support the fact that stress on the spine, muscles, joints and ligaments during manual handling activities in early life results in rheumatic disorders as people get older.

In industrial handling situations, therefore, there is an urgent need to instruct operators in correct techniques of movement and posture. Above all, they must be made aware of the importance of the correct assessment and planning of a task such as moving a particular load prior to tackling it.

Assessment prior to handling

Before examining the various problems of handling, the first important rule must be recognised, namely: 'If you think you can't manage to move the load, get help'. This may be help from another person or use of a mechanical handling aid. The decision must ultimately be left to the person who is doing the job. There will rarely be a single deciding factor, however. The size, shape, weight, degree of rigidity, outside surface of the load, conditions such as the height of the load, state of the ground surface, headroom and temperature and, most important of all, the physical and temperamental characteristics of the individual concerned, must be considered. These factors are discussed below.

Size

Sizes of loads vary in terms of their actual volume. For instance, a sack of cement weighing 50kg needs a totally different lifting technique from a box of feathers, measuring 1m x 1m x 1m but of the same weight. The centre of gravity of the load should be as near to the body as possible (as with any lifting machine). Moreover, the wider the arms are stretched and the further the hands are in front of the body, the greater the tension on the shoulders, chest and back muscles. Often the use of straps, hooks and other handling aids will assist when moving large loads. There is also a considerable difference between handling indoors and outdoors, where wind velocity can affect individual lifting ability, especially where the handling of sheet materials or large lightweight loads is concerned.

Shape

It is essential to carry a load at the point of balance. Many loads are carried off balance and, in the case of a moving load in a container – eg liquids, loose items – the point of balance constantly changes.

Where more than one person is moving a large object, it is essential that the weight be evenly distributed among the people concerned, and that the contents of any container, box, drum, packing case or sack are known.

Weight

Many organisations and individuals have attempted to identify a maximum weight that people of different sexes and ages could handle safely. Indeed, this concept was embodied in several sets of regulations. However, such philosophy is not practicable for a number of reasons:

- all people are different in terms of physical strength, height, degree of physical fitness and body weight
- if statute stipulated a maximum weight, the implication would be that the handling of a weight in excess of that figure was illegal and vice versa; this philosophy is suspect, since many strain injuries occur when moving the lightest of loads and
- the weight of an object is only one factor in determining whether or not to move a load. For instance, reducing the overall weight of a load might be considered salutary, but a person is likely to take greater care when moving a large heavy load than a light one, and he can abuse his body more easily with small light loads than with large heavy ones.

Lack of rigidity

A load likely to change its overall shape during handling can create difficulties in terms of grip and hold. Many materials are packed in sacks or bags. When these are pressure-filled, the 'floppy' nature of the load can pull a person off balance. A typical example here is in the nursing profession. Lifting patients, who may be totally or partially incapable of assisting, is the principal reason why this profession has such a bad record of muscular strain injuries. The fact that the load is live aggravates the problem, coupled with the need to provide careful support not only to the torso but to individual limbs. The difficulty in obtaining a satisfactory grip without harming the patient, who may have been injured, compounds the problem.

Outside surfaces

The material in which a load is packed can directly affect the ease with which it is handled. In the days of hessian sacks the handler used hooks, such as the docker's hook, and the roughness of the material enabled him to acquire a better grip and hold on the load. The increasing use of plastics has reduced this ability for obtaining a good hold. Moreover, the practice of shrink wrapping of goods has created its own handling problems in terms of gripping the load properly. The use of purpose-designed gloves can help in overcoming many of these problems. Such gloves are useful for moving smooth-surfaced loads, whether plastic-sacked goods, domestic appliances or even glass sheets.

Height

The location of a load and the positioning of the person's hands will affect the ease with which the load is moved. Hands can only perform a task efficiently when they are placed directly in front of the body, and close to it, in an area between the chest and thigh levels. Handling loads below the feet or above the head is inadvisable, but there are times when this is unavoidable. The use of hooks and other aids can assist when the load is below feet level. A typical example is keys used to lift manhole tops. Handling loads above head level is made the more hazardous because the handler cannot see the top of the load. This exposes him to risk of other items falling on his head. The weight of a load should always be known when it is to be taken from a shelf, so that the person is not 'taken off guard' when he initially receives it. Here the use of staging or steps to permit the load to be at waist level is advantageous.

Ground or floor surface

Balance depends upon the stability of the base. If a person stands or moves on an unstable base, muscles will automatically be tensed to safeguard balance. Icy or wet surfaces also create this stiffening. When a person walks over a loose surface, this creates tension in the legs and lower parts of the body, eg walking over sand dunes. Suitable footwear should, therefore, be worn. When selecting footwear there is a tendency to consider the protection afforded to the toes only. However, on certain surfaces, the sole of the boot or shoe can stabilise the body. The use of safety shoes, with high-grip soles, generally improves body stability.

Headroom

Whenever a person needs to lower his head, he tends to adopt a top-heavy bending action. Many tasks are performed with restricted headroom, eg mining, and loading and unloading vans and other forms of transport. The removal of unconscious passengers from window seats of many airliners creates almost insurmountable problems for airline staff. Acquiring the ability to perform instinctively good 'balance movements' as distinct from 'top-heavy bending' will reduce the risk of strain in such cases.

Temperature and humidity

Temperature and humidity affect the way and speed with which a person moves. If it is too cold, muscles tend to stiffen; a 'warming up' period should be allowed – not, however, using movements that cause 'stiffening up' but rather using gentle movements to stretch and shorten muscles by relaxing and tightening. An advantage of working in high temperatures is that the worker tends to move more slowly, reducing the discomfort of perspiring, and the tendency to employ sudden or snatching movements. Injury statistics for tropical climates indicate fewer strain injuries. Moreover, use of the correct clothing is important. Clothing should not be tight yet should be sufficiently close fitting to give freedom of movement. Gaps, especially around the waist, should be avoided when working outdoors.

Physical and psychological characteristics

It is not only the physical shape and size of a person that is important but posture and muscular condition. There are quite heavy jobs which can be undertaken successfully by small people. What they lack in body bulk, they may compensate for in dexterity, suppleness and timing. Age is also relevant, particularly the inevitable stiffening which accompanies the ageing process. So, too, is the temperament of an individual and the degree of mental stress which can affect muscular tension. The more placid the individual, the more likely he is to be a relaxed mover, making more fluid and 'segmental' movements than the jerky staccato-type movements associated with a tense person. Equally, a person's own physical performance will often vary from day to day, depending upon factors such as general state of health, food intake, amount of sleep, tasks performed the day before and general mental state.

All the above factors must be considered when assessing handling procedures. No single factor should be considered in isolation. It is incorrect to adopt a black-or-white approach to every situation, and frequently a compromise must be reached. Often, the really awkward job does not create difficulties when extra care and thought are given, but the simple everyday job, apparently with few risks, in some cases leads to severe injuries being sustained.

Handling techniques

General rules for safe lifting

- No-one should ever attempt to lift anything beyond their capacity. If in doubt, get help.
- Where mechanical lifting aids are provided, they should be used.
- Extra care should be taken when lifting awkwardly shaped objects.
- In the analysis of individual posture and movement considerable observation of the operator is necessary. The following should occur at the moment the force is exerted on the load:
  - Position the feet correctly. The feet should be placed hip-width apart to provide a large base. One foot should be put forward and to the side of the object which gives better balance.
  - Bend or 'unlock' the knees and crouch to the load. The weight will then be safely taken down the spine and the strong leg muscles will do the work.
  - Get a firm grip. The load should be gripped by the roots of the fingers and the palm of the hand. This keeps the load under control and per-

mits it to be distributed more evenly up the arms. Use of the finger tips only can produce excessive tension in the forearms and possible loss of grip.

- Extend the neck upwards by tucking in the chin. This will automatically straighten the back as the load is taken. This does not mean in a vertical position, but inclined at an angle of approximately 15°. This prevents pressure on the abdomen, reduces the risk of hernia and ensures an even pressure on the intervertebral discs.
- Keep the arms close to the body. This reduces muscle fatigue in the arms and shoulders and the effort required by the arms. It ensures that the load moves with the body and becomes, in effect, part of the body.
- Use the leg muscles. Lifting should utilise the strong thigh muscles. Lifting should proceed by straightening the legs lifting in one smooth and progressive movement from floor to carrying position. Push off with the rear foot.

Note: The above points should be considered as features of an overall smooth lifting movement and not a sole means of instruction.

- Hand protection, and arm protection where appropriate, should always be used, particularly when lifting rough loads, or loads with sharp edges or projections.

4

HUMAN KINETICS

This section examines the concepts of kinetics, first by observing the human being as a handling machine and, second, by relating these observations to the problems involved in handling which were discussed earlier, eg size, shape, weight, lack of rigidity. Correct and incorrect methods of movement are also considered.

Human kinetics follows from the detailed study of body reactions, and may be defined as 'the study of mechanical, nervous and psychological factors which influence the functions and structure of the human body as a means of producing higher standards of skill and reducing cumulative strain'. A simpler definition might be 'a technique of moving in a more relaxed and efficient way'.

Physiology of kinetics

Many injuries and conditions arise from a common cause, namely cumulative strain, or stiffening of the body structures. When body structures are unduly tense, the adaptability is reduced, and they are more easily injured and tired. Body structures are elastic, given to stiffening and relaxing, shortening and lengthening. If they are maintained in either state over a period of time, they will lose their elasticity. Indeed, one of the inevitable effects of growing old is the loss of suppleness accompanied by general stiffening throughout the body.

Human tissues undergo structural changes as a result of reasonable activity regularly performed. Moreover, structural adjustment of tissue can be beneficial. It enables people to perform a particular task more easily, thereby developing a skill or 'knack' in the job, especially if the working method is related to sound kinetic principles. The kinetic method of movement depends upon good balance adjustment and tissue elasticity. In this case structural changes produced by regular, but not excessive, use of the tissues tend to be healthy and beneficial. In contrast, where the actions are carried out by sheer muscular effort and brute force, this increases the risk of strain and expedites development of other harmful conditions, such as rheumatism and fibrositis.

Rhythmic muscle contraction and relaxation have a salutary effect on body tissues whether movements are carried out performing a task or as a specific exercise. Sustained tension in the muscles inhibits their nourishment, restricts absorption of muscle waste products and causes fatigue, thereby undermining efficiency of effort. Where tension is sustained in a muscle, a 'muscle-bound' condition develops. The connective tissue which binds the muscle fibres becomes contracted so that it tends to resist expansion of muscle fibres and makes proper relaxation of the muscles impossible. Conversely, when the muscles are relaxed, the connective tissue will become sufficiently loose to allow the blood to circulate freely in the small blood vessels which carry nourishment to and waste materials from the muscle fibres. If the connective tissue is contracted for too long, the muscle fibres begin to lack vitality, become slower in action and more easily tired.

When a muscle contracts or tightens, it does not lose bulk. What it loses in length, it gains in breadth. Connective tissue is important to the economy of body movement, and sustained tension, which causes connective tissue to shorten, undermines the health and efficiency of the body. A good muscle is one that reacts quickly and accurately to the demands imposed by retaining or reacquiring elasticity in the connective tissue.

A large percentage of strains occur in experienced operators who have been doing a particular job for years prior to injury. It is sometimes cynically suggested that this problem arises as a result of carelessness brought about by overfamiliarity. Such suggestions are fallacious, however. The most common cause of injury in experienced workers is cumulative strain, usually arising from incorrect methods of working. Most strains and injuries arise as a result of repetitive incorrect body usage, contributed to by poor workplace design, systems of work or environmental factors. Additionally, however, body conditions dictate the way the body is used. Muscles are powerful in relation to their size, and the natural tendency to be proud of physical strength leads to muscle abuse. To use the body intelligently, individuals must learn to employ skill instead of brute force, thereby cultivating sensitivity rather than muscle bulk.

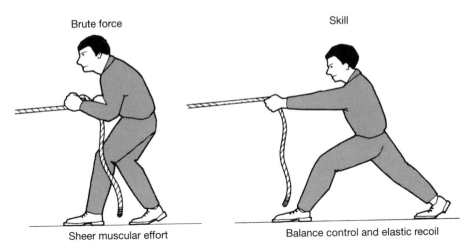

Brute force · Skill

Sheer muscular effort · Balance control and elastic recoil

FIG 4.4 Conflicting ideas of movement
Real strength depends upon skilful use of body weight, good balance adjustment and elasticity of body structures

This can be illustrated by the two methods of pulling on a rope (see Figure 4.4). If a 'doubled-up' position is adopted, brute force and sheer muscular effort are used, thereby explaining why there are so many strains and ruptures throughout industry. In a 'top-heavy' movement, the initial head-bending action causes concentration of pressure on the toes, simultaneously stimulating a chain of stiffening reactions throughout the body. Similarly, the doubled-up position puts a needless load on the abdominal and lower back muscles, causing congestion in the lower abdomen and pelvis, and leading to rupture or hernia. However, in the correct 'skilful' position the feet are so placed that the maximum amount of body weight is deployed and arm muscles, which are strongly contracted in the 'brute force' method, are under less strain when the arms are kept straight (see Figure 4.5).

The character and effects of a movement are determined by how the movement begins. For example, if the position in a pushing action has been assumed by leaning forward in a top-heavy manner, the operator will increase resistance by pushing the load into the ground. There would also be excessive tension throughout the body. On the other hand, if the action had first started by unlocking the knees, the feet would adjust and the operator could push the load over the ground, thereby reducing resistance and requiring less muscular effort with correspondingly more effective use of body weight.

The human being is like a puppet on a string. Any task that requires lowering of the head or hands starts by unlocking the knees and the feet and works progressively upwards. Any upward movement starts by raising the head and works progressively downwards. This principle applies irrespective of the movement to be performed, eg lifting, pulling, pushing, thrusting, down pulling or just sitting or kneeling down. All movements start by relaxing or unlocking the knees to allow the feet to adjust to safeguard balance.

FIG 4.5 Healthful movement
Progressive relaxation results from unlocking both knees as hands are lowered.
Raise the head as the hand takes the load automatically

The correct and the incorrect way of moving

Good movement

Good movement is that which fulfils its function efficiently with the minimum of effort and cumulative strain. The key to this is co-ordination of muscular action, ie reciprocation between:

- muscles which contract to produce movement and those which elongate to allow it to take place
- muscles concerned with maintaining and readjusting balance throughout the movement and
- muscles which stabilise the spinal joints and the bases of the limbs during movement.

The most 'expensive' form of muscle work, in terms of energy expended and cumulative strain, is that involving sustained contraction of muscles. At home, often the most tiring jobs are working at the sink and ironing, which involve standing up with the feet side by side and bending the upper trunk, resulting in gradual build up of excessive tension and stiffening of body tissues, ie cumulative strain.

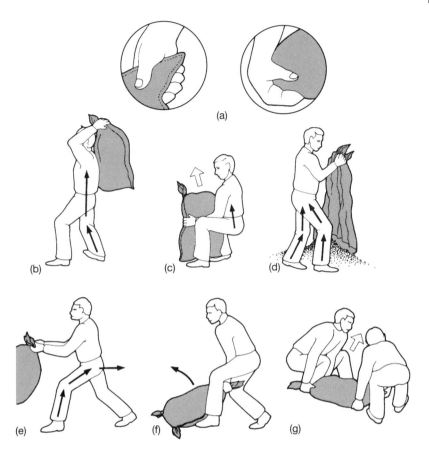

FIG 4.6 Bag and sack handling

(a) Gripping – Take hold from below. Grip with the palms and the roots of the fingers.

(b) Carrying – Relax the knees, arms in, and forward foot pointing in the direction of travel. Straighten knees to lift the load clear. Thrust strongly with rear foot to pivot and move off.

(c) Lifting – Raise the head and straighten the back. Correct feet positioning enables the handler to swing the load forward then upwards. The leg muscles then do the work.

(d) Emptying – Relax the knees. Keep the elbows tucked into the body.

(e) Laying a sack down – Use front foot straight forward to thrust, with knee bent to let body move back as far as possible. Stretch rear foot well out to improve balance. Tuck the chin in to keep the shoulders stable. Keep the arms straight.

(f) Standing a sack up – Lower the hands by relaxing the knees. Take a proper hold and position the feet correctly, one between the lugs, and one forward alongside the sack. Move forward and upwards in one rhythmic movement.

(g) Team lifting – The same principles apply as for single lifting. The lift must be co-ordinated by the team leader.

(Source Creber, 1967)

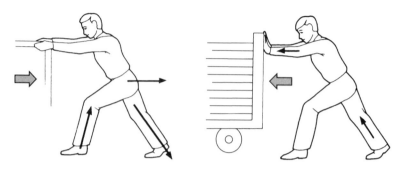

FIG 4.7 Pulling and pushing

Tuck the chin in, keeping the back and arms straight. In pushing, the front foot should balance the body, while the rear foot, pointing forward, gives the thrust. In pulling, the back foot safeguards balance while the front leg, with knee bent to allow the body to move back, does the thrusting.

(Source Creber, 1967)

FIG 4.8 Stowing and stacking

When stacking to high level, make the legs do the work. Relax both knees when approaching the stack and thrust upwards with a swinging movement, one foot following through.

(Source Creber, 1967)

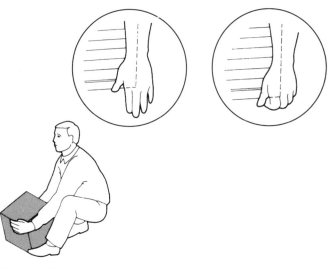

FIG 4.9 Box handling

Grip with the palms to reduce finger strain. Position the feet as shown to maintain balance and give a strong thrust forward and upwards off the back foot. The arms should be close to the sides and the hands placed diagonally. The legs will then do the lifting.

(Source Creber, 1967)

4

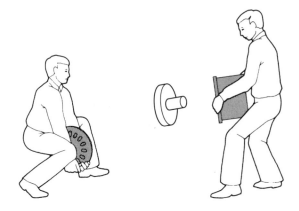

FIG 4.10 Spool handling

The head is raised, the chin tucked in and the back straight. To lift or lower, relax the knees, keep the arms into the body, stabilising one forearm inside the thigh, feet apart, with one foot forward, pointing in direction of travel. Grip with the palms and the roots of the fingers.

(Source Creber, 1967)

Body balance

Good balance is a prerequisite of most physical activities, from maintaining stationary positions to balance readjustment whilst performing movements. The slightest limb movement can change the centre of gravity, requiring balance readjustment. There are two ways of maintaining balance:

- by simply stiffening the legs or
- by relaxing or unlocking the legs so that the feet can readjust to safeguard balance.

All movements performed in an upright position are either top-heavy or base movements. Top-heavy movements are those which begin by bending the head, upper trunk and arms, so that the legs and back stiffen to prevent the body falling. This leads to a staccato-type movement which concentrates stresses in the shoulders, neck and lower back. Sustained tension in the legs leads to circulatory deficiency, loss of resilience and predisposition to injury in the legs and back.

A good movement (see Figure 4.5) always begins as a base movement and is segmental. In contrast to the initial stiffening of the legs in a top heavy movement, it begins by relaxation of the legs so that one foot can move automatically to safeguard balance. Simply bending the knees, however, is not necessarily relaxing to the legs. People tend to bend their knees excessively, leading to awkwardness in movement. In a good movement, action in the knees is rather a 'giving' or unlocking of the joints.

Conclusion

Human kinetics is not simply a new type of drill routine to be employed in performing certain tasks, but a method of thinking which involves fundamental changes in attitude and physical habits. First, the problem itself must be clarified before deciding on the methods to be employed in dealing with that problem. Much confusion arises when body movements are discussed because of different interpretations of the terms employed. For instance, if 12 people in a class were asked to 'arch' their backs, half would bend forwards and the other half backwards.

Whilst some people have a natural sense of good movement, in most instances individuals must be encouraged to change long-established physical habits and acquire a new way of thinking regarding the mechanical use of their bodies. Instructors themselves must learn to feel reactions in their own bodies and acquire skill in getting others to do the same. Teaching should concentrate on practical experiments which make clear the basic principles of good movements, followed by explanations of how and why they influence the body structures. Practical demonstration speaks louder than words!

Even when trainees are fully convinced that kinetic methods of moving are more beneficial, there is a likelihood that old habits will reassert themselves when the individual ceases to think about his movements. It is for this reason that the main emphasis in teaching should be on cultivating good base movements, so that when movements begin correctly the correct movements will follow.

No matter how efficiently the primary instruction is carried out, long-established habits cannot be changed overnight. There should always be some form of follow-up. The role of immediate supervision is essential. The man who supervises the job has the most influence on how the individual carries out the job. Because of this, all supervisors should have an understanding of the basic aspects of good movement.

Human kinetics is a way of life and should be taught at a very early age. Waiting until people reach adulthood, before introducing them to the subject, may be too late.

MANUAL HANDLING OPERATIONS

Principles of safe manual handling

Injuries associated with manual handling of raw materials, people, animals, goods and other items are the principal form of injury at work. Such injuries include prolapsed intervertebral (slipped) discs, hernias, ligamental strains and various forms of physical injury. It is essential, therefore, that all people required to handle items be aware of the basic principles of safe manual handling.

The following principles should always be considered in handling activities and in the training of people in manual handling techniques.

Feet positions
Place feet hip breadth apart to give a large base. Put one foot forward and to the side of the object to be lifted. This gives better balance.

Correct grip
Ensure that the grip is by the roots of the fingers and palm of the hand. This keeps the load under control and permits the load to be better distributed over the body.

Arms close to body
This reduces muscle fatigue in the arms and shoulders and the effort required by the arms. It ensures that the load, in effect, becomes part of the body and moves with the body.

Flat back
This does not mean vertical, but at an angle of approximately 15°. This prevents pressure on the abdomen and ensures an even pressure on the vertebral discs. The back will take the weight but the legs do the work.

Chin in

It is just as easy to damage the spine at the top as it is at the bottom. To keep the spine straight at the top, elongate the neck and pull the chin in. Do not tuck the chin on to the chest as this bends the neck.

Use of body weight

Use of body weight to move the load into the lifting position and to control movement of the load.

Planning the lift

When considering moving a load, make sure your route is unobstructed and that there are no obstructions or tripping hazards.

Ensure there is an area cleared to receive the load. If your route requires you to wear a safety helmet, eye protection or hearing protection, put them on before you lift.

Assessing/testing the load

The majority of injuries occur when actually lifting the load. People involved in handling operations should be instructed to assess the following:

- *Are there any rotating or moving parts?* If so, do not use them to lift with.
- *Is the load too big to handle?* If so, get help.
- *Is the load too heavy?* Rock the load. This will give a rough idea of its weight. If too heavy, get help.

Protective clothing

The provision and use of the correct PPE is an essential feature of safe manual handling. The following instructions should be incorporated in manual handling training and activities.

Hand protection

Examine the load for evidence of sharp edges, protruding wires, splinters or anything that could injure the hands. Wear the correct type of glove to prevent hand injury.

Feet protection

Wear footwear which is suitable for the job:

- with steel toe caps to protect the feet against falling objects or if the feet could get trapped under the load
- steel insoles to protect against protruding nails
- soles that will resist heat, oil and acid.

Two-man lift

Use all the principles involved in a one-man lift, with one variation. The leading foot should point in the direction of travel.

One man should give the order to lift, ensuring that his partner understands the order.

It is vital that there be unison in the movement of both men and load.

Manual Handling Operations Regulations 1992

Under these regulations, each employer shall, so far as is reasonably practicable, avoid the need for his employees to undertake any manual handling operations at work which involve a risk of their being injured. However, where it is not reasonably practicable to avoid same, he must make a suitable and sufficient assessment of all such manual handling operations, using the checklist shown in Figure 4.11, and then take appropriate remedial action aimed at preventing manual handling injuries (see also Figure 4.12).

MECHANICAL HANDLING

4

A host of equipment is available to ease the task of handling goods and, whenever possible, mechanical handling systems should be used in preference to manual handling. There are four principal forms of mechanical handling, namely conveyorised systems, elevators, internal factory transport and the use of goods vehicles. The choice of mechanical handling system will depend on several criteria such as the weight, shape, size, form, distance and frequency of movement of loads, together with space restrictions, storage systems and the nature of the material to be handled.

Conveyors

The following are the most commonly used conveyors.

Belt conveyors
These may be flat or troughed and are commonly used for transporting materials over long distances. The flat type is largely used to convey bulky packages or boxed goods, whilst the trough type is employed to carry loose materials, such as coal and aggregates. These materials are prevented from falling over the sides of the belt because it forms a cross-sectional 'trough' which prevents side spillage unless the belt has been overloaded.

Roller conveyors
Roller conveyors, which can be of the gravity type or the powered type, are used for the movement of unit loads. The powered type is used where level

Manual handling of loads
EXAMPLE OF AN ASSESSMENT CHECKLIST

Note: This checklist may be copied freely. It will remind you of the main points to think about while you:

- consider the risk of injury from manual handling operations
- identify steps that can remove or reduce the risk
- decide your priorities for action.

SUMMARY OF ASSESSMENT	
Operations covered by this assessment: .... Locations: .... Personnel involved: .... Date of assessment:	Overall priority for remedial action: Nil/Low/Med/High* Remedial action to be taken: .... Date by which action is to be taken: .... Date for reassessment: .... Assessor's name: ....Signature: ....

*circle as appropriate

Section A – Preliminary:

Q1   Do the operations involve a significant risk of injury?   **Yes/No***
If 'Yes' go to Q2. If 'No' the assessment need go no further.
If in doubt answer 'Yes'. You may find the guidelines in Appendix 1 helpful.

Q2   Can the operations be avoided / mechanised / automated at reasonable cost?   **Yes/No***
If 'No' go to Q3. If 'Yes' proceed and then check that the result is satisfactory.

Q3   Are the operations clearly within the guidelines in Appendix 1?   **Yes/No***
If 'No' go to Section B. If 'Yes' you may go straight to Section C if you wish.

Section C – Overall assessment of risk:

Q   What is your overall assessment of the risk of injury?   **Insignificant / Low / Med / High***

If not '**Insignificant**' go to Section D. If '**Insignificant**' the assessment need go no further.

Section D – Remedial action:

Q   What remedial steps should be taken, in order of priority?
i ....
ii ....
iii ....
iv ....
v ....

And finally:

- complete the SUMMARY above
- compare it with your other manual handling asessments
- decide your priorities for action
- TAKE ACTION.......................AND CHECK THAT IT HAS THE DESIRED EFFECT

FIG 4.11   Example of an assessment checklist

Section B – More detailed assessment, where necessary:

Questions to consider: (If the answer to a question is 'Yes' place a tick against it and then consider the level of risk)	Yes	Level of risk: (Tick as appropriate)			Possible remedial action: (Make rough notes in this column in preparation for completing Section D)
	Yes	Low	Med	High	
The tasks – do they involve: • holding loads away from trunk? • twisting? • stooping? • reaching upwards? • large vertical movement? • long carrying distances? • strenuous pushing or pulling? • unpredictable movement of loads? • repetitive handling? • insufficient rest or recovery? • a workrate imposed by a process?					
The loads – are they: • heavy? • bulky/unwieldy? • difficult to grasp? • unstable/unpredictable? • intrinsically harmful (eg sharp/hot?)					
The working environment – are there: • constraints on posture? • poor floors? • variations in levels? • hot/cold/humid conditions? • strong air movements? • poor lighting conditions?					
Individual capability – does the job: • require unusual capability? • hazard those with a health problem? • hazard those who are pregnant? • call for special information/training?					
Other factors – Is movement or posture hindered by clothing or personal protective equipment?					

Deciding the level of risk will inevitably call for judgement.
When you have completed Section B go to Section C.

4

FIG 4.11 Continued

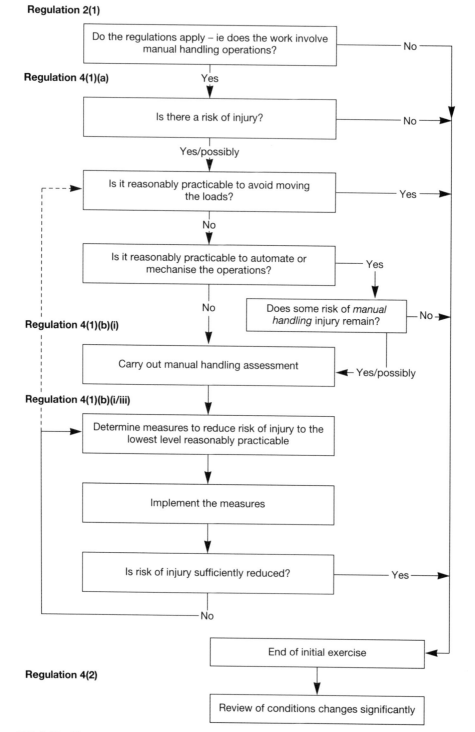

Regulation 2(1)

Do the regulations apply – ie does the work involve manual handling operations? — No

Regulation 4(1)(a)

Yes

Is there a risk of injury? — No

Yes/possibly

Is it reasonably practicable to avoid moving the loads? — Yes

No

Is it reasonably practicable to automate or mechanise the operations? — Yes

No

Does some risk of *manual handling* injury remain? — No

Regulation 4(1)(b)(i)

Carry out manual handling assessment — Yes/possibly

Regulation 4(1)(b)(i/iii)

Determine measures to reduce risk of injury to the lowest level reasonably practicable

Implement the measures

Is risk of injury sufficiently reduced? — Yes

No

End of initial exercise

Regulation 4(2)

Review of conditions changes significantly

FIG 4.12   How to follow the Manual Handling Operations Regulations 1992

or slightly rising runs are installed, where manual pushing of loads is impracticable, or where the incline necessary for gravity movement is not possible.

Chain conveyors

These are often of the 'scraper' type, used for pushing or pulling materials along a fixed trough. Overhead chain types employ 'hangers' attached to the chain from which are suspended the objects requiring transfer. 'Trolley' types comprise specially-designed trolleys mounted on a guide system, and are used, for instance, for the transfer of vehicle bodies during vehicle assembly.

Screw conveyors

This type of conveyor is used mainly for the transfer of loose or freeflowing solid materials, generally over short distances, eg solid fuel from bunker to boiler furnace or grain from storage to processing plant.

Slat conveyors

These conveyors comprise a series of spaced wooden or metal slats moving on side chains. They are commonly used for the transfer of boxed or sacked goods, and can operate on inclined levels for the transfer of goods between floors.

Hazards associated with conveyors

The main hazards associated with conveyors of different types are:

- traps or 'nips' between moving parts of a conveyor, eg between a conveyor chain and chain wheels, or between a moving belt and rollers, particularly drive and 'end' rollers and also belt tensioning rollers
- traps between moving and fixed parts of a conveyor, eg between the screw of a screw conveyor and the edge of the feed opening in the transfer tube
- hazards associated with sharp edges, eg on worn conveyor chains and belts, which may be exposed
- traps and nips created by the drive mechanism, eg V-belts and pulleys, chains and sprockets and
- traps created at transfer points between two conveyors, eg between a belt conveyor and roller conveyor.

Specific aspects of conveyor guarding

Whilst all conveyors present similar trapping and contact hazards, the various forms of conveyor need guarding in different ways. The hazards and guarding requirements are outlined below.

Belt conveyors

Traps formed between belt and rollers: Traps formed between the belt and drive, driven and tension rollers (see Figure 4.13) should be covered with fixed guards extending to 850 mm from the trapping point. Side guards should be provided along the whole length of the conveyor and extend to 25 mm below the return belt. Where there is pedestrian access, and the underside of the belt is carried by return roller, this section of the conveyor should be enclosed.

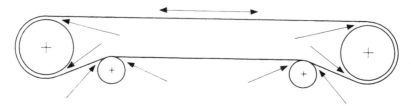

FIG 4.13   A reversible conveyor showing trapping points

Traps between belts and end plates: In addition to providing guards as outlined above, a horizontal guard plate should be fitted (see Figure 4.14). Clearance between plate and belt should not exceed 4 mm.

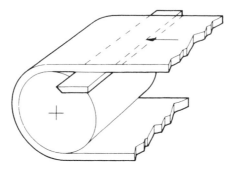

FIG 4.14   Guarding of conveyor end using a horizontal guard plate

Traps at belt conveyor transfer points: Where static transfer plates (dead plates) are fitted at the junction of two belt conveyors, the gap between the top surface and the belt should not exceed 4 mm (see Figure 4.15).

Traps between items conveyed and fixed structures: The risk associated with traps formed between a heavy item conveyed, eg a heavy crate, and fixed structures should be minimised by ensuring that there is a clearance of at least 50 mm between the item and any fixed structure. Support members should be free from sharp edges.

Hazards from worn and defective belts: Worn and defective belts and belt joints can create a hazard. Belts should be examined regularly and belt joints should be designed to be as smooth as possible. Worn belts or belts with loose fasteners should be replaced.

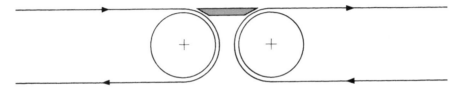

FIG 4.15 Use of a dead plate where two conveyors meet

Roller conveyors

Traps between rollers and fixed structures across the conveyor: The gap between the rollers and fixed structures should be either 4 mm or less, or greater than 50 mm, to minimise trapping.

Hazards from rotating ends of exposed roller shafts: Rotating ends of roller shafts should be contained within the supporting frame for the rollers or flush with the bearing housing. They may, however, be exposed without guards outside the bearing housing up to a distance of 25 mm, provided they are smooth. If they extend more than 25 mm beyond the bearing housing, or if they have protrusions or irregularities, they should be fitted with fixed caps which completely enclose them.

④

Hazards from missing or jammed rollers: Missing, worn or jammed rollers may cause instability of the conveyed load and increased risk of trapping. These rollers should be replaced.

Hazards at transfer points: Where a roller conveyor is fed from another conveyor and the gap between the conveying surface is less than 50 mm, the first roller should not be power-driven, but so arranged that it would be displaced from its position should a hand be trapped between conveyors (see Figure 4.16). Such a roller is termed a jump-out roller.

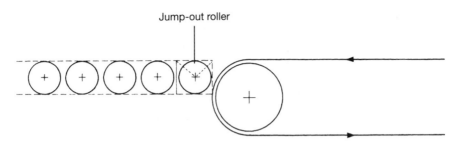

FIG 4.16 Junction of a roller conveyor and belt conveyor showing position of jump-out roller

Chain conveyors

Traps between the conveyor chain and chain wheels: Fixed side and end guards (see Figure 4.17) should be fitted at both the powered and free chain wheel ends of the conveyor, except where the conveyor is fitted in to the floor. Clearance between the lower edge of the guards and the floor, so as to facilitate cleaning, is allowable up to 180 mm, provided that the return chains are carried in guides and the guard extends to not less than 50 mm below the guide. On the top run of the conveyor, fixed in-fill plates should be fitted in the gaps between the chain guides and the side and end guards or the adjacent floor. All guards should be extended to 850 mm from the trapping points or otherwise prevent access. Clearance between guard and conveyor chain, where it runs over the chain wheel, should be 6 mm or less. Where a chain passes through a guard, clearance should not be less than 50 mm.

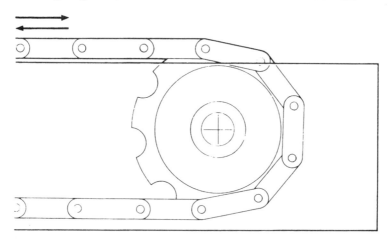

FIG 4.17   Guarding at the end of a chain conveyor by enclosure of the sprocket wheels and nip points

Traps at overlapping sections between chains and chain wheels: At overlapping sections, side guards or in-fill plates should be fitted. Alternatively, only side guards need to be fitted, provided that the reach distance to the trapping points over the side of the guards corresponds with Table 2 of Appendix A of BS 5667; Part 19 **'Specification for Continuous Mechanical Handling Equipment – Safety Requirements: Belt Conveyors – Examples for Guarding of Nip Points'**.

Traps between return chains and guide shoes, guide wheels and adjacent supporting structures: The return and carrying chain, where practicable, should be carried in continuous guides. Where this is not practicable and short guides, guide wheels or guide shoes are used, the chain should be free to lift 100 mm above the guide so as to reduce the risk of trapping. Guide wheels which have spokes or similar apertures should be fitted with discs to prevent hand and finger access.

Traps between carrying and return chains: Where carrying and return links of a chain run close together in guides, the return links should be positioned below guide level so as to reduce risk of trapping.

Hazards on bends caused by the chain slipping from its guide: The tendency for a chain to slip out of its guide on a bend can be reduced by:

- inclining the guide away from the centre of the bend
- use of wedge-shaped strips and plastic wearing strips so as to deflect the chain downwards in the guides and
- fitting of specially coated metal blocks in place of guides.

On the return chain, a plate can be fitted on top of the guide to prevent the chain from slipping out.

Screw conveyors

Traps between the rotating auger (screw) and the fixed parts: A fixed or interlocked guard should be fitted to prevent access to the screw. Where mesh or bar guards are fitted to allow free passage of materials, there must be sufficient distance between the guard members and the screw flight to prevent contact with the screw.

Slat conveyors

Traps between the conveyor chain and chain wheels: Fixed side guards should be fitted below conveyor track level along the whole length of the conveyor. The clearance between the guard and the chain should be 4 mm or less, and the guards should extend below the return chain so that the distance between the chain and the bottom of the guard is not less than 25 mm. Guards to enclose the chain underneath are not generally necessary, except where there is pedestrian access beneath the conveyor.

Traps between conveyor chain wheels and fixed structure: Safeguarding should be provided as above.

Traps between conveyor chain and end plates, dead plates, rails and fixed structures: Safeguarding should be provided as above. In addition, fixed guards should be fitted at the driven end of the conveyor where the chain passes close to the end plate. The clearance between the guard or a dead plate and the conveyor chain should be 4 mm or less.

Traps between the slats of biplanar chain conveyors where the slats open and close on bends and are inadequately supported: Biplanar chains should, at bends where the slats open and close, be supported underneath by solid fixed plates extending to the edge of the slats, and guarded by protective hoods, as shown in Figure 4.18, over the return point to a distance of not less than 850 mm.

Traps between rotating corner plates and fixed structures or conveyor chains: Fixed nip guards should be provided at circular corner plates where the plate is in-running with the conveyor chains or runs up to a fixed structure.

Hazards from corner plates with exposed sharp edges: Before the edge of the corner plate becomes sufficiently sharp, it should be replaced or protected by a guard around the entire periphery.

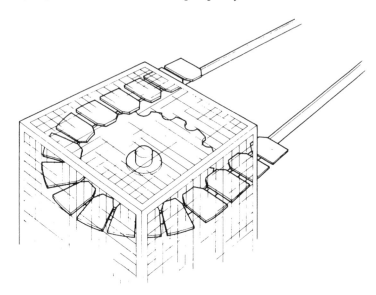

FIG 4.18 Protective hood over the return point of a conveyor
(Source BS 5667 Pt 18)

Hazards from conveyor chain with exposed sharp edges: Before chain edges become sufficiently sharp, they should be replaced.

General aspects of conveyor guarding

Types of guard

Fixed guards: Fixed guards should be used wherever practicable and must be securely fixed in position when the conveyor is in motion or likely to be put in motion. It should not be possible to open or remove these guards without the aid of a specific tool. Moreover, the fastener should be captive to the guard. Fixed guards may be an integral part of the conveyor or freestanding from the floor and securely fixed to the floor of the conveyor structure. Guards should not allow space for a person to be trapped between the guard and the conveyor.

Interlocked guards: An interlocked guard should be so connected to the machine controls that:

- until the guard is closed the machine cannot operate and
- either the guard remains locked closed until the dangerous movement has ceased or, where overrun is insufficient to create danger, opening the guard disengages the drive. The interlocking system should be fail-safe.

Interlocked guards should be provided for dangerous parts of a machine where the operator needs frequent access. (*'A part of machinery is dangerous if it is a possible cause of injury to anybody acting in a way in which a human being may be reasonably expected to act in circumstances which may reasonably be expected to occur'* – per du Parcq J in **Walker v Bletchley-Flettons Ltd** [1937] 1 AER 170.)

Tunnel guards: A tunnel guard is a form of distance guard preventing access to a danger point by reason of the relationship of the guard opening dimensions to length of tunnel. Where tunnel guards are used, the guards should be so designed and fitted that the relationship between the opening and the distance from the opening to the danger point complies with BS 5304: '**Safeguarding of Machinery**', cl. 10, Fig. 5, 'Openings in Fixed Guards'. Clearance between the sides of the opening to the tunnel guard and the items being conveyed should be not less than 50 mm.

Other safety aspects

- Where practicable, arrangements should be made for lubrication with the guards in position, eg through suitably located small openings which do not allow access to danger points.
- To minimise the risk of conveyed items jamming or falling from conveyors, the radius of all bends should be maximised at the design stage.
- All fixed support members, including guide rails, should be free from sharp edges.
- Where conveyors rise to more than one metre above floor or walkway level, suitable rails or side members should be provided to a sufficient height above the conveyor to contain the top item of the load being conveyed.

Emergency devices

- Where a conveyor is greater than 20 metres in length, an emergency stop (trip) wire should be provided. (The alternative is a series of emergency stop buttons.)
- Emergency stop buttons, which must be easily identifiable and designated as such, should be provided. An emergency stop button, however, is not a substitute for effective guarding. It is a device for cutting off the power in order to stop the conveyor. The position and number of stop buttons should be determined by the following criteria:
  - plant layout and product flow associated with the unit as a whole
  - the operator positions about the plant; no point on the conveyor should be more than 10 metres from an emergency stop button and
  - at any point on a conveyor where an emergency stop button is not visible, eg where a conveyor passes through a wall, a further stop button should be provided.

Emergency stop buttons should be palm- or mushroom-shaped and coloured red. They should remain in the 'off' position until reset. Releasing the emergency stop button should not cause equipment to restart.

Elevators

Most elevators operate in a fixed position. In certain industries, however, mobile elevators, which can be moved from one point to another, are used for loading and unloading tasks.

Fixed elevators

Fixed elevators may be of the vertical or the adjustable angle type. Vertical elevators may take the form of:

- bucket elevators for transferring loose materials, such as grain or
- bar elevators, on which items are placed or hung, eg sacked or boxed goods.

The elevator may be enclosed in a fixed shaft or hoistway and is generally continuous in operation, often being linked with a horizontal conveyor prior to and/or after elevation. One of the greatest hazards with elevating loose materials is dust explosions, and in flour mills, for instance, all elevator heads must be fitted with explosion reliefs. To prevent the spread of fire between floors in mills using bucket elevators in particular, all hoistways and floor openings must be fire-proofed with fire-resistant materials giving a notional period of fire resistance of 30 minutes.

Adjustable angle elevators are commonly used for loading and unloading the holds of ships, particularly where loose materials such as grain, metal ores and coal are involved.

Both types of elevator normally run in either direction. A fixed guard should be installed at the base of the elevator to prevent direct access to the moving flights and in-running nips formed between the chain and sprocket.

Mobile elevators

Mobile elevators are used for loading and unloading commodities such as sacked goods, regular shaped containers, and luggage into and out of aircraft. They may be of the bucket or bar type. A trap is created at the in-running nip between the elevator chains and sprockets, and both ends of the elevator should incorporate fixed guards. A further hazard is that such elevators can be run at variable speeds. Hand, arm and shoulder injuries have been sustained by operators because they have been unable to keep up with the speed of the elevator. Adequate supervision and control over the operation of these elevators is, therefore, crucial to the prevention of accidents.

INTERNAL TRANSPORT

Internal transport operations, principally through the use of various forms of lift truck, are a standard feature of many workplaces. Lift trucks are used in the loading and unloading of delivery vehicles, the handling of bulk products and in the transfer of palletised loads. They may also be used for access purposes using specifically-designed safe working platforms.

In 1982 the HSE produced an analysis of fatal accidents in transport activities. ('Transport Kills' – HSE (1982)) Statistics showed that, for all types of vehicle, 20 per cent of the fatal accidents were due to reversing vehicles, 15 per cent were associated with vehicles under repair or maintenance, 12 per cent involved loading or unloading operations, 10 per cent were caused by all classes of vehicle overturning and seven per cent specifically involved lift trucks overturning. An analysis of the causative factors which resulted in these fatal accidents revealed the following:

Safe systems of work not provided	34%
Inadequate information, instruction and training	23%
Human error	15%
Failure to follow safe system of work	14%
Lack of maintenance/faulty vehicle	14%
Poor management organisation	11%

Fundamentally, four specific aspects need consideration in preventing accidents associated with internal transport, namely the driver, the truck, the working environment and the system of work. The close co-ordination of these aspects is vital for maintaining high levels of lift truck safety.

The driver

A lift truck driver should be in a good state of health, with particular reference to vision and hearing. Drivers should be subject to a pre-employment health examination by an occupational health nurse prior to appointment, with follow-up health examinations at annual intervals. Drivers should be over 18 years.

All drivers should be trained according to the standards and criteria outlined in the HSC Approved Code of Practice and Supplementary Guidance 'Rider operated lift trucks – operator training'. This document distinguishes between three areas of training, that is basic training, specific job training and familiarisation training, and provides guidance on such aspects as selection of trainees, accrediting bodies for instructor training, test of operator skills, training records and programmes. Training should be undertaken by trainers who are experienced in the specific tasks to be carried out by trainees. Furthermore, it should be provided for all truck operators even if they have been trained by a former employer. Supplementary or refresher training should be given, for instance, when there has been a significant change in the operational layout, on transfer to a new operational area, when new or different equipment is introduced and when there has been a lapse in safe driving standards.

All trainees should be tested and, on passing the truck driving test, should receive a 'permit to drive', or similar written company authorisation, for certain identified classes of truck. A record of all authorised drivers should be maintained incorporating the serial numbers of permits to drive issued.

Operators should be provided with safety footwear and a safety helmet and, where appropriate, hearing protection, together with protective clothing appropriate to weather and/or temperature conditions.

Line managers should ensure that all drivers are adequately trained and working safely, that supervision is efficient and frequent, that they are undertaking the appropriate checks on their truck and that the system for reporting deficiencies in trucks is being used.

The truck

Trucks should be subject to clearly defined maintenance programme based on the manufacturer's recommendations for inspection, maintenance and servicing. Servicing records should be maintained. Apart from daily checks undertaken by operators, weekly maintenance on the truck should incorporate an operational examination of steering gear, lifting gear, battery, masts, forks, attachments and of any chains or ropes used in the lifting mechanism. Trucks should also be subject to six-monthly and annual examinations. In the case of the six-monthly examination (or 1,000 running hours) all parts of the truck should be examined by either a trained fitter or a representative of the manufacturer and a certificate issued by the examiner to the effect that the truck is safe to use. Lifting chains should be inspected on an annual basis and certificated in accordance with the requirements of the FA 1961.

Where a working platform is used in conjunction with a truck, eg for high level maintenance and cleaning, such platforms should be specifically designed for use with the truck.

The working environment

Well-designed layout and regular maintenance of operating areas is crucial to safe truck operation. Floors should be of adequate load-bearing capacity, reasonably smooth-surfaced and level. The edges of loading bays should be protected when not in use and 'tiger-striped' to warn the driver of such hazards. Sharp bends and overhead observations, such as pipes and cables, should be eliminated. Ramps should be installed to prevent displacement of the load at changes in floor level. Bridge plates should incorporate an adequate safety margin to support loaded equipment. Aisles should be of an adequate width and overhead clearance to facilitate turning and safe movement, and should be kept clear at all times. Where speed ramps are installed, a bypass for trucks should be provided.

Lighting should be adequate, that is a minimum of 100 lux internally and 50 lux externally. If a permanent level of 100 lux is not available in working areas, auxiliary lighting should be installed on the truck and so arranged to avoid glare to pedestrians and other truck operators.

In truck battery-charging bays, ventilation should be sufficient to prevent accumulations of hydrogen gas. Smoking and the use of naked lights in these areas should be prohibited. Refuelling areas for petrol-driven trucks should be located outside the building.

The system of work

Many accidents, particularly to other persons, and damage to vehicles and structures, are associated with the absence of or failure to follow safe systems of work. Typical causes of overturning of trucks are due to drivers exceeding the maximum-rated load capacity or failing to place the load dead centre. Where loads are being carried by the use of slings, slinging should be at designated slinging points on the truck. The movement of unsafe loads and the use of defective or under-strength pallets is a common cause of pallet loads collapsing during movement. Movement of trucks in unlit or badly lit external areas can result in accidents involving people and property. Convex mirrors should be installed prior to bends and junctions.

When powered industrial trucks are used on public highways, they must comply with the road traffic acts and regulations, particularly with regard to brakes, lights and steering.

To comply with the requirements of the HSWA, formal safe systems of work, which identify the hazards and precautions necessary on the part of drivers, should be produced. This is particularly necessary for routine operations and certain high risk operations. Safe systems of work should form an important feature of the induction and orientation training for drivers, and line management must ensure such safe systems of work are closely followed.

Operator safety rules

The following safety rules should be enforced, including taking disciplinary action where necessary. These rules should be incorporated in the company permit to drive issued to all approved truck drivers.

1 Regulate speed with visibility.

2 Use the horn wherever necessary, but particularly at blind corners.

3 Pay particular attention to pedestrians and other vehicles.

4 Travel with the forks down; no movement of the forks when in motion.

5 Drive in reverse when the load obscures vision.

6 Use the prescribed truck routes; no short cuts.

7 Take care when reversing, using the horn where necessary.

8 Passengers must not be carried at any time.

9 Adhere to the speed limit eg 10mph.

10 Slow down on wet or bad surfaces; no quick turns.

11 No parking in front of fire exits or equipment.

12 Use the handbrake and tilt mechanism correctly.

13 Take care on ramps; no turning on ramps.

14 When leaving the truck at any time, follow the procedure below:
   (a) controls in NEUTRAL
   (b) forks down
   (c) power off
   (d) brakes on and
   (e) remove the key or connector plug.

15 Carry out the daily check prior to starting or handover – brakes, lights, horn, steering, battery, hydraulics, speed controls.

16 Report any defects immediately to your supervisor.

It should be recognised that lift truck accidents can result in death, major injury, damage to property, plant and the truck itself. Damage costs to trucks can be substantial. It is essential that truck drivers are adequately trained and supervised in their operations. Unsafe driving practices should result in various levels of disciplinary action. Appropriate standards of truck maintenance are also significant in the prevention of accidents, together with well-maintained surfaces and good cleaning and housekeeping levels in operational areas.

Mobile handling equipment

A wide range of equipment is used in storage and handling operations. Although such equipment is necessary for speedy movement of goods, its use has frequently led to accidents. The basic requirements for the safe operation of mobile handling equipment, such as fork-lift trucks, are careful selection and use of the right equipment in the right place by the right people. With any mechanical handling task, the selection of the appropriate equipment for the material to be handled is important. The type and layout of the storage system, type, weight and shape of the materials to be handled, construction and layout of buildings and operational areas, as well as the potential for accidents, must be considered. Before acquiring mechanical handling equipment, manufacturers and/or suppliers should be consulted to ensure that the equipment selected matches the performance requirements. Where new storage systems are being developed, the manufacturer and/or supplier should again be consulted.

Classification of mobile mechanical handling equipment

Pedestrian-operated stacking trucks

These are of two types, manually operated and power-operated stackers (see Figure 4.19). A manually operated stacker is normally restricted in operation to moving post pallets or heavy machinery. It has a manual shift with hydraulically operated lift, and cannot pick up directly from the floor. It has a capacity of 0.25 to 0.5 tonne, with a maximum lift of approximately 1.5 metres.

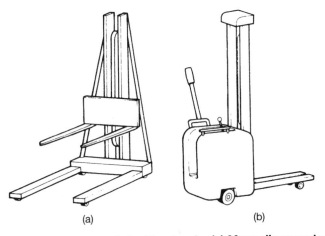

(a)   (b)

FIG 4.19 Pedestrian-operated stacking trucks (a) Manually operated stacker (b) Power-operated stacker

Power-operated stackers can be pedestrian or rider controlled, with power operation vertically and horizontally. They can pick up pallets from the floor. This type of stacker has a capacity of 0.5 to one tonne and a maximum lift of approximately three metres.

Reach trucks

A reach truck is a fork-lift truck that enables the load to be retracted within the wheel base, minimising overall working length and allowing reduced aisle widths. There are two separate forms, the moving mast reach truck and the pantograph reach truck (see Figure 4.20). The former is rider-operated. Forward-mounted load wheels enable the fork carriage to move within the wheel base, so that forks can reach to pick up or deposit the load. The mast, forks and load move together. This truck has a capacity of 0.5 to three tonnes, with a maximum lift of 10 metres.

A pantograph reach truck is a rider-operated truck in which reach movement is by pantograph mechanism, whereby the fork and load can move away from the static mast. This truck has a capacity of 0.5 to 2.5 tonnes and a maximum lift of 10 metres.

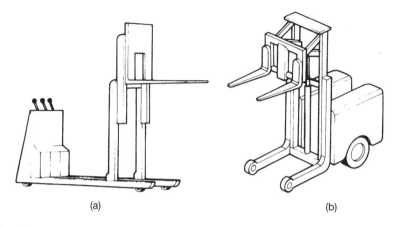

FIG 4.20   Reach trucks (a) Moving mast reach truck (b) Pantograph reach truck

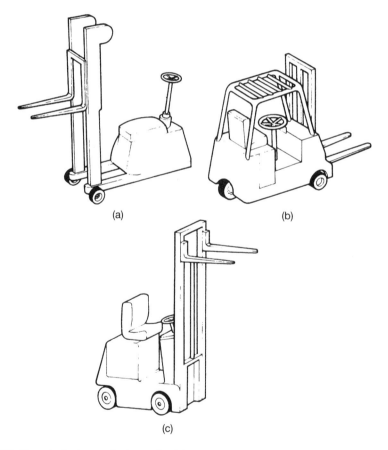

FIG 4.21 Counterbalance fork trucks (a) Lightweight pedestrian controlled
(b) Lightweight rider controlled (c) Heavyweight rider controlled

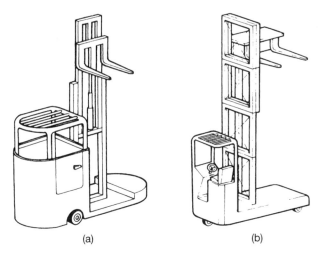

(a)   (b)

FIG 4.22   Narrow aisle trucks (a) Side loader (b) Counterbalance rotating load turret truck

Counterbalance fork trucks

Such trucks are battery, petrol, diesel or gas powered. They carry the load in front which is counterbalanced to the weight of the vehicle over the rear wheels. They take three specific forms, namely lightweight pedestrian controlled trucks, lightweight rider controlled trucks and heavyweight rider controlled trucks (see Figure 4.21). The lightweight pedestrian controlled type is normally a three-wheeled vehicle, and is used mainly where stacking rather than transfer is important. Such trucks provide a greater load-carrying capacity than the pedestrian stacker. They have a capacity of 0.5 to one tonne and maximum lift of approximately three metres.

The lightweight rider-controlled truck is similar to the pedestrian controlled truck, except that the operator sits inside the truck. The handling rate is higher. Such trucks have a capacity of 0.5 to 1.25 tonnes and a maximum lift of six metres.

The heavyweight version is a four-wheeled truck, the high counterbalance weight over the rear wheels giving it a high load capacity. Many attachments, such as cradles, are available to suit different loads. They have a capacity from one to nine tonnes and maximum lift from six to 12 metres.

Narrow aisle trucks

This type of truck differs from a reach truck in that the base of the truck does not turn within the working aisle to deposit or retrieve its load. This enables the aisle width to be kept to a minimum. This type of truck takes two forms, namely side loaders and counterbalance rotating load turret trucks (see Figure 4.22). Side loaders are ideal for long runs down narrow aisles. They are, however, only capable of stacking down one side of the aisle at a time and a large turning circle is needed at each end of the aisle in order to serve both faces of a racking system. Reach trucks have a capacity of up to 1.5 tonnes and a maximum lift of nine to 12 metres.

The counterbalance rotating load turret truck has a rigid mast with telescopic sections. It incorporates a head which rotates through 180°, enabling it to slide sideways to deposit or retrieve a load. This type of truck can serve both faces of a racking system, and is guided by tracks or rails at floor level. They have a capacity of one to 1.5 tonnes and a maximum lift of 12 metres.

Both types of narrow aisle truck are rider-operated.

Order pickers

This device is derived from the fork-lift truck, incorporating a protected working platform permanently fixed to the lift forks. Thus the operator can pick goods from racking above floor level or place them in a racking system. The truck is operated from the picking platform and incorporates side shift, rotating mast and other purpose-added features. Order pickers allow maximum utilisation of racked storage areas owing to the narrowness of the aisles within which they can operate. Order pickers operate on a conventional basis or can be purpose designed for a specific task (see Figure 4.23). Conventional order pickers operate on the same basis as a fork-lift truck with a cage fitted for the operator. The case incorporates a small platform for the placement of goods picked from the racking. They have a capacity of 0.5 to one tonne with a maximum lift of six to nine metres.

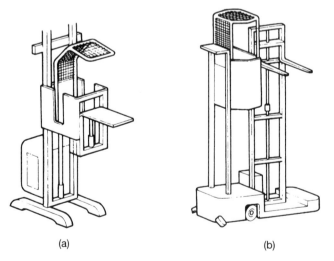

(a)   (b)

FIG 4.23 Order pickers (a) Conventional (b) Purpose designed

Order pickers can be designed for a multitude of storage tasks. The heavy-duty type can incorporate traversing load masts or dual mast with independent load/operator control, and generally operates along rails or tracks within narrow aisles. With purpose designed order pickers, capacity and maximum lift would be specified at the ordering stage.

Safe operation of mobile handling equipment

Equipment
The operation of mobile handling equipment results in many industrial accidents. The following rules should be applied to such operations:

- Untrained and/or unauthorised personnel should not drive or operate powered mechanical handling equipment.
- Rider trucks left unattended should have the forks lowered and be immobilised by:
    - leaving the controls in the neutral position
    - shutting off the power
    - applying the brakes and
    - removing the key or connector plug.
- The maximum rated load capacity of the equipment, as stated on the manufacturer's identification plate, should never be exceeded.
- On no account should passengers be carried, unless in a properly constructed cage or platform. (See **Use of fork-lift trucks as working platforms** later in this chapter.)
- When powered industrial trucks are used on public highways, they must comply with the Road Traffic Acts and be fitted with lights, brakes, steering, etc.
- The keys to the truck should be kept in a secure place when the equipment is not in use. Keys should be issued to authorised operators only and be retained by such persons until the end of the work period, when they should be returned to the manager responsible for the operation.
- A clearly defined maintenance programme, based on the manufacturer's recommendations for inspection, maintenance and servicing, should be operated. Repairs and maintenance should be carried out only by trained and experienced staff. Drivers should be trained to undertake simple periodic maintenance checks, and there should be a formal procedure for reporting defects identified in such checks and during normal operation. A typical daily check by the operator would include an examination and/or test of lights, including warning beacon, horn, tyres, brakes, steering, tilting, lifting and manipulation systems, operator controls, fluid levels, security of the overhead cage/guard and load backrest, as well as the integrity of hydraulic pipes, pipe joints and connections.
- Weekly maintenance on a truck should include all the operator checks mentioned above, together with an operational examination of steering gear, lifting gear, battery, mast, forks, attachments, and any chains or ropes used in the lifting mechanism.

- Mobile handling and lifting equipment should also be subject to a six-monthly and an annual examination. In the case of the six-monthly examination (or 1,000 running hours) all parts of the truck should be examined by either a trained fitter or a representative of the manufacturer and a certificate issued by the examiner to the effect that the truck is safe to use. Lifting chains should be inspected on an annual basis and certificated in accordance with statutory requirements.

Operating area

Layout and maintenance of operating areas for mobile handling equipment are important in ensuring safe operation. The following points are relevant:

- Floors and roadways should be of adequate load-bearing capacity as well as being smooth-surfaced and level. Moreover, a designer or consultant engineer of a factory or other workplace who fails to provide for this requirement can be sued for negligence (**Greaves & Company (Contractors) Ltd v Baynham Meikle & Partners** [1975] 1 WLR 1095). Where 'sleeping sentries' ('sleeping policemen') are installed to slow down vehicular traffic, a bypass for mobile handling equipment should be provided. Furthermore, the edges of loading bays should be protected when not in use and 'tiger-striped' to warn the driver, particularly when operating at night. Sharp bends and overhead obstructions, such as electric cables and pipework, should be eliminated where possible.

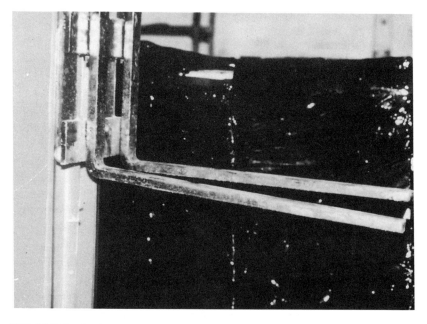

FIG 4.24(a)   Serious distortion of the forks of a hand fork-lift truck due to overloading

FIG 4.24(b)   The fractured bracket (arrowed) attached the steering base to the fork-lift truck and affected the ability of the driver to steer the truck effectively
(Reproduced by courtesy of National Vulcan Engineering Insurance Group Ltd)

- Ramps should be installed to prevent displacement of the load at gutters, changes in floor level, etc.
- Gradients should not exceed 10 per cent and there should be a smooth gradual change of gradient at the bottom and top of the slope.
- Bridge plates should incorporate an adequate safety margin to support loaded equipment. These should be clearly and permanently marked with the maximum permissible load, secured to prevent accidental movement, and surfaced with a high-friction finish.

- Aisles should be of adequate width and overhead clearance to facilitate turning and safe movement, and should be kept clear at all times.

- Lighting should be adequate with a minimum overall illuminance level of 100 lux. If a permanent level of 100 lux is not available, auxiliary lighting should be installed on the equipment and so arranged to avoid glare which could affect other operators.

- Adequate general vehicle parking facilities should be provided away from the main operating areas and preferably in a secure compound.

- Actual layout of operating areas is crucial to the prevention of accidents. Doorways and overhead structures low enough to form an obstacle should have suitable warning notices displayed above them. Clear direction signs, marked barriers, electrically operated warning devices and convex mirrors should be used in order to prevent pedestrians coming into direct contact with trucks. Additionally, instructions to drivers to sound the horn and restrict speed should be posted at prominent positions. Separate routes, designated crossing places and barriers, clearly marked at frequent intervals, should be arranged so as to restrict access by pedestrians to operational areas. Where pedestrians and handling equipment use the same access between parts of a building, a separate pedestrian access door should be available; alternatively, tubular steel barriers should be installed one metre from the side of the opening to provide a pedestrian passageway at the side. Windows or ports should be installed in rubber doors through which trucks frequently pass. Columns, pipework, racking, exposed electrical conduits and items of plant should be protected by impact-absorbing barriers.

- In truck battery-charging bays ventilation should be sufficient to prevent accumulations of hydrogen gas. Although not a statutory requirement, smoking should be forbidden and other sources of ignition eliminated. Notices prohibiting smoking, the use of naked lights and other sources of ignition should be displayed. Moreover, before disconnecting the truck battery from the charger, the current should be switched off to reduce the risk of sparking.

- Refuelling areas for petrol-driven trucks should ideally be located outside the building.

The operators

To ensure the safe operation of mobile handling equipment, it is essential that operators be responsible persons and physically fit for the job. They should be trained, and there should be an effective system for documentation of authorised operators, eg permits to drive. In particular:

- A high level of supervision and control should be exercised over all product- and goods-handling activities.

- Operators of mobile handling equipment should be physically and mentally fit, intelligent, mature and reliable. Handicapped persons need not be excluded, but medical advice should be sought as to suitability for specific tasks.

- Training should be given to operators and supervisors, and to managers responsible for areas where mobile handling is in operation, particularly to cover emergency situations.

- Operator training should be undertaken by trainers who are experienced in the specific tasks to be undertaken by trainees. Such training comprises three specific parts:
  - acquisition of the basic skills and knowledge required to operate the equipment safely and to undertake the required daily equipment checks.
  - specific job training in a 'safe' working area to develop operational skills, and
  - familiarisation training under close supervision in the workplace. Training should be provided for all operators, even if they have been trained by a former employer. Supplementary or refresher training should be undertaken:
  - when there has been a significant change in operational layout;
  - on transfer to a new operational area;
  - when new or different equipment is introduced; or
  - when there may have been a lapse in operator standards;

- Trainees should be tested. On passing a truck driving test, the operator should receive a 'permit to drive' for the class of truck on which he has qualified. Management should not allow persons to operate any mechanical handling equipment without this written authority. Additionally, a record should be maintained of all authorised operators and the serial number of the permit to drive issued. The date of training, and that of the refresher training which will be required in the future, should also be recorded.

- Operators should be provided with safety footwear and a safety helmet and, where appropriate, hearing protection, together with protective clothing to suit weather and/or temperature conditions. For example, for work in cold stores or on external loading, donkey jackets and gloves should be provided.

- Supervisors are responsible for ensuring that all operators are trained and working safely, that they carry out periodic checks and that there is a system for reporting deficiencies.

The HSC Approved Code of Practice and Supplementary Guidance '**Rider operated lift trucks – operator training**' provides excellent advice on this matter.

Use of fork-lift trucks as working platforms

There is now widespread industrial use of fork-lift trucks as a means of elevating workers and contractors to undertake tasks at high level, eg painting, cleaning, maintenance, repairs. Although, in principle, the use of a fork-lift truck affords considerable advantages for this type of work, nevertheless its primary function is the carriage and manipulation of materials and not as a means of support for a working platform. Therefore, if trucks are to be used for such purposes, certain safeguards are essential. Where practicable, the truck should be specifically designed for this purpose. In most cases, however, this is not the case and consequently working platforms are usually fitted to the forks of trucks. A platform designed for use on one particular truck should never be employed on any other type of fork-lift truck.

Where trucks are specially designed for or are regularly used with working platforms, movement of the platform should be controlled by the person on the platform. When trucks are only occasionally used with working platforms, either full platform controls or a platform-mounted emergency stop control should be provided.

Precautions with working platforms on fork-lift trucks

- The manufacturer's opinion as to the suitability of a truck for use in connection with a specific working platform should always be obtained.

- The weight of the platform and total superimposed load thereon should be not more than half of the truck manufacturer's rated capacity at the rated load centre distance of the truck at maximum lift height. A plate should be affixed to the platform indicating the maximum superimposed load and minimum rating of the truck on which it may be used.

- The platform should be secured to the forks and either the edges fenced to a minimum height of one metre either by guard rails comprising top rails, intermediate rails and toe board, or a steel mesh enclosure of similar height should be constructed.

- A locking device should be fitted to ensure that the mast remains vertical.

- Where controls are located on the platform, they should be of the 'dead man's handle' type, whereby the actuating lever or switch must be held or pressed continuously to effect motion of the platform. Preferably, controls should be positioned midway across the platform and at the rear to keep the operator away from the edges of the platform whilst it is in motion. This recommendation does not preclude provision of emergency controls at floor level which may be desirable to lower the platform in the event of breakdown or emergency. When fitted, such controls should be located and designed so as to prevent accidental or unauthorised operation.

- A prominent notice should be affixed to the platform with the instruction 'ENSURE THAT PARKING BRAKE IS APPLIED BEFORE ELEVATING PLATFORM'.

- On all machines designed specifically for, or likely to be used for, access purposes there should be a minimum of two suspension ropes or chains.

- No person should remain in the elevated working position when the truck is moved from one point to another.

- The appliance should only be used on well-maintained and level floors.

(See reference earlier to the case of **Greaves & Company (Contractors) Ltd v Baynham Meikle & Partners**.)

- All trapping points should be screened or guarded to protect persons carried on the platform, eg where a chain passes over sprockets, or where there is a crushing or shearing action between parts of the mast or its actuating mechanism.

Goods vehicles

Rail vehicles

Rail movement in depots and industrial complexes is a major hazard, frequently owing to poor visibility. The danger is greatly increased where long rafts or wagons are being shunted, especially by one-man diesel locomotives. Here the number of crossing places should be kept to a minimum and they should be clearly defined by signs and barriers. 'STOP, LOOK AND LISTEN' signs should be displayed well ahead of level crossings located in rail depots. Each crossing should be well lit at night and during bad weather. Shunting locomotives should be fitted with flashing beacons which operate during movement. Further guidance on rail vehicle operations is provided in the Locomotives in Sidings in Factories Regulations 1906.

Motor vehicles

Many of the requirements for industrial powered trucks apply to the operation of motor vehicles within the boundaries of a factory or industrial complex. The careful layout of loading bays, approaches, and other areas will minimise those hazards which can exist when vehicles need to manoeuvre in awkward or confined spaces.

Although goods vehicles visiting factory premises are not 'machinery' for the purposes of the FA 1961, section 14(1) (per Viscount Dilhorne in **British Railways Board v Liptrot** [1967] 2 AER 1072), they come within the general requirements for a safe system of work, as laid down in HSWA, section 2(2) and at common law. Consequently, drivers of such vehicles, whether company employees or those of another company delivering to the premises, must not reverse vehicles, unless guidance is given by an authorised person. In particular, where there is extensive vehicle manoeuvring in a loading area, marshalling stewards should be employed to ensure the safe reversing, loading and unloading of vehicles.

LIFTING MACHINERY AND EQUIPMENT

Definitions

Lifting machinery

The statutory definition of *lifting machinery* is '*a crane, crab, winch, teagle, pulley block, gin wheel, transporter or runway'* (FA, section 27(9)). Also included are hoists, cranes, elevators and lifts, whether used for carrying people, goods or both.

Lifting tackle

The statutory definition of *lifting tackle or lifting equipment* is *'chain slings, rope slings, rings, hooks, shackles and swivels'* (FA, section 26(3)). Hence the general meaning of lifting tackle is taken to include various types of ropes, chains, hooks, eyebolts, 'D' rings and other items.

Note: The Construction (Lifting Operations) Regulations 1961 lay down detailed requirements in respect of lifting appliances and lifting equipment used in building operations and works of engineering construction.

Lifting machinery – legal aspects

Lifting machinery may be classified thus:

- hoists
- cranes and
- lifts.

Outline of statutory requirements relating to machinery

Principal legal requirements covering lifting plant and equipment are incorporated in the FA (sections 22–27), the Shipbuilding and Ship-repairing Regulations 1960, the Construction (Lifting Operations) Regulations 1961, the Offices, Shops and Railway Premises (Hoists and Lifts) Regulations 1968 and the Docks Regulations 1988, all of which were amended by the Lifting Plant and Equipment (Records of Test and Examination etc) Regulations 1992.

Hoists and lifts – general requirements
Every hoist or lift shall be:

- of good mechanical construction, sound materials, adequate strength and properly maintained (section 22(1)) and
- examined by a competent person once every six months at least and a report produced; the details of the examination must be attached to or entered in the general register within 28 days; where defects indicate that future operation of the equipment may be unsafe the HSE must be notified by a competent person within 28 days (section 22(2)).

Every hoistway or liftway shall be efficiently protected by a substantial enclosure fitted with gates of such design and layout as to prevent, when the gates are shut, any person falling down the way or coming into contact with any moving parts of the equipment. Any such gate must be fitted with an efficient interlocking device (section 22(4)).

Every hoist or lift and every enclosure shall be so constructed as to prevent any part of any person or any goods carried from being trapped between any part of the hoist or lift and any fixed structure or between the counterbalance weight or any other moving part (section 22(7)).

The safe working load of the hoist or lift must be conspicuously marked and must not be exceeded (section 22(8)).

Hoists and lifts for carrying persons

The following requirements, in addition to those listed above, apply:

- provision of efficient automatic devices to prevent the cage or platform overrunning (section 23(1)(*a*))

- provision of a gate on every side where access to a landing is afforded; efficient devices must be provided to prevent the cage being set in motion when the gate is open and to ensure that the cage will come to rest when the gate is opened (section 23(1)(*b*)) and

- where the platform or cage is suspended by a rope or chain, there must be at least two ropes or chains separately connected to the cage or platform, each rope or chain and its attachments being capable of carrying the whole weight of the platform or cage and its maximum working load; efficient devices must be provided and maintained which will support the platform or cage with its maximum working load in the event of a breakage of the ropes or chains or any of their attachments (section 23(3)).

Teagle openings

A teagle opening is an opening in the fabric of a building above ground level through which goods can be hoisted into the building. Such openings are common in flour and agricultural mills in particular. They also feature in older types of factories and in warehouses. The FA, section 24, requires that every teagle opening or similar doorway used for hoisting or lowering goods or materials, whether by mechanical power or otherwise, must be securely fenced and provided with a secure handhold at each side. The fencing must be properly maintained and kept in position, except when hoisting or lowering goods or materials.

Work at teagle openings and platform edges

What constitutes 'secure fencing' within the requirements of section 24 is a matter for legal interpretation, but it is quite common to see openings fenced solely by a metal bar or wooden beam set horizontally approximately one metre from the floor. This arrangement relies heavily on operators replacing the bar after loading or unloading operations, and there is always the risk of operators falling over or under the bar. Furthermore, the sole provision of handholds at each side of the opening is of limited value in preventing falls from teagle openings and platform edges.

In recent years a number of safety barriers for high-level openings have been developed, the Ajax safety barrier being the most common. It is designed to give continuous protection to anyone working at a high-level loading point or teagle opening. The barrier operates on the basis that when a load has to be placed on a platform or through a teagle opening, the barrier is pivoted laterally through 180° and comes to rest in a similar position some distance back from the edge of the platform or opening. Once the materials have been placed on the platform, the barrier is pivoted upwards and over the load until it rests in its original position at the platform edge so that the load can be removed. The moving part of the barrier is spring-loaded for ease of operation and a simple automatic catch locks the barrier in the closed position.

While the standard application is at loading points on platforms or mezzanine floors, the barrier can also be made to suit difficult installations where it is not practicable to make structural alterations, such as teagle openings, where doors may be involved or the pallet load is too large for standard type of barrier.

Cranes and other lifting machines

- All parts and working gear shall be of good construction, sound materials, adequate strength and free from patent defect, and be properly maintained (section 27(1)).

- All parts and working gear shall be examined by a competent person at least once every 14 months, a report containing the prescribed particulars of every such examination must be kept where defects indicate that operation of the equipment may be unsafe in future (section 27(2)).

- All rails on which a travelling crane moves and every track on which the carriage of a transporter or runway moves shall be of proper size and adequate strength and have an even running surface; any rails or track must be properly laid, adequately supported or suspended and properly maintained (section 27(3)).

- The safe working load or loads must be plainly marked on every lifting machine. In the case of a jib crane, so constructed that the safe working load may be varied by raising or lowering the jib, there must be attached to it either a safe working load indicator or a table indicating the safe working loads at corresponding inclinations of the jib or corresponding radii of the load (section 27(4)).

- Except for the purposes of a test (proof testing), no lifting machine must be loaded beyond the safe working load (section 27(5)).

- No lifting machine may be taken into use in a factory for the first time unless it has been tested and all parts thoroughly examined by a competent person; a certificate of the test and examination, specifying the safe working loads of the machine, must be issued and signed by the person making the test and examination, and the certificate must be kept available for inspection (section 27(6)).

- If any person is employed or working on or near the wheel-track of an overhead travelling crane in any place where he would be liable to be struck by the crane, effective measures must be taken, eg by warning the driver of the crane, to ensure that the crane does not approach within about six metres of that place. Where any person is working at a place above floor level, where he would be liable to be struck by an overhead travelling crane or its load, effective measures must be taken to warn him of the approach of the crane, unless his work is so connected with or dependent on the movements of the crane as to make a warning unnecessary (sections 27(7) and 27(8)).

Safety aspects of lifting machinery

Cranes

Cranes have numerous applications in industrial activities, construction, docks and shipbuilding, and on railways. The principal hazard associated with any crane operation is the risk of collapse or overturning of the crane which can be caused by a variety of factors such as overloading, incorrect slewing or even incorrect construction of the crane. One of the principal causes of crane overturning is associated with the crane operator exceeding the 'maximum permitted moment' which is the product of the load and the radius of operation of the crane. (The radius of operation is the horizontal distance between the crane's centre of rotation and a vertical line drawn through the crane hook.) If the maximum permitted moment is exceeded, the crane is in danger of overturning or collapse.

There are many types of crane in use. Several of the more common forms of crane are discussed below.

Some defects in cranes which could result in accidents are illustrated in Figures 4.25–4.28.

Fixed cranes

This type of crane is permanently fixed in one location, such as wharf, loading bay, dock or rail siding. It may incorporate a fixed angle or adjustable angle jib, and may rotate through 360°. Accidents involving fixed cranes with resultant crane collapse, fall of the load and/or injury to operatives can occur in many ways. One principal cause of accidents is the failure to lift vertically. This may arise through the physical impossibility of getting the load directly below the lifting point, or the use of a fixed crane in a deliberate attempt to drag a load sideways, a very dangerous practice. Loads treated in this way can overstress the crane and cause collapse, or the load may swing violently, crushing people and damaging property. Alternatively, loads being raised or lowered may catch in a fixed structure causing damage. The 'snatching' of loads, instead of operating a slow and steady lifting action, can cause crane failure. Moreover, attempting to pull an object from under other material can impose loads of up to one hundred times that anticipated, often with disastrous results. Cranes with adjustable angle jibs have collapsed through the operator's failure to observe the reduction in the safe working load as the jib moves towards the horizontal.

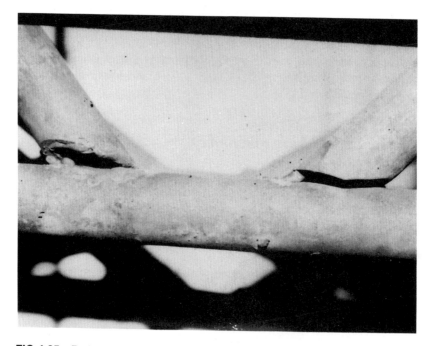

FIG 4.25   Defects in cranes. Unsatisfactory welds between braces to the jib of a mobile crane. This could seriously reduce the strength of the crane and lead to failure

Similar observations apply in the case of rotational cranes. Accidents are caused by incorrect lifting and slewing, failure of the rotating gear when slewing and, more commonly, slewing too fast. Variations in wind speed, particularly while slewing, have a direct effect on the strength and stability of this type of crane.

Tower cranes

These cranes are covered by the Construction (Lifting Operations) Regulations 1961, and are highly complex items of plant. Accidents are caused through incorrect assembly of the crane, and insufficient access to the jib, mast and driver's cab. The need for the driver to reach the cab safely is well recognised, but safe access to other parts of the crane is necessary during inspection, maintenance and repair, and in the course of erection or dismantling. Modifications to tower cranes may affect their strength and stability, and the manufacturer's advice should be sought prior to any modification. Rail-mounting arrangements and the system for maintenance of such cranes must be considered in any assessment of safe working operations.

FIG 4.26   A close-up of cracking originating from a weld in a 57mm diameter tubular section of a part of a crane jib head fabrication. Further development of this defect, aided by internal corrosion of the member, could lead to jib failure.

Mobile cranes

Mobile cranes are used increasingly for lifting heavy items into specific locations. Some incorporate a telescopic or articulated boom and rotate through 360° on the chassis of a purpose-built road vehicle. In addition to the precautions outlined previously for fixed cranes, it is imperative that any lift takes place on solid level ground, using the vehicle's outriggers fully extended to spread the load through the vehicle to the ground. The principal cause of accidents is the use of cranes on uneven sloping ground, where the centre of gravity of the load combined with that of the crane has fallen outside the wheel base of the vehicle, resulting in overturning.

Overhead travelling cranes

The most common application of this crane is in heavy fabrication shops and foundries where the crane runs along a fixed traverse. The crane may be fixed to operate in one position or to rotate through 360°. The main hazards are derailment due to overloading, obstructions on the traverse or rail track, and the absence of adequate stops at each end of the traverse or rails. With

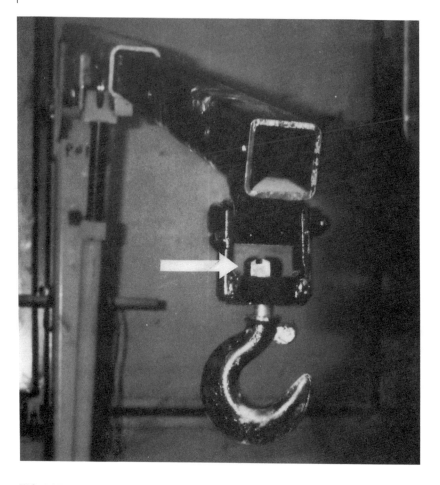

FIG 4.27   A dangerous situation with a manual hydraulic portable jib crane.
The hook-retaining nut is only engaging one or two threads. Provision was made
for locking the nut with a split pin which is missing.

rail-mounted cranes, either the crane must be fitted with effective brakes for
the travelling motion, or sprags, scotches or chocks must be provided and
used.

Many accidents are attributed to overhead travelling cranes crushing or
striking operators working in the vicinity of the track. Previous reference has
been made to the requirements of the FA, section 27(7), whereby effective
measures must be taken to prevent a crane approaching within about six
metres of any place where a person may be working on or near the wheel
track of such a crane. The only reliable 'effective measures' are the complete
isolation and locking off of the electrical supply to the crane, coupled with the
issue of a permit to work indicating that the isolation procedure has been carried out and that it is safe for work to proceed in the vicinity of the crane

track. The mere switching off of the electrical supply at a control box, even with the display of a cautionary notice on the switchbox itself, is not considered sufficient. The starter switch should be physically locked in the OFF position, or where this is not possible, the fuses removed from the operating circuit.

FIG 4.28   Cracks in the spokes to a jib head sheave of a large crane. Such cracking would eventually result in failure of the crane
Reproduced by courtesy of National Vulcan Engineering Insurance Group Ltd

Hand signals to be used when directing the driver of an overhead travelling crane are shown in Figure 4.29.

Hoists and lifts

The FA, Section 25, broadly defines a hoist or lift as a *'platform or cage whose movement is restricted by a guide or guides'*. A similar definition is incorporated in the Construction (Lifting Operations) Regulations 1961, and the Hoists Exemption Order 1962 exempts certain classes or types of hoist or lift from some or all of the requirements under the FA. Sections 22, 23 and 25 prescribe comprehensive requirements for the design and mechanical construction of hoists and lifts. The requirements differ for hoists operated by power and by hand. In general, all hoistways and liftways must be protected by a substantial enclosure fitted with gates so as to prevent a person from falling down the way or coming into contact with any moving part of the hoist. Automatic devices are required on hoists and lifts used for carrying people to prevent the cage or platform of a hoist from overrunning. All cage gates must be interlocked so that a cage cannot be moved until the gates have been shut and will come to rest as soon as a gate is opened. The interlocking system must ensure that the hoistway gate cannot be opened unless the cage or platform is at that level.

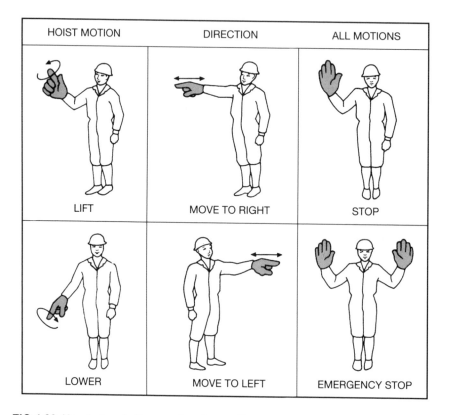

FIG 4.29 Hand signals for overhead travelling crane operation. Signaller should stand in a secure position where he CAN SEE the LOAD and CAN BE SEEN CLEARLY by the driver. Face the driver if possible. Each signal should be distinct and clear.

Hoistways and liftways inside buildings must be completely enclosed with fire-resisting materials, and all means of access to the hoist or lift fitted with doors of fire-resisting material. The top of a hoistway, however, must be enclosed only by material easily broken by fire, or be provided with a vent at the top (section 48(4)).

The provisions of FA, sections 22 and 23, and the Offices, Shops and Railway Premises (Hoists and Lifts) Regulations 1968 (as subsequently amended) require that every power-driven lift be properly maintained and thoroughly examined by a competent person once every six months. Legal responsibility for ensuring that lifts are, at all times, properly maintained, and that statutory examinations are carried out, rests generally with the occupier of the premises.

New lifts

There is no statutory requirement for new lifts to be tested before being taken into service. It is recommended, however, that all new lifts be tested and examined in accordance with Part 7 of BS 2655 'Lifts, Escalators, Passenger Conveyors and Paternosters' and a test certificate obtained.

Examination of personnel lifts

The purpose of periodic examination is to determine whether the condition of the lift installation is such that it can continue to be operated safely. The design and construction of many lifts are such that occasionally component parts will need to be dismantled. There is a need to consider at periodic examinations those parts which are not normally accessible. Recommendations should be made for the testing of safety equipment. The following items should be subject to examination within the periods stated:

- landing and car door interlocks – not exceeding 12 months
- worm and other gearing – not exceeding 10 years
- shafts, bearing and pulleys – not exceeding 10 years
- stepped diameter shafts – regularly
- governors – not exceeding four years.

If safety gear has been fully tested and certified before hand-over as specified in BS 2655, Part 7, then a full speed test should be required only after a major overhaul involving a change of rated load or rated speed, or the disturbance of the car sling and/or safety gear assembly. The checking of linkages and the moving parts of safety gear for free and effective operation should be carried out at every periodic examination. In the case of suspension ropes, examination should take into account the number of broken wires, their position, surface wear, the presence of excessive stretching, inequality in rope tension and diameter, internal conditions and corrosion (as opposed to surface rust). Where overload protection devices are fitted, a full load calibration test should be carried out at intervals not exceeding 12 months.

Maintenance work on both personnel and goods lifts should incorporate the complete isolation and locking off of the electrical supply to the lift, together with the operation of a permit to work system. Apart from the risk of injury to maintenance engineers, there is the risk of members of the public falling down a lift shaft during routine servicing. A high degree of supervision and control is needed, therefore, possibly to the extent of employing personnel to direct people away from the lift entrance area and/or the provision of fencing and notices, particularly where the gates will be left open for long periods.

Goods lifts

There must be an efficient gate, and a device to ensure that the cage or platform cannot be raised or lowered unless the gate is closed and will come to rest when the gate is opened, or, where it is not reasonably practicable to fit such a device, the gate should be kept closed and fastened when the cage or platform is at rest at the gate, ie not being loaded or unloaded. Personnel must not travel on specifically designated goods lifts. The hoistway of a goods lift should be properly enclosed and maintenance requirements apply similar to those for personnel lifts.

Man hoists

This is a continuous belt hoist within the meaning of the FA, section 25(2). Man hoists are commonly installed in flour mills and other premises where there is a continuous need for operators to move between floors. Provisions relating to belt diameters and strengths, clearance at the top of the man hoist, monthly inspections in addition to statutory annual examination, the provision of guards above and below the floor, the provision of hand-holds, emergency ladders, arrangement of ladders, openings in floors, the warning notices necessary and maximum permitted speeds are outlined in the revised recommendations on man hoists produced by the National Joint Industrial Council for the Flour Milling Industry (1956), in their *Health and Safety Handbook*.

Paternoster lifts

This type of lift is defined as *'a continuous running appliance for transporting passengers in a substantially vertical direction, in which a number of cars are suspended by two endless chains attached to the cars diagonally, so that the car floors are substantially horizontal when changing direction at the extremities of travel'*. Fundamentally, a paternoster lift is another form of continuous hoist within the meaning of the FA, section 25(2). The lift does not incorporate a front gate, and comprises a series of compartments or cars capable of holding four to six persons, moving at a speed of 18–20 metres per minute. Platforms are hinged at the front to prevent trapping of feet between the landing opening and the moving floor of the compartment. This type of lift can be dangerous if the level of supervision is poor. Its safety relies heavily on the visual perception of the user in deciding at what point to step onto the slowly moving platform. Such lifts are not suitable for use by the aged, the infirm, the disabled or children. The same provisions relating to testing and examination of lifts apply to paternosters.

Powered working platforms

These platforms are now commonly used where quick and safe access to overhead machinery and plant, electrical installations, lighting equipment and stored goods is needed, and for lifting people and equipment into position where high-level maintenance of buildings, ships, aircraft and public service vehicles is undertaken. Where height, reach and mobility are required, these aerial working platforms have substantial advantages over other systems such as fixed or rolling scaffolding, access towers, bosun's chairs and working platforms fitted to fork lift trucks. They are completely mobile, operating from either a self-propelled electric trolley or a light trailer. Their operations take three specific forms:

- self-propelled hydraulic boom operation
- semi-mechanised articulated boom operation and
- self-propelled scissor lift operation.

Safety procedures for powered working platforms

Whilst such platforms do not come within the general definition of lifting machines or appliances under the FA, a number of aspects relating to their safe use should be considered. Above all, the user and operator must be aware from a study of the manufacturer's specification, of the scope and capabilities of the machine, and the machine must not be used beyond its recommended design capabilities. The following points must be considered in their operation and use.

Siting
Platforms should be sited on firm level working surfaces, and attention paid to the risk of aerial collision with nearby platforms and cranes, and possible contact with electrical conductors and power lines. Ample room must be allowed for passing vehicles; traffic cones and barriers, to warn approaching vehicles, should always be used when these platforms are in use.

Transportation
Care must be taken when loading and unloading platforms from road transport trailers, and ramps should always be used. Platforms should be driven by trained personnel only. When towing platforms on sites, it must be appreciated that the majority of self-propelled platforms do not have automatically applied brakes when under tow. Platforms should be lowered and correctly stowed before transporting and wheels chocked. Care should be taken in lifting any powered platform by crane or fork-lift truck. The manufacturer should always be consulted prior to any lifting operation of this type.

Overturning
Hazards from overturning may be created by overloading of the platform, wind loading, impact or shock loading, and improper use. The maximum lifting capacity must be marked on the platform and shown in the manufacturer's specification. In no circumstances should this be exceeded. If any tools or equipment are carried, their extra weight must be considered. When assessing the weight of person to be carried in terms of overall safe working

load, it is good practice to work on the basis of the first person weighing 100kg and each subsequent person 75kg.

For normal applications, it is considered impracticable to operate a working platform in wind speeds above Force 4 (Beaufort Scale), ie fair breeze, which is equal to 16mph or 7.3m/sec or 14 knots. Care must be exercised when using a platform on high-rise structures, eg bridges, elevated roadways.

Shock loading through dropping heavy materials or articles onto the platform should be avoided, and particular care exercised when using a platform or folding extension for overreach purposes. Platforms should never be used for jacking or as lifting appliances unless specifically designed for this purpose, and only when written approval, together with a test certificate, has been granted by the manufacturer. Moreover, the platform should not be moved in an elevated condition on uneven surfaces. Outriggers must only be operated with a platform in the lowered position. They must always be used where recommended by the manufacturer and for greater stability. The maximum gradient for safe use must not be exceeded, and on soft ground or unsurfaced areas supporting plates of timber mats should be used. (All platforms are rated for use on firm level ground, even when supplied with rough-terrain wheels.) Care must be taken when using the machine close to excavation or trenches, or on embankments. (Maximum gradient=1:40.)

Falls and trapping

Personnel working on a platform should wear safety harness with lanyards attached to the platform and not to an adjacent structure. Loose tools and articles should be properly stowed on the platform. No attempts to extend the working height of the platform with boxes, steps, planks, trestles, etc should be permitted. Operators should not use excessive force against the hand rails.

Trapping can occur between the chassis and a wall or by the working platform against roof trusses, overhead cranes, pipelines and bridges. Guards fitted around a scissor mechanism and baseframe must be adequately maintained and kept in position.

Electric cables and bare conductors present a major hazard. No platform must come within six metres, with the platform at maximum elevation, of a power cable. Inside this limit, a permit to work system should be used, in conjunction with the power supply authority. (See also HSE Guidance Note GS6, 'Avoidance of Danger from Overhead Electric Lines'.)

Maintenance

Regular maintenance is crucial to platform safety. The manufacturer's instructions should be followed and fitters trained in specific maintenance procedures. When undertaking maintenance on, or inspecting, the working platform mechanism, a 'scotch' or mechanical locking bar should be used to sustain the platform in a raised position should the hydraulics, etc fail. (Numerous fatal and severe accidents are on record where this vital advice has not been followed.)

Operators

No one should be allowed to drive a power-operated platform unless he has been selected, trained and authorised. Operators should be reasonably fit and intelligent. Persons suffering from disorders such as epilepsy, poor hearing and/or poor eye-sight should be health screened before a decision as to their fitness to operate is made. Operator training should be taken in three stages by the company operating the platform, ie basic operating skills and knowledge of the platform operation; specific job training for the particular needs of the site employer; and familiarisation training at the work area, eg emergency procedures.

Lifting tackle and equipment – legal aspects

The main law relating to chains, ropes and lifting tackle is embodied in the FA, section 26, and the Construction (Lifting Operations) Regulations 1961. This chapter confines itself to mention of the provisions of the FA.

Section 26(1) lays down specific provisions in respect of every chain, rope or lifting tackle used for the purpose of raising or lowering persons, goods or materials.

- No chain, rope or lifting tackle shall be used unless it is of good construction, sound material, adequate strength and free from patent defect (section 26(1)(*a*)).

- Subject to section 26(2) (ie safe working load plainly marked), a table showing the safe working loads (SWLs) of every kind and size of chain, rope or lifting tackle in use and, in the case of a multiple sling, the SWLs at different angles of the legs, shall be posted in the store in which the chains, ropes or lifting tackle are kept, and in prominent positions on the premises, and no such items not shown in the table shall be used (section 26(1)(*b*)).

- No chain, rope or lifting tackle shall be used for any load exceeding its SWL (as shown by the table mentioned in section 26(1)(*b*) or marked as mentioned in section 26(2) (section 26(1)(*c*)).

- All chains, ropes and lifting tackle in use shall be thoroughly examined by a competent person at least once every six months or at such greater intervals as the minister may prescribe (section 26(1)(*d*)).

- No chains, rope or lifting tackle, except a fibre rope or fibre rope sling, shall be taken into use in any factory for the first time unless it has been tested and thoroughly examined by a competent person and a certificate of test and examination, specifying the SWL, and signed by the person making the test and examination, has been obtained and is kept available for inspection (section 26(1)(*e*)).

- Every chain and lifting tackle, except a rope sling, shall (unless of a class or description exempted by certificate of the chief inspector upon the ground that it is made of such material or so constructed that it cannot be subjected to heat treatment without risk or damage, or that it has been subjected to some form of heat treatment (other than annealing) approved by him) be annealed at least once every 14 months or, in the case of slings or chains of 12.7mm (half inch) bar or smaller, or chains used in connection with molten metal or slag, every six months; but chains and lifting tackle not in regular use need be annealed only when necessary (section 26(1)(f)).

Exception to SWL requirements

Section 26(1)(b) shall not apply in relation to any lifting tackle if its SWL or, in the case of a multiplying sling, the SWL at different angles of the legs, is plainly marked upon it.

Safety aspects of chains, ropes and lifting tackle

Ropes

Natural fibre ropes

This is a rope made from material of vegetable origin, generally comprising manila hemp, sisal, coir and cotton. Manufacturers do not normally provide a certificate stating the SWL. However, the purchaser should obtain the guaranteed breaking strength from the manufacturer in order to assess the SWL. For new ropes used on a direct lift, the factor of safety (ie ratio of ultimate stress to the maximum design stress) should not be less than six under favourable conditions. For ropes used for slings, the factor of safety should be increased to at least eight. Fibre ropes are not legally required to have a test certificate before being taken into service. They do, however, require examination every six months (and hence be capable of identification), and when deterioration takes place to such an extent that the SWL cannot be guaranteed, the rope must be withdrawn and destroyed. Great care must be taken with fibre ropes. When they have become damp or wet they should be dried naturally, as direct heat will cause brittleness. They should be kept in a well-ventilated store, hung on wooden or galvanised steel pegs, within a temperature range of 13–19 °C.

When lifting loads with sharp edges, the rope should be protected with packing. When reeved through blocks, the sheaves must be of adequate diameter, with the grooves of the sheaves of adequate diameter and in sound condition to allow the rope to seat correctly. Fibre ropes should be inspected before use by opening the strands slightly and checking for serviceability. If discoloured, weak or rot (mildew) has occurred, the rope should be destroyed. A reduction in circumference will generally indicate that the rope has been overloaded. The rope should also be examined for chemical action, particularly by acids. (Nylon or terylene ropes are recommended where there is any possibility of acid attack.)

Figure 4.30 illustrates ropes which are dangerously worn.

4

FIG 4.30 Dangerous ropes. This is the condition of a closing rope found during examination of a 1.13 cubic metre grab. The frequent examination of ropes is crucial in these situations

Wire ropes

There are many types of wire rope specified for cranes, lifts, hoists, elevators, construction site equipment, such as excavators, and those for use in general engineering. Wire rope is designated by diameter, except when used in shipping, and the tensile strength of the wire used ranges within 1,550–700 N/mm^2 (100–10 tons/in^2) and 1,700–850 N/mm^2 (110–20 tons/in^2). The diameter is normally measured by rope callipers and the average of three measurements, taken at intervals of about 127mm, is construed as the rope diameter. A wire rope is made up of strands and the number of wires per strand is termed the 'construction' of the rope. Thus a rope of 6x19 construction has six strands each having 19 individual wires. Ropes of ordinary or regular 'lay' have the direction of the lay of the strands opposite to the direction of helix of the individual wires which balance the rope against twist. Where flexibility is needed, then a rope with a greater number of wires should be selected. Thus a 6x24 rope is more flexible than a 6x19 rope, and a 6x37 rope even more flexible than a 6x24 rope for the same approximate strength. If, however, hard wear is significant, a 6x19 rope would be more suitable because of the larger size of wires.

FIG 4.31 A badly worn rope on a trolley crane. Failure of the rope would result in the trolley travelling towards the mast with possible impact and consequent risk to people below and to the main structure of the crane itself
Reproduced by courtesy of National Vulcan Engineering Group Ltd

In a wire rope, broken wires must be regarded as a warning sign, but the actual position of the breaks is significant. If the breaks occur over a short distance, or occur in one or two strands, then the rope should be removed from service and the cause investigated. If breaks occur as a result of normal service over a reasonable period, this may well indicate that the rope is reaching the end of its life and should be replaced. In the interests of safety, however, there must be a limit to the number of broken strands. When broken wires appear, more frequent examination of the rope is needed. The ends of the wires should be manipulated until they break off inside the rope and should never be trimmed with pliers.

During manufacture, wire ropes are thoroughly impregnated with a lubricant to reduce wear, exclude moisture and delay corrosion. Frequent relubrication is necessary depending upon the nature of service and the degree of use. A number of proprietary lubricants are available.

Wire ropes should never be knotted as a means of joining ropes. They may be joined by the use of sockets, swaged ferrules, bulldog clips or by splicing. Proof testing may be required in any event as a splice is never as strong as the parent rope and strength may vary from 85 to 95 per cent according to rope size. Where a mechanical splice is used, proof loading to twice the safe working load is required before placing the wire rope into service.

Wire ropes should be stored in a clean dry place. Wire rope slings should be cleaned after use, inspected and hung on pegs to prevent corrosion and kinking.

Man-made fibre ropes

Ropes of this type, generally manufactured in nylon or terylene, have the following advantages over natural fibre ropes:

- higher tensile strength
- greater capacity for absorbing shock loading
- freedom from rotting, mildew formation, etc
- they can be stored away whilst still wet
- their performance is the same whether wet or dry
- some degree of immunity from degradation due to contact with oil, petrol and many solvents and
- resistance to acids and other corroding agents.

Procedures for the care of man-made fibre ropes are similar to those for other types of rope, viz. clean dry storage, frequent inspection for cuts, abrasions, signs of overloading and evidence of chemical attack and exposure to extreme heat. Exposure to strong sunlight may weaken the fibres and unnecessary exposure should be avoided.

Chains

Despite the increased use of wire rope, chain is still one of the principal components of lifting gear. For the same safe working load, it is five to six times heavier than rope but it has a longer life, stands up to rough usage, is almost 100 per cent flexible and can be stored externally for long periods without deterioration. Chains do not kink or curl; they grip the load better and possess superior shock-absorbing properties. Moreover, chain is available in several grades – mild steel, high tensile steel and alloy steel – and it is common practice to designate these grades by their minimum ultimate strength in terms of the diameter of the bar from which the links are made – ie breaking strength=$30d^2$ – measured in tons or tonnes.

Classification of chain strengths

Wrought iron: Each link is hand-welded by a scarf weld at the end or crown of the link. The weld is distinctive and serves to identify the chain. The safe working load of the chain under normal working conditions is $6d^2$ and minimum breaking strength is $27d^2$. The skin of wrought iron chain is liable to embrittlement due to impact in service causing fine hairline cracks. These act as stress leading to failure without stretching. Under the FA, section 26, wrought iron chains must be annealed every 14 months or more frequently when used in connection with molten metal. Annealing involves the chain being heated uniformly until the whole of the metal has attained a temperature of between 600 and 650°C, after which it is withdrawn from the furnace and allowed to cool in still air. Wrought iron chain has largely been superseded by alloy steel chain.

Mild steel: Mild steel chain incorporates a machine-made butt or flash resistance welded joint in the middle length of the link. The safe working load is assessed at $6d^2$ and the minimum breaking strain is $30d^2$, identified by the figure '3' on the links. Mild steel is liable to embrittlement and should be subject to 'normalising', a form of heat treatment, at frequent intervals. The use of mild steel chain is rapidly declining.

High-tensile steel grade 40: This grade of steel has mechanical properties which are superior to those of mild steel, the safe working load being 30 per cent higher. The safe working load is assessed at $8d^2$ and the minimum breaking strain is $40d^2$, identified by the figures '4' or '04' on the links.

Alloy steel grade 60: This type is 50 per cent stronger than high-tensile steel grade 40 chain and twice as strong as mild steel chain. It is suitable for most lifting purposes. The safe working load is assessed at $12d^2$ and the minimum breaking strain is $60d^2$. Such chain is subjected to hardening and tempering during manufacture and is marked '06' on each twentieth link.

Alloy steel grade 80: Grade 80 chain is designed for specific purpose, for instance as load chain for pulley blocks and similar applications which require an accurately calibrated chain of great strength and wear resistance. Its proof load is only one and a half times the safe working load due to the fact that the standard proof load of twice the safe working load for other chains listed above can disturb the pitch of the links. The safe working load is rated at $24d^2$, and the minimum breaking strain is $80d^2$. This type of chain is not suitable for slings. It requires considerable technical and manufacturing resources, as does the actual servicing of it. The length of the chain is regarded as a complete unit; individual links are not marked but the chain is identified by a disc attached.

Chain breakages

Generally, chains break for one of three reasons:

- from a defect in one of the links
- through the application of a static load in excess of the chain's breaking load or
- through the sudden application of a load which, but for the shock, the chain would have been capable of withstanding.

In no circumstances should nuts and bolts be used to replace broken chain links, nor must chains ever be knotted.

A comparison of the strengths of the various types of chain is shown in Table 4.3.

Table 4.3 Comparison of chain strengths (12.7mm (½") diameter)

Type	SWL (tonnes)	Proof load (tonnes)	Minimum breaking (tonnes)	Marking
Wrought iron	1.5	3.0	6.75	–
Mild steel grade 30	1.5	3.0	7.15	3
HT steel grade 40	2.0	4.0	10.00	4 or 04
Alloy steel grade 60	3.0	6.0	15.00	06
Alloy steel grade 80	3.5	8.0	20.00	08

Lifting tackle

The same safety principles as those for ropes and chains apply to items of lifting tackle such as slings, hooks, grips and eyebolts. In the majority of cases, the complete set of tackle in a lifting situation must be viewed as one specific unit. For instance, it is unwise to use a particular sling for a particular lifting job if the rope or chain being used for the lift is of inadequate strength.

Slings

Slings should be made of chains, wire ropes or fibre ropes (whether man-made or natural) of adequate strength. Rings, hooks, swivels and end links of hoisting chains should be fabricated in the same metal as the chain. Tables showing the maximum safe working loads for slings at various angles should be conspicuously displayed (see Figure 4.32 and Table 4.4), and workers

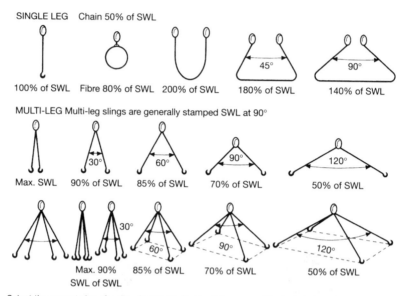

Select the correct size of a sling for the load taking into account the included angle and the possibility of unequal loading in the case of multi-leg slings

Figure 4.32 Maximum safe working loads for slings at various angles
Reproduced by courtesy of G. W. Sparrow & Sons plc

Table 4.4   Estimation of sling leg angles

Sling angle	Distance apart of legs
30°	½ leg length
60°	1 leg length
90°	1½ leg length
120°	1⅔ leg length

Table 4.5   Relationship between sling leg angle and tension in leg

Sling leg angle	Tension in leg (tonnes)
90°	0.7
120°	1.0
151°	2.0
171°	6.0

using slings should be trained in the use of these tables, particularly the fact that sling leg tension increases rapidly with increase in leg angle. For instance, for a one tonne load, the tension in the leg increases as shown in Table 4.5. Reference to this table indicates how important it is for anyone dealing with multi-leg slings to appreciate fully how changes in the angles of the legs affect the safe working load, particularly for angles in excess of 120°.

Slings that show evidence of cuts, excessive wear, distortion (see Figures 4.33 and 4.34) or other dangerous defects should be withdrawn. Wire rope slings should be well lubricated. To prevent sharp bends in slings, corners of loads should be packed. When multiple slings are used, the load should be distributed evenly among the ropes, and where double or multiple slings are used for hoisting loads, the upper ends of the sling should be connected by means of a ring or shackle and not put separately into a lifting hook. When bulky objects are being raised, the correct number of slings should be selected to ensure stability and support the weight of the load (see Figure 4.35).

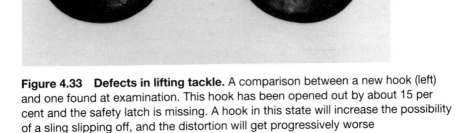

4

Figure 4.33 Defects in lifting tackle. A comparison between a new hook (left) and one found at examination. This hook has been opened out by about 15 per cent and the safety latch is missing. A hook in this state will increase the possibility of a sling slipping off, and the distortion will get progressively worse

Hooks

Hooks for lifting appliances should be manufactured from forged steel or an equivalent material, and fitted with a safety catch shaped so as to prevent the load from slipping off (see Figure 4.36). In certain situations a hook must be provided with an efficient device to prevent displacement of a sling, or be of such a shape as to reduce, as far as possible, the risk of displacement (Regulation 36 of the Construction (Lifting Operations) Regulations 1961 is a typical example).

Figure 4.34 Badly distorted chain links in a sling which could lead to failure of the sling
Reproduced by courtesy of National Vulcan Engineering Insurance Group Ltd

In potentially dangerous lifting operations, hooks should be provided with a hand rope (tag line) long enough to enable workers engaged in loading to keep clear. Parts of hooks likely to come into contact with ropes and chains should have no sharp edges.

Pulley blocks

Pulley blocks should be manufactured from shock-resistant metal, eg mild steel. Axles of pulleys should be made of metal of suitable quality and of adequate dimensions. The diameter of the pulley should be at least 20 times the diameter of the rope to be used. The axle in the blocks should be capable of lubrication and a suitable lubricating device provided. (Regular and

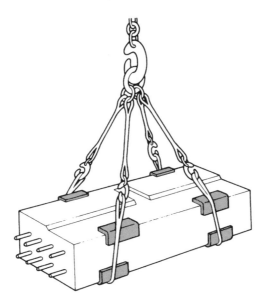

Figure 4.35 When lifting a bulky object, use a lifting ring and pack the edges of the object

4

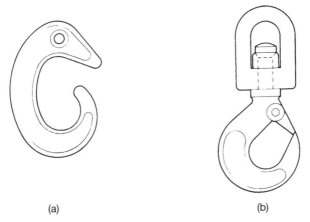

(a)   (b)

Figure 4.36 Hooks for lifting appliances

(a) Hook specially shaped to prevent the load from slipping off
(b) Hook incorporating a safety catch

adequate lubrication of pulley blocks is essential.) The sheaves and housing of blocks should be so constructed that the rope cannot become caught between the sheave and the side of the block, and the grooves in the sheaves should be such that the rope cannot be damaged in the sheave. (Badly worn blocks should be taken out of use.) Blocks designed for use with fibre rope should not be used with wire rope. A pulley within reach of workers should be provided with a guard that effectively prevents a hand being drawn in.

Shackles

Shackles used for joining lines should have a breaking strength of at least 1.5 times that of the lines joined. In the case of shackles used for hanging blocks, the breaking strength should be at least twice that of the pulling lines, and the pins should be secured by locked nuts or other suitable means. Shackle pins should be secured by keys or wire, unless bolts are employed.

Eyebolts

Eyebolts are used for lifting loads which may be heavy and concentrated. (Three common types of eyebolts are shown in Figure 4.37.) The use of the wrong type of eyebolt is a common contributory cause of accidents. A typical example of this is when a dynamo eyebolt is used for other than a vertical lift.

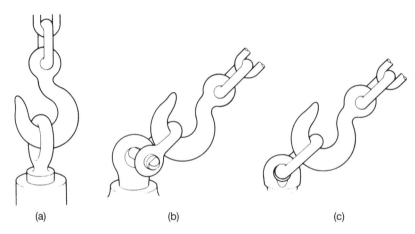

(a)   (b)   (c)

Figure 4.37   Eyebolts (a) Dynamo eyebolt (b) Collar eyebolt (c) Eyebolt with link

Dynamo eyebolts are large enough to receive a hook of a comparable safe working load, but should only be used for a vertical lift because the eye is so large that it is likely to bend, should an inclined load be placed upon it. Furthermore, a load which is only slightly out of the vertical plane places an undue stress on the screw threads of the eyebolt shank. Where dynamo eyebolts are fitted in pairs, a spreader bar should form an integral part of the lifting gear used to move the load. The dynamo eyebolt is designed to receive the hook directly, and in all cases the hook should be able to operate freely. It is extremely dangerous to use a hook which jams in an eyebolt because, under load, serious weakening of both hook and eyebolt could occur leading to failure at some later date. If the hook available for the eyebolt is too large, a shackle of adequate size should be fitted to the eyebolt to accommodate the hook.

Where inclined loads are encountered, eg when a multi-leg sling is in use, collar eyebolts or eyebolts with links must be used. The collar eyebolt, or service eyebolt, has a squat eye that is too small to accommodate a hook, so a shackle is always necessary. Collar eyebolts are intended for permanent attachment to heavy pieces of equipment and are usually fitted in pairs for use with shackles or two-leg slings. When two pairs of eyebolts are fitted to a single load, then two-leg slings and a spreader bar (lifting beam) should be used in lifting (see Figure 4.38).

Figure 4.38   Typical lifting beam (spreader bar)

The third type of eyebolt, that incorporating a link, is intended for general lifting. Although its rated load decreases as the angle of the load to the axis of the screw thread increases, by virtue of its special construction these rated loadings are greater than those of a collar eyebolt of equivalent vertical safe working load.

Lifting beams (spreader bars)

A lifting beam is a special purpose device which enables a particular load to be lifted in a particular way, often to prevent horizontal stressing of eyebolts. Lifting beams are commonly used in foundries for transporting vats of molten metal prior to casting or for the transport of engines in vehicle assembly. This is far safer than the use of multiple slings. Lifting beams incorporate three basic parts:

- the beam, which is made from rolled steel section or plate
- the means of attaching the beam to the lifting machine, such as a ring, shackle, eyebolt or hole in the main structure of the beam and
- the means of fixing the beam to the actual load to be lifted, such as chain

or wire rope slings which are fixed to the beam with fittings at the ends for securing the load, such as shackles or locking pins.

Lifting beams are designed using standard steel rolled section or plate, angles, tees, universal beams or hollow sections. To ensure rigidity and resistance to accidental damage, the thickness of metal should not be less than 6mm. This thickness can be reduced to 4.5mm with hollow sections provided that they are adequately sealed against ingress of water or other damaging material. Many beams will be left outside and exposed to all weather conditions, so care must be taken in their design to avoid places where water might lodge; where this is not practicable, suitable drainage holes should be provided. If corrosion is the agent most likely to affect the beam, an allowance of up to 2mm should be added to the minimum dimensions determined from all other strength calculations.

Lifting Plant and Equipment (Records of Test and Examination etc) Regulations 1992

These regulations remove the legal requirement to report the results of testing and examination of lifting plant and equipment by a competent person on prescribed forms. They also remove the requirement to provide a written report, except when required by an inspector, thus allowing for the storage of records of tests etc by electronic means.

On this basis the competent person may provide the record by a means that suits him and the owner or user of the plant and equipment. Effectively this means a competent person is able to use the same form on which to provide the written record for the majority of lifting plant and equipment likely to be tested, etc or, if he wishes, he can record the results of the test etc by electronic means. The only proviso is that the record must contain the particulars prescribed by these regulations, which are outlined in the schedule and Appendix 1 to same.

Prescribed particulars

The prescribed particulars covering:

- record of test, test and examination or test and thorough examination of lifting plant and equipment and
- record of thorough examination of lifting plant and equipment

are shown opposite.

Record number or other identification _____

RECORD OF TEST, TEST AND EXAMINATION OR TEST AND THOROUGH EXAMINATION OF LIFTING PLANT AND EQUIPMENT

Description of the equipment (including date of manufacture)_____

Name and address of owner of equipment and its location _____

Identification mark of the equipment _____

The safe working load or loads and (where relevant) corresponding radii, jib lengths and counterweights _____

Details of the test, tests and examination or test and thorough examination carried out _____

Dates or date of completion _____

I hereby declare that the equipment described in this record was tested, tested and examined or tested and thoroughly examined in accordance with the provisions on _____, and that the above particulars are correct.

Signature _____

Name and address of person making above declaration

_____

Date the record is made _____

4

Record number or other identification _____

RECORD OF THOROUGH EXAMINATION OF LIFTING PLANT AND EQUIPMENT

Description of equipment _____

Identification mark of the equipment _____

Name and address of owner of equipment and its location _____

Date of the most recent test and examination or test and thorough examination and date and number or other identification of the record issued on that occasion_____

Date of last thorough examination and number or other identification of the record issued_____

Safe working load or loads and (where relevant) corresponding radii _____

Details of any defects found (if none state NONE) _____

Date(s) by which the defects described above must be rectified _____

Any other observations _____

What parts, if any, were inaccessible? _____

(TO BE COMPLETED ONLY AFTER A THOROUGH EXAMINATION OF A HOIST OR LIFT)

Latest date by which the next thorough examination must be carried out _____

I hereby declare that the equipment described in this record was thoroughly examined in accordance with the appropriate provisions and found free from any defect likely to affect safety other than those listed above on _____, and that the above particulars are correct.

Signature or other authentication _____

Name and address of person authenticating the record_____

Date of making the record _____

Name and address of person responsible for the thorough examination _____

_____

TRANSPORT OF DANGEROUS CHEMICALS BY ROAD

Under the HSWA, employers have a duty to protect members of the public from hazards arising from their activities. This duty applies particularly in the case of the transport of dangerous substances and is reinforced by the Dangerous Substances (Conveyance by Road in Road Tankers and Tank Containers) Regulations 1981 (SI 1981 No. 1059). The regulations apply to the conveyance of dangerous chemicals by road in a tanker or tank container, including any loading and unloading activities at premises. The regulations contain an 'Approved List' of dangerous substances (approved substance identified numbers, emergency action codes and classifications for dangerous substances conveyed in roads tankers and tank containers). A dangerous substance is defined with reference to the approved list as:

> any substance (including any preparation) which is either contained in Part I of the approved list (unless it is in such a diluted form as not to create a risk) or any other substance which by reason of its characteristic properties creates a risk to the health and safety of any person in the course of conveyance by road, which is comparable with the risk created by substances which are specified in the approved list.

These characteristic properties are listed in Schedule 1. An approved code of practice, '**Classification of Dangerous Substances for Conveyance in Road Tankers and Tank Containers**', gives practical guidance on how substances not on the approved list can be classified to see whether or not they come within the regulations.

Vehicles or tanks must be properly designed, of adequate strength and of good construction from sound and suitable material before they can be used to convey dangerous substances by road. Operators must bear in mind the nature and circumstances of the journey and the characteristic properties and the quantity of substances being carried. Provision has been made for the testing and examination of tanks on road tankers and tank containers.

Under the regulations, specific duties are placed on operators and drivers.

The 'operator' in relation to a road tanker or other vehicle is the person who holds, or should hold, an operator's licence for the use of the vehicle for the carriage of goods by road or, if no licence is required, the keeper of the vehicle. In the case of a tank container, the operator is:

- the owner of the tank container or his agent, if that person:
  - has a place of business in Great Britain and
  - is identified as the owner of or, as the case may be, as the agent of the owner of the tank container on the tank container itself, or on a document carried on that vehicle or
- otherwise the operator of the vehicle on which the tank container is conveyed.

Considerable duties and responsibilities are placed on operators. They must ensure that they are aware of the risks by obtaining, from the consignor or others, relevant information on the dangerous substances. They must ensure that drivers are informed, in writing, of the identity of the substance and nature of the dangers to which the substance could give rise, together with the emergency action which should be taken (emergency action codes for each substance are shown in the approved list). All operators must provide adequate instruction and training for their drivers, together with documentation of this training.

Specific duties on drivers include ensuring that vehicles, when not in use are safely parked or supervised when they are carrying prescribed substances. They must also take the precautions necessary for the prevention of fire or explosion. This latter duty is imposed on every person who is engaged in the conveyance by road of a dangerous substance.

Tanker and tank container marking

All road tankers and tank containers must carry at least two hazard warning panels to the specification outlined in Schedule 4 of the regulations. The panels must be weather-resistant, indelibly marked and rigidly fixed. Details relating to the form and specification of hazard warning panels and compartment labels are outlined below.

The form of the hazard warning panel is indicated in Figures 4.39(*a*) and 4.39(*b*). The allocation of the five spaces, as numbered in Figure 4.39(*a*), is as follows:

(1) emergency action code

(2) substance identification number and, if included, the name or, in the case of multi-loads, the word 'multi-load'

(3) hazard warning sign

(4) telephone number or other approved text

(5) optional manufacturer's or owner's name or house symbol or both.

The colour of the hazard warning panel must be *orange* and conform to the specification for that colour in Part 2 of Schedule 4 of the regulations, except that the space for the hazard warning sign must be *white*, and the borders, internal dividing lines, letters and figures, *black*.

Specification for hazard warning panels for single loads is as shown in millimetres in Figure 4.39(*b*).

The specification for hazard warning panels for multi-loads is set out in Figure 4.39(*c*).

Where the emergency action code or the multi-load emergency action code, ascertained from Schedule 1 or 2, is a *white* number and/or letter on a *black* background, it/they must be displayed on the panel as *orange* on a *black* background; the letters must appear in a *black* rectangle, having the height of 100mm and a width of 10mm greater than the width of the letter.

The form of the compartment label for multi-loads of substances of differ-

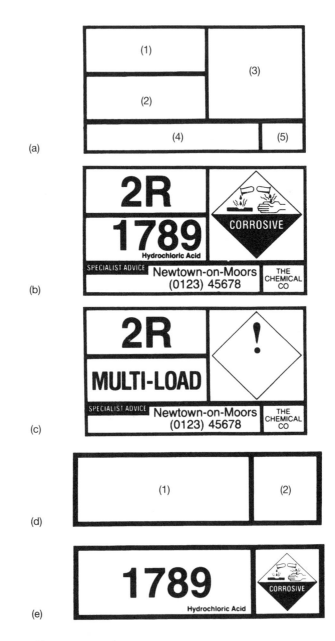

Figure 4.39 Hazard warning panels and compartment labels, as required by the Dangerous Substances (Conveyance by Road in Road Tankers and Tank Containers) Regulations 1981

(a) Hazard warning panel: layout   (d) Compartment label (multi-load): layout
(b) Hazard warning panel (single load)   (e) Compartment label (multi-load): completed
(c) Hazard warning panel (multi-load)

ent hazards is set out in Figure 4.39, and the spaces must be used for the following purposes:

(1) substance identification number and, if included, name and

(2) hazard warning sign.

An example is shown in Figure 4.39(*e*).

Where the multi-load consists of substances subject to the same hazards, the square labelled (2) in Figure 4.39(*d*) can be omitted from the compartment label.

The colour of the compartment label must be *orange* and conform to the specification for that colour in Part 2 of Schedule 4, except for the space for the hazard warning sign (where one is required), which must be *white* and the borders *black*.

The specification for compartment labels is set out, with dimensions in millimetres, in Figure 4.39(*e*).

Definitions

Within the Dangerous Substances (Conveyance by Road in Road Tankers and Tank Containers) Regulations 1981, the following definitions are relevant:

The approved list is the list of dangerous substances published by HSC on 25th July 1984 under the title '**Information Approved for the Classification, Packaging and Labelling of Dangerous Substances**'. It lists approved substance identification numbers, emergency action codes and classifications. Part 2 of the list specifies a method for ascertaining the multi-load emergency action code. (The list may be revised from time to time.) Information contained in the list will enable operators to comply with the various duties imposed by these regulations. The name of the substance (as given in this list) can include an alternative name in parentheses and/or the concentrations or conditions referred to in regulations 9(*c*) in italics.

Classification: a substance is classified either by HSC and hence appears in the approved list or, for a substance not on the list, by reference to Schedule 1 of the regulations. The substances in the approved list are normally single chemical substances. However, Schedule 1 should be used to classify any other substance, mixture or preparation which possesses one or more of the characteristic properties listed in Column 1 of this schedule; for such a substance the classification will be determined by whichever is the most hazardous property. Practical guidance on how to determine which property is, in a given case, the most hazardous will be found in the ACOP '**Classification of Dangerous Substances for Conveyance in Road Tankers and Tank Containers**'.

The *Emergency Action Code* informs the emergency services of the action to be taken in the event of an accident. The codes approved by HSC for dangerous substances are specified in the approved list and have to appear on the hazard warning panel, fitted to vehicles, as required by these regulations. Where a substance is not in the approved list, the hazard warning panel must not show an emergency warning action code.

Multi-load is defined as a '**load consisting of two or more dangerous substances in separate compartments or tanks**', but regulation 16, relating to the labelling requirements for road tankers and tank containers conveying multi-loads, only applies to certain multi-loads, ie those carried in separate tanks or compartments in the tank when conveyed in a road tanker, or in a compartmented tank container.

The definition of *road tanker* includes both rigid and articulated road tankers, and also draw-bar trailers which have a tank structurally attached to the frame of the trailer.

A *tank*, within the definition of the regulations, is so constructed that it can be securely closed, except for the purpose of relieving excessive pressure, during the course of conveyance by road. This has the consequence that a tank which has any opening, other than for relieving excessive pressure, which cannot be securely closed by means of valves or covers, is not a tank for the purposes of these regulations.

Tank containers is any tank, with a capacity in excess of three cubic metres, which is not a tank or road tanker. This would normally be:

- tank contained within an ISO framework (but would also include a large gas cylinder of the type used for compressed hydrogen or helium) or
- any other tank not within an ISO framework, if its capacity was in excess of three cubic metres.

Electrical safety

THE NATURE OF ELECTRICITY

Electricity is a form of energy passing from one point to another in the form of an electric current. Electric current represents a flow of charged particles or electrons passing along some element, a **conductor**, which permits the passage of this flow, such as a metal wire, a liquid or a gas. In order for this electron flow to take place, there must be a continuous **circuit** of appropriate conducting material. Conductors include virtually all metals, certain gases and water. Certain substances, such as wood, plastic and rubber which do not conduct electricity well may have an insulating effect (**insulators**). This insulating effect can be an effective form of protection against current passing through the human body due to the high resistance to flow of an insulator. This resistance to flow is directly related to the form of material and size of the conductor or insulator. The unit of measurement of resistance is the **ohm**. The strength of, or amount of energy in, an electric current is determined by the pressure of flow (**voltage**) and the number of electrons contained in the flow (**current**). Current is measured in **amperes** (amps), whereas electrical pressure is measured in **volts**.

Ohm's Law

Ohm's Law states that at a constant temperature, the current through a conductor is directly proportional to the potential difference across its ends.

The **ohm** is the practical unit of resistance being that resistance which allows a current of one amp to flow through it when the potential difference across it is one volt.

Thus:
$$\text{resistance} = \frac{\text{pressure}}{\text{current}} = \frac{\text{volts}}{\text{amps}}$$

Similarly: volts = amps x ohms

Hence **power**, measured in **watts**, may be found from the following formula, although in strict alternating current theory, it is somewhat more complicated mathematically.

Watts = volts × amps

= amps² × ohms

$$= \frac{volts^2}{ohms}$$

Features of an electrical circuit

Fundamentally, an electrical circuit incorporates:

- a source of electrical current
- various conductors and
- some form of appliance, machine or equipment powered by the current.

The source of the current can be an electrical generator or a battery. This supplies electrical charges along a cable (the conducting element) to the equipment or appliance, such as an electric fire, a fan or a light bulb. Initial current supply is by a **phase conductor** (or **line conductor**) and an electric current will flow once the voltage is applied. At the appliance, the electrical flow, in the case of an electric fire, is converted to heat. Completing the circuit, the current is returned to its source via a **return (neutral) conductor**. (See Figure 5.1)

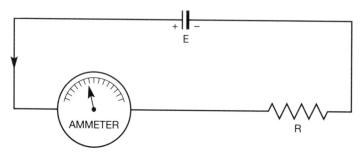

FIG 5.1 Simple circuit

An electric current will pass along a conductor if there is a difference in pressure between the ends of the conductor. This difference in pressure, the **potential difference**, is measured in volts. These potential differences can be produced in the magnetic fields created by generators. Similarly, the chemical reaction produced in a torch battery can produce potential differences.

Direct and alternating current

Direct current (dc) is current which flows in one direction only. **Alternating current** (ac), on the other hand, is current where the direction of flow alters at regular intervals. The natural current generated is alternating in kind (ac) which, in a normal single cycle of 1/50 second, alternates in value from zero to maximum in one direction, back to zero and to maximum in the opposite direction, and back to zero again, thus producing the 50 cycles per second (50 hertz) system used in the UK. (The number of complete alternations or cycles in one second is the **frequency** of the alternating current. The unit of frequency is the **hertz (Hz)** (formerly cycle per second)).

Single and three phase systems

A single phase ac system, normally at 240 volts, is one in which the circuit comprises two conductors ("live" and "neutral") usually with an additional conductor for "earth". In the UK, the public electricity supply is set at 240 volts ac, which is cyclical. One of the problems is that this public supply peaks at 338 volts, and this cyclical variation is unsuitable for certain equipment and installations. To eliminate this problem, a **three-phase system**, namely three specific supplies of electricity fed to the equipment, each of which is out of phase with the others but which, in combination, produce a steady current, is used.

A three phase ac system, normally at 415/240 volts, has four conductors. Three of them are live and the fourth is neutral. The three phase supply system is for larger equipment and the maximum voltage of the system (415 volts) is utilised. But 240 volts may be obtained between one of the live phase conductors and neutral.

The **earth conductor** in a circuit is linked to the general mass of earth which is at zero potential. By connecting all exposed metal parts which should not carry a current to earth, any fault current is provided with a path to earth so that the exposed metal parts cannot become live.

ELECTRIC GENERATORS

Simple generation

A simple basic generator comprises two main parts, the **rotor**, which is the rotating part, and the **stator**, the fixed part. The rotor contains conductors wound around a metal cylinder and, as it rotates under the action of an external mechanical power source, these conductors cut across a magnetic field from the electromagnet housed in the stator. The laws of electromagnetism, which apply to the interrelationship between electricity and magnetism are such that this action causes voltage to be induced in the rotor conductors. By suitably connecting these conductors to an external circuit, the electric current thus produced can be tapped and used.

Alternatively, the conductors and electromagnets can be housed in the stator and rotor respectively, without affecting the generation of electricity in the conductors. It is the motion of the conductors in relation to the magnetic field that matters. The value of the current, voltage, etc depends upon the characteristics of the generator. In modern power stations, for example, the generators (usually called **alternators**) may each have output in excess of 500MW, ie 500 million watts.

Small portable and mobile generators

These are used for a variety of purposes. On construction sites, for example, they are used to provide an emergency and temporary supply of electricity or to serve particular items of plant, such as electric arc welding sets. Most generators on construction sites are capable of supplying at 240 volts and 120 volts which enables them to supply a 55 volt system via special transformers available for this purpose. The generator's frame, metallic parts of the transformer and centre point of the secondary winding of the transformer should be bonded electrically and suitably earthed.

It is important that the manufacturer's instructions on the installation and use of generators are known and understood by operators and other staff involved. (For further information see BS Code of Practice CP 1017.)

HAZARDS ASSOCIATED WITH ELECTRICITY

Hazards associated with the use of electricity can broadly be divided into two categories, namely the risk of injuries to people and the risk of fire and/or explosion.

Injuries to people

Human injury is associated with shock, burns, injuries from explosions, microwaves, accumulators and batteries and eye injuries.

Electric shock

This is the effect produced on the body and, in particular, the nervous system by an electric current passing through it. The effect varies according to the strength of the current which, in turn, varies with the voltage and the electrical resistance of the body. The resistance of the body will vary according to the points of entry and exit of the current and other factors, such as body weight and/or the presence of moisture.

Common cause of death is ventricular fibrillation (spasm) of the heart muscle which occurs at 0.05 amps. The vascular system ceases to function and the victim dies of suffocation.

> **Remember. It's the current that kills!**

First aid
First aid for a victim of electric shock must be cardiac massage plus mouth-

to-mouth resuscitation until normal breathing and the heart action return. A victim who is 'locked on' to a live appliance must not be approached until the appliance is electrically dead. (See Figure 5.2.)

Table 5.1   Typical responses to current/voltage

Voltage	Response	Current
15 volts	Threshold of feeling	0.002–0.005 amps
20–25 volts	Threshold of pain	–
30 volts	Muscular spasm (non-release)	0.015 amps
70 volts	Minimum for death	0.1 amps
120 volts	Maximum for 'safety'	0.002 amps
200–240 volts	Most serious/fatal accidents	0.2 amps

Burns

A current passing through a conductor produces heat. Burns can be caused by contact with hot conductors or by the passage of a current through the body at the point of entry and exit. Electric arcing from short circuits may also cause burns.

Explosion

Electrical short circuit or sparking from the electrical contacts in switches or other equipment is a common cause of explosions and subsequent human injury or death. This presupposes the presence of a flammable atmosphere eg vapour, gas, dust.

Eye injuries

These can arise from exposure to ultraviolet rays from accidental arcing as in short circuits or arcing in a process, such as welding.

Microwave apparatus

Microwaves can damage the soft tissues of the body.

Accumulators and batteries

Hydrogen gas may be produced as a by-product of battery charging which can cause explosive atmospheres with the risk of burns.

Fire

Electricity is a common source of ignition for major fires. Some insulating materials and materials used for electrical connections may be flammable and can give rise to small fires in switchgear, distribution boxes or sub-stations. The risk of losses from fire increases when these local fires go undetected and result in major fires. Sources of electrical ignition include:

- **Sparks** – between conductors or conductor and earth.
- **Arcs** – are a larger and brighter discharge of energy and are more likely to cause fire.
- **Short circuits** – arise where a current finds a path from live to return other than through apparatus resulting in high current flow, heating of conductors to white heat and arcing.
- **Overloading** – where too much current flows causing heating of conductors.
- **Old and defective/damaged wiring** – through break down of insulation resulting in short circuit, or the use of progressively more equipment on an old circuit resulting in overloading.

PRINCIPLES OF ELECTRICAL SAFETY

The prime objective of electrical safety is to protect people from electrical shock, and also from fire and burns, arising from contact with electricity. There are two basic preventive measures against electric shock, namely:

- protection against direct contact, eg by providing proper **insulation** for parts of equipment liable to be charged with electricity and
- protection against indirect contact, eg by providing effective **earthing** for metallic enclosures which are liable to be charged with electricity if the basic insulation fails for any reason.

When it is not possible to provide adequate insulation as protection against direct contact, a range of measures is available, including protection by barriers or enclosures, and protection by position, ie placing live parts out of reach.

Earthing

This implies connection to the general mass of earth in such a manner as will ensure at all times an immediate discharge of electrical energy without danger. Earthing, to give protection against indirect contact with electricity, can be achieved in a number of ways, including the connection of extraneous conductive parts of premises (radiators, taps, water pipes) to the main earthing terminal of the electrical installation. This creates an equipotential zone and eliminates the risk of shock that could occur if a person touched two different parts of the metalwork liable to be charged, under earth fault conditions, at different voltages. When an earth fault exists, such as when a live part touches an enclosed conductive part, eg metalwork, it is vital to ensure that the electrical supply is automatically disconnected.

1 RECOGNISE A LACK OF OXYGEN

Arising from
ELECTRIC SHOCK
DROWNING
POISONING
HEAD INJURY
GASSING etc

May be causing
UNCONSCIOUSNESS
NOISY OR
NO BREATHING
ABNORMAL COLOUR

2 ACT AT ONCE

SWITCH OFF ELECTRICITY, GAS etc
REMOVE CASUALTY FROM DANGER
SEND SOMEBODY FOR HELP
GET A CLEAR AIRWAY
REMOVE ANY OBSTRUCTION ... then

LIFT
JAW

TILT
HEAD
BACK

BREATHING MAY RESTART ... IF NOT ...

3 APPLY RESCUE BREATHING

START WITH FOUR
QUICK DEEP BREATHS
SEAL NOSE AND
BLOW INTO MOUTH
or
SEAL MOUTH AND
BLOW INTO NOSE
KEEP FINGERS ON JAW
BUT CLEAR OF THROAT
MAINTAIN HEAD
POSITION

AFTER BLOWING INTO
MOUTH or NOSE,
WATCH CASUALTY'S
CHEST FALL AS
YOU BREATHE IN

REPEAT EVERY 5 SECS

**AFTER FIRST FOUR
BREATHS TEST FOR
RECOVERY SIGNS**

1. PULSE PRESENT?
2. PUPILS LESS LARGE?
3. COLOUR IMPROVED?   PULSE POINTS

4 IF NONE, COMBINE RESCUE BREATHING & HEART COMPRESSION

PLACE CASUALTY   BREASTBONE
ON A FIRM SURFACE
COMMENCE
HEART COMPRESSION
HEEL OF HAND ONLY
ON LOWER HALF OF
BREASTBONE
OTHER HAND ON TOP,   **HEART**
FINGERS OFF CHEST

KEEP ARMS STRAIGHT
AND ROCK FORWARD
TO DEPRESS CHEST
$1\frac{1}{2}$ INCHES (4 cm)

APPLY 15 COMPRESSIONS
ONE PER SECOND ... then
GIVE TWO BREATHS

RE-CHECK PULSE ...
IF STILL ABSENT
CONTINUE WITH
15 COMPRESSIONS
TO TWO BREATHS
IF PULSE RETURNS
CEASE COMPRESSIONS
BUT CONTINUE
RESCUE BREATHING

5

FIG 5.2   Resuscitation procedure
(Source RoSPA)

This protection is brought about by the use of **overcurrent devices**, ie correctly rated **fuses** or **circuit breakers**, or by correctly rated and placed **residual current devices**. The maintenance of earth continuity is vital.

Fuses

A fuse is basically a strip of metal of such size as would melt at a predetermined value of current flow. It is placed in the electrical circuit and, on melting, cuts off the current to the circuit. Fuses should be of a type and rating appropriate to the circuit and the appliance it protects.

Circuit breakers

These devices incorporate a mechanism that trips a switch from 'ON' to 'OFF' position if an excess current flows in the circuit. A circuit breaker should be of the type and rating for the circuit and appliance it protects.

Earth leakage circuit breakers (residual current devices)

Fuses and circuit breakers do not necessarily provide total protection against electric shock. Earth leakage circuit breakers provide protection against earth leakage faults, particularly at those locations where effective earthing cannot necessarily be achieved.

Reduced voltage

Reduced voltage systems are another form of protection against electric shock, the most commonly used being the 110 volt centre point earthed system. In this system the secondary winding of the transformer providing the 110 volt supply is centre tapped to earth, thereby ensuring that at no part of the 110 volt circuit can the voltage to earth exceed 55 volts.

Socket outlets and plugs

Socket outlets are the means of 'tapping' into the circuit to allow electricity to be used to supply an appliance. A plug, attached to a flexible cable supplying the apparatus, is used to connect into the socket outlet and thus form another circuit. Fixed apparatus, such as large electric motors which drive equipment, do not require socket outlets and are supplied from their own circuit, controlled by a separate motor control which not only incorporates 'STOP' and 'START' facilities, but also protection against overload.

Safe systems of work

Where work is to be undertaken on electrical apparatus or a part of a circuit, a formally operated safe system of work should be used. This normally takes the form of a **permit to work system** which should ensure the following procedures:

- switching out and locking off the electricity supply, ie isolation
- checking by use of an appropriate voltage detection instrument that the circuit or part of same to be worked on is dead before work commences
- high levels of supervision and control to ensure the work is carried out correctly
- physical precautions, such as the erection of barriers to restrict access to the area, are implemented and
- formal cancellation of the permit to work once the work is completed satisfactorily and return to service of the plant or system in question.

PRACTICAL CONTROLS

Prevention of injury

The principal precautions which need attention include:

Equipment

- earthing of supply circuit
- earthing of equipment
- insulation of all live conductors and equipment
- isolation of switchgear etc in lockable switch rooms and sub-stations and
- the use of low voltage equipment.

Supply circuit design

- fuses
- current operated circuit breakers
- voltage operated circuit breakers and
- thermal trip devices.

Working system

- use of protective equipment, ie rubber gloves and insulated tools
- use of rubber mats
- isolation and locking off of circuits prior to work
- portable step-down transformers and low voltage (not more than 110 volts) equipment
- trained and competent staff
- operation of safe systems of work, eg permit to work systems and
- use of monitoring procedures.

FIRE AND EXPLOSION PREVENTION

The principles of insulation, isolation, circuit protection and minimising supply and equipment voltages apply equally to the prevention of fire and explosion as to the prevention of injury.

Further protection of potentially flammable atmospheres using flameproof or sparkproof equipment and/or the siting of switchgear, etc away from risk areas must also be considered.

Automatic inerting of switch rooms and sub-stations or flooding with extinguishant gas (BCF) is often used as a precaution against potential fire damage where equipment value is high, eg computer installations.

WORK ON HIGH VOLTAGE SYSTEMS

Generally, a high voltage system is taken to mean any system which operates in excess of 650 volts. Clearly the risk is far greater in this situation and it is essential that, in order to comply with the competent persons requirements of the Electricity at Work Regulations, personnel working on such systems are adequately trained to a higher level of competence than those working on lower voltage systems. The assessment of an individual's competence rests with the employer, who must consider that person's level of skill, knowledge, training and experience in making such an assessment.

It is also common practice for organisations to designate in writing certain trained persons as **authorised persons** for certain classes of work on electrical equipment, such as switching operations, for access to high voltage areas and for the issue of authorisations for work on high voltage systems.

High voltage areas

Because of the risks associated with these areas, only authorised persons should be allowed access. In the case of routine and other types of maintenance work, attention must be paid to isolation systems before access is made. A safe operating procedure will also include the installation and maintenance of physical barriers with lockable entrance/exit points to prevent unauthorised persons gaining access. Operators should always be accompanied and not operate on a lone worker basis, particularly where testing procedures imply high test voltages. There should be adequate space available to prevent danger and, in the case of uninsulated conductors in most high pressure systems, a clear height of not less than 8′0″ (2.44m) and a clear width of not less than 3′6″ (1.07m) should be maintained.

PORTABLE ELECTRICAL EQUIPMENT

The hazards described above for all electrical equipment and circuits apply but are made worse by the portable nature of the equipment and tools. The following precautions should be considered in the use of portable electrical equipment:

- safe means of connection to the electrical supply
- the vulnerability of flexible cables to physical damage
- the potential for metal components and/or casings becoming live if in contact with a live conductor
- the need for the frequent handling of equipment and manual contact with supply outlet switches and cables which raises the probability of human injury.

Specific precautions

Specific precautions relating to portable electrical equipment and appliances include:

- the use of low voltage circuits and equipment
- the use of all-insulated appliances, ie conductors are insulated plus a protective case of tough insulating material
- the use of double-insulated appliances, ie conductors insulated together with a general insulation beneath the metal cladding or the case
- the use of current operated circuit breaker adaptation to power outlets
- regular checks on earth continuity, condition of flexible cables and cable connections and circuit protection in circuits used for portable equipment.

FLAMEPROOFING

The use of electrical equipment in flammable atmospheres is a highly specialised matter. Electrical equipment which can give rise to heat or sparking will provide a source of ignition for a flammable atmosphere of the right mixture, and it is therefore necessary to take adequate precautions. Potentially flammable hazardous areas are classified according to a graded probability of an explosive gas or vapour concentration occurring.

The principal of flameproofing is to ensure that the apparatus so described is constructed to withstand any explosion, within the apparatus, arising from ignition of flammable gas that may enter through the casing or other enclosure. All flanges and other joints of the casing or enclosure of the apparatus must be well-designed and constructed so as to prevent any internal ignition of gas from moving out of the enclosure and igniting a surrounding flammable atmosphere.

Potentially flammable hazardous areas are classified according to a graded probability of an explosive gas or vapour concentration occurring. Three classifications, or zones, are usually referred to as follows:

- **Zone 0** – which is a zone in which a flammable atmosphere is known to be continuously present, or present for long periods.
- **Zone 1** – which is a zone in which a flammable atmosphere is likely to occur, at least during normal working.
- **Zone 2** – which is a zone in which a flammable atmosphere is unlikely to occur save under abnormal conditions, such occurrence being of only short duration.

The particular zone is predetermined at the design stage and it is in everyone's interest to design out the more hazardous zones so far as possible.

Types of protection

The type of protection required for electrical equipment which is to be placed at a particular location depends upon the zone. First, the possibility of excluding electrical equipment from the zone should be considered. If this is not a practicable proposition, consideration should be given to segregation of the electrical equipment within the zone, say by suitable barriers. However, the installation of electrical equipment in hazardous areas may be unavoidable, in which case special types of protection are available and designated as in the following examples.

Type N equipment

This equipment is designed for use in zone 2 conditions and is so constructed that, properly used, it will not ignite flammable atmospheres under normal conditions.

Type E equipment

This includes equipment such as transformers and squirrel cage motors. They do not normally produce sparks and are suitable for zone 2 conditions.

Pressurising or purging methods

These are methods of using pressurised or inert gases to prevent ingress of flammable gases, and are suitable for all zone locations.

Intrinsically safe equipment

This is used for instrumentation and low energy equipment. Intrinsically safe equipment is categorised 'ia' or 'ib' if it can be used in zones 1 and 2. Exceptionally, category ia may be used in zone 0 if sparking contacts are not part of the equipment.

Flameproof equipment

This is probably the most familiar term and is a well-tried British approach to the problem. The principle of flameproofing is that the apparatus so described is constructed to withstand any explosion within the apparatus, arising from ignition of flammable gas that may enter through the casing or other enclosure. All flanges and other joints of the casing or enclosure of the apparatus are well designed and constructed so as to prevent any internal ignition of gas from moving out of the enclosure and igniting a surrounding flammable atmosphere. By its nature, flameproof equipment is substantial, heavy and rather costly. It is intended for application in zones 1 and 2 but is not suitable for use in zone 0.

Marking

Each item of electrical equipment for use in hazardous atmospheres should be marked with an appropriate group number for the range of gases it was designed for, and also with a temperature classification indicating the maximum allowable surface temperature of the equipment used.

5

Circuitry

Electrical apparatus for use in hazardous atmospheres has to be supplied with electricity via a cable circuit and control gear. As much as possible of this should be located outside the hazardous zone. Within the zone, however, the suitability of the metallic cable sheathing, armouring or conduit must be ensured, with the provision of special cable sealing glands and fittings. Earthing requires particular attention.

ELECTRICAL TESTING

Electrical testing is necessary to ensure that the design, construction and performance specifications of the items being tested are maintained at an adequate standard for the anticipated continued use. Electrical testing also enables faults to be detected so that remedial measures can be taken before the fault develops and damage or personal injury arises.

Procedures include resistance and insulation tests for correct connection and operation. Those undertaking the tests should be competent. The layout of the work area should be such as not to expose anyone to live and other dangerous parts. 'Anyone' means not only the tester but other persons present.

Testing of electrical installations

A prerequisite to such testing is visual inspection to ensure all circuits and equipment comply with an accepted standard and are properly installed, and that circuit protection and earthing arrangements appear in order.

The method adopted for testing should not, of course, be liable to endanger people or plant. Thus the testing operation must be under proper control and the testing equipment suitable for the required use.

Ordinary test lamps, and leads with exposed test prods or even bare ends, have caused numerous flashovers, and the dangerous practice of using metal lampholders is, unfortunately, still encountered. Properly designed, protected and approved test equipment, employing current limiting resistors, well-shrouded test prods, and properly insulated handles are available, and should always be used.

It is a requirement of the IEE Wiring Regulations that on final circuits the circuit protective device, eg fuse or miniature circuit breaker, will, in the event of a fault to earth, operate within 0.4 seconds for socket outlets in bathrooms and outdoor circuits and within 0.5 seconds for circuits supplying fixed equipment.

Testing of electronic telecommunications and similar equipment

The dangers of working on and testing components inside television sets, for instance, without first having disconnected the set from the power supply, are obvious. Repair and testing bays in workshops should be earth-free areas, set apart, with special arrangements such as the provision of a single isolating transformer and appropriate test benches and equipment.

The testing of electronic equipment with earthed metal casings requires special precautions to remove the risk of electric shock through the casing. This may be achieved by provision of current limiting devices for the testing circuit. Testing is a specialised operation and reference should be made to the latest edition of the Institution of Electrical Engineers' Wiring Regulations (see later in this chapter) and current HSE publications.

TRAINING OF PERSONNEL

A key to safe working on electrical installations and apparatus is that all those engaged on such work shall have been adequately trained. The training, supported by relevant experience in a working environment, should be aimed to ensure that the trainee acquires the skills, related knowledge and attitudes necessary for safe and efficient working. Both off-the-job and on-the-job training must be properly supervised, and at each stage the trainee must be made aware of the extent and limitations of the job in hand, the hazards that may be present, and the precautions that have to be taken to ensure safe working.

ELECTRICAL SAFETY IN OFFICES

General electrical safety requirements

- All accessible parts of electrically-operated equipment should be efficiently earthed.
- All live terminals should be efficiently screened. In particular, operator access to parts of equipment should not allow access to live electrical parts at the same time.
- Where interlock switches are provided for guards, they should be of such design or construction as to prohibit inadvertent operation. The standard and frequency of maintenance and testing respectively is important.
- All flexible cords, plugs, sockets and couplers should be of good quality and standard. Flexible cables should be of adequate size, construction and protection, with approved connections and colour coding.
- Mains input switches should be suitably placed on equipment with the 'ON' and 'OFF' positions identified and accessible.
- An effective overcurrent protective device should be provided in each phase of the circuit and so arranged as to disconnect the electricity supply to the equipment in the event of overload or short circuit.
- All high voltage terminals and live conductors should be securely screened and a suitable warning notice indicating the danger displayed in a prominent position.
- Where fluids are used in any machine, they should be used and housed so that they do not come into contact with electrical conductors and components. In the case of flammable liquids, special attention should be given to the machine enclosure to prevent dangerous concentrations of vapour. All electrical conductors and components should be specifically housed or constructed so as to avoid a risk of fire or explosion.
- Where heating elements are incorporated in any machine, they should be placed and installed so as to cause no deterioration of electrical equipment or overheating that could create hazards to individuals.

Electrical installations

- The installation, repair and maintenance of all electrical installations and equipment should be undertaken only by competent persons.
- Equipment should be regularly inspected and serviced and staff should be encouraged to report defects, such as worn or damaged cables, loose connections, damaged or unearthed equipment, badly placed trailing cables, broken plugs, sockets and switches, and overloaded sockets and circuits. Defective equipment should be taken out of service immediately.
- Before anyone attempts to repair, service or adjust any electrically-

operated machine or equipment, or to remove covers, it should be disconnected from the power supply.

● All wiring, whether of a permanent or temporary nature, should be sound and regularly maintained.

● Circuits should not be overloaded, particularly by the use of a single-socket outlet for more than one item of equipment. All circuits should incorporate overcurrent protection in the form of properly rated and positioned circuit breakers or fuses.

● Staff should be trained in safety procedures and treatment in the event of electric shock.

STATIC ELECTRICITY

An atom is comprised of a central nucleus containing positively charged particles (**protons**) surrounded by an equal number of negatively charged **electrons**. The charges on a proton and an electron are equal and so an atom as a whole is normally electrically neutral.

When two particular substances are rubbed together, they can become electrostatically charged. For instance, when a strip of white polythene is rubbed with a cloth it becomes charged. The production of charges is caused by the transfer from one material to another. In this case electrons pass from the polythene surface to the cloth, leaving the polythene surface short of electrons, that is, positively charged. The cloth now has more electrons than protons and becomes negatively charged.

Hazards from static electricity

The main risk associated with static electricity is the potential for the discharge of very high voltages to earth which can ignite flammable environments and atmospheres. Most people are familiar with the static electricity produced when a person combs their hair. Static electricity can be produced, however, in a variety of industrial and other situations, for instance where liquids flow through an orifice, during the flow of powders in a pipeline, in the manufacture of certain man-made textiles, such as nylon, and, in some cases, by the flow of air or gases.

Static electricity can be a source of danger if sparking takes place in flammable atmospheres, resulting in explosions and fire. For instance, where high voltages are involved, a **flashover**, which is sufficient to ignite a flammable atmosphere produced by a dust or a gas, can take place.

Precautions necessary

The development of static charge over a period of time, or the possibility of static discharge, can be reduced significantly by the use of the following precautions:

- the maintenance of a humid atmosphere around 50 per cent which allows static charge to drain away
- the use of special conducting footwear by operators to enable the charge to drain away from the body
- the earthing of all exposed metalwork which does not carry current
- inerting of the space above powders and liquids, thereby reducing the chance of ignition
- the use of air ionising devices
- increasing the conductivity of insulator material to minimise the development of static charge
- the use of anti-static products, such as anti-static flooring and
- in some cases, reducing the rate of a manufacturing process, may reduce the level of static charge building up over a period of time.

POWER LINES

5

Power lines running both overhead and underground can be a significant source of danger. Power lines operate at a wide range of voltages from as low as 240 volts to 400,000 volts. Where people come into contact with overhead lines, the result is commonly electrocution, whereas contact with an underground cable most frequently results in varying degrees of burns and, in a limited number of cases, death by electrocution. The precautions necessary in work involving underground cables and overhead lines vary considerably.

Underground cables

The principal cause of damage to underground cables is that from excavation operations, frequently due to crushing of the cable by excavation plant and penetration of same with pneumatic drills, spades and other hand tools. This form of damage to cables frequently results in arcing currents accompanied, in some cases, by fire and explosion. The result can be extensive, and often fatal, burns to operators.

Before any excavation work is commenced, it is essential that a safe system of work be established, perhaps through the use of a method statement. This should be accompanied by perusal of any plans indicating the layout of cables, their precise location, depth below ground and the age of the cables. Liaison with the local electricity authority, local authority and owners of the land should take place at a very early stage of the operation. Where there is uncertainty as to the precise location of cables, cable locating devices should be used and the lines of the cables marked conspicuously above ground.

Once the line of the cable has been established using available plans and detecting devices, trial holes should be dug by hand at specific points to expose the route of the cables. Clearly, considerable care is needed in such an exercise. It is essential that such work is undertaken by trained operators who have been briefed before commencing work.

Overhead lines

Overhead lines are not generally insulated. Whilst they present no risk to the public in general, occasions can arise where construction-related activities can bring operators in close proximity to same. This includes people erecting or working on scaffolding, roof workers, or people driving vehicles, such as cranes, mobile platforms and excavating machinery.

As with work below ground, planning of the exercise is essential, particularly on construction sites. In certain cases, by arrangement with the electricity authority, it may be possible to divert overhead lines or make them dead for a specific period in order to ensure safe working. Where this is not possible, it is necessary to take other precautions which ensure safe clearance distances from the lines.

In situations where the owner/operator has not been consulted, no part of a vehicle, plant or equipment should approach or work in a position where it is liable to be within:

- 15m of lines suspended from steel towers
- 9m of lines suspended from wooden poles.

The owner should be consulted as soon as practicable in order that an appropriate safe system of work can be operated. Broadly, precautions necessary involving work with overhead lines can be split into three specific aspects, no work or passage of plant beneath lines, passage of plant beneath lines, and work carried out beneath lines.

No work or passage of plant beneath lines

In this case, the area should be cordoned off using heavy barriers at least six metres from the lines in order to prevent close approach. Barriers, which may take a number of forms, such as heavy duty fencing, tension wire fencing earthed at each end, earth banking to at least one metre high or baulks of stout timber, which act as wheel stops for vehicles, should be installed prior to any work commencing. Flags and markers should be used to indicate the boundary line, together with bunting or flags three to six metres above the ground.

Passage of plant beneath lines

Where such operations are essential, the width of the passageway should be restricted to no more than 10m, preferably at right angles to the lines. Passageway routes should be defined with fencing, with goalposts formed at each end to act as entrances/exits in the barriers which run parallel to the lines. Goalposts should be constructed in non-conducting material, eg timber, plastic pipes. They should display cross bar clearance heights prominently together with instructions to crane drivers to lower any jib to well below the identified clearance height. In winter months, or where night work is undertaken, warning barriers, goalposts and precautionary signs should be illuminated.

Work carried out beneath lines

Barriers, goalposts and precautionary signs must be installed. However, further precautions may be required, such as close supervision of operations to ensure safe working procedures, the use of a horizontal barrier of insulating material installed below the lines and, in effect, forming a roof above the area of operations, and the modification of cranes by various physical restraints on jibs to prevent their extension into a danger zone. It is common practice in certain operations to use an earthed steel net over the area of lifting operations.

In all the above cases, where safe clearance distances are necessary to ensure safe working, special attention must be paid to any variations in ground level caused by excavations and excavated materials, the uncontrolled dumping of waste materials, abnormal ground conditions, the presence of large quantities of deposited building materials or natural variations.

THE WIRING REGULATIONS

These regulations are produced by the Institution of Electrical Engineers as a code of best practice. Whilst they have no legal status compared, for instance, with the Electricity at Work Regulations 1989, compliance with the Wiring Regulations should ensure a high level of electrical safety and compliance with certain aspects of the above regulations.

Objectives of the Wiring Regulations

The main objectives of the Regulations are to:

- establish safety standards for people who design and work with electrical installations, such as designers, installers, erectors and testers of both permanent and temporary installations and
- protect employees and people generally from the hazards associated with electricity namely electric shock, fires, burns and the movement of electrically-operated work equipment.

The regulations apply only to installations operating at up to 1000 volts ac.

Principal requirements

The Wiring Regulations are split into a number of parts.

Part 1

This part emphasises the need for sound standards of workmanship and the competence of operators, and the use of suitable and correct materials to the relevant standard/specification.

Part 2

In this part various definitions of voltages are outlined. These include:

- **Extra-low voltage** – not exceeding 50 volts ac or 120 volts dc.
- **Low voltage** – exceeding extra low but not over 1000 volts ac or 1500 volts dc between conductors, or 600 volts ac or 900 volts dc between conductors and earth.

Part 3

This part deals with the factors which installation designers must consider including the purpose of the installation, any external influences, maintainability, maximum demand, the number of conductors, earthing arrangements, the type of supply and possible future extensions to be installation.

Part 4

This part provides guidance on methods of protection against the hazards of shock, burns, fires and excess current.

Designers must consider direct and indirect shock protection, including the use of low or reduced voltages, limitation of energy, insulation of live parts, use of barriers/enclosures/obstacles/location out of reach, earthed equipotential bonding and automatic disconnection, non-conducting locations and electrical separation.

Specific measures to prevent fires and burns from fixed equipment are considered, along with short circuit protection and the means of isolating and switching provided.

Part 5

This deals with the selection and erection of equipment to ensure that it is fit for the purpose. Considerable emphasis is given to compliance with British Standards. Where no standard exists, the specifier should be satisfied the equipment meets the other requirements of the IEE Wiring Regulations.

Part 6

This part is concerned with procedures for inspection and testing to ensure any installation is safe and complies with the Wiring Regulations.

The tests should be carried out in a particular order to identify faults before the installation is energised by the supply.

ELECTRICITY AT WORK REGULATIONS 1989

These regulations are made under the HSWA and apply to all work associated with electricity. The purpose of the regulations is to require precautions to be taken against the risk of death or personal injury from electricity in work activities.

The regulations impose duties on persons ('duty holders') in respect of systems, electrical equipment and conductors and in respect of work activities on or near electrical equipment. They replace the 1908 and 1944 regulations and extend to all premises and not just those defined as factories under the Factories Act 1961.

These regulations establish general principles for electrical safety rather than state detailed requirements. Further detailed advice is given in the supporting Memorandum of Guidance and other authoritative documents such as the IEE Wiring Regulations, British and European standards and HSE publications.

Because the regulations state principles of electrical safety in a form which may be applied to any work activity having a bearing on electrical safety they apply to all electrical equipment and systems wherever manufactured, purchased, installed or taken into use, even if this pre-dates them. If, however, electrical equipment does pre-date the regulations it does not of itself mean that the continued use of such equipment is prohibited. The equipment may continue to be used provided the requirements of the regulations can continue to be satisfied, in other words, the equipment need only be replaced if it becomes unsafe or there is a risk of injury.

Duties in some of the regulations are subject to the qualifying term '**reasonably practicable**'. Where qualifying terms are absent, the requirements is said to be **absolute** and must be met regardless of cost or any other consideration.

Regulation 29 provides a defence for a duty holder who can establish that he took **all reasonable steps and exercised all due diligence** to avoid committing an offence under certain regulations.

Regulation 2 – interpretation

This regulation incorporates a number of important definitions.

- **Circuit conductor** means any conductor in a system which is intended to carry electric current in normal conditions, or to be energised in normal conditions, and includes a combined neutral and earth conductor, but does not include a conductor provided solely to perform a protective function by connection to earth or other reference point.

- **Conductor** means a conductor of electrical energy.
- **Danger** means risk of injury.
- **Electrical equipment** includes anything used, intended to be used or installed for use, to generate, provide, transmit, transform, rectify, convert, conduct, distribute, control, store, measure or use electrical energy.
- **Injury** means death or personal injury from electric shock, electric burn, electrical explosion or arcing, or from fire or explosion initiated by electrical energy, where any such death or injury is associated with the generation, provision, transmission, rectification, conversion, conduction, distribution, control, storage, measurement or use of electrical energy.
- **System** means any electrical system in which all the electrical equipment is, or may be, electrically connected to a common source of electrical energy, and includes such source and such equipment.

Regulation 3 – persons on whom duties are imposed

Equal levels of duty are imposed on four classes of person (duty holders), ie employers, the self-employed, the manager of a mine or quarry and employees.

PART II – GENERAL

Regulation 4 – systems, work activities and protective equipment

- All systems shall at all times be of such construction as to prevent, so far as is reasonably practicable, danger.
- As may be necessary to prevent danger, all systems shall be maintained so as to prevent, so far as is reasonably practicable, such danger.
- Every work activity, including operation, use and maintenance of a system and work near a system, shall be carried out in such a manner as not to give rise, so far as is reasonably practicable, to danger.
- Any equipment provided under these regulations for the purpose of protecting persons at work on or near electrical equipment shall be suitable for the use for which it is provided, by maintained in a condition suitable for that use, and be properly used.

Regulation 5 – strength and capability of electrical equipment

This regulation places an absolute duty to ensure that the strength and capability of electrical equipment in use are not exceeded in such a way as to give rise to danger.

The defence provided by Regulation 29 is available.

Regulation 6 – adverse or hazardous environments

Full account must be taken of any reasonably foreseeable adverse or hazardous environmental conditions that equipment may be subjected to ie equipment intended for outdoor use must be selected on this basis.

The adverse or hazardous environments are:

- mechanical danger
- the effects of the weather, natural hazards, temperature or pressure
- the effects of wet, dirty, dusty or corrosive conditions or
- any flammable or explosive substance including dusts, vapours or gases.

Regulation 7 – insulation, protection and placing of conductors

Regulation 7 requires that all conductors in a system which may give rise to danger (eg electric shock) shall either:

- be suitably covered with insulating material and as necessary protected so as to prevent, so far as is reasonably practicable, danger or
- have such precautions taken, including their being suitably placed, as will prevent, so far as is reasonably practicable, danger.

Regulation 8 – earthing or other suitable precautions

There is an absolute duty under the regulations to safeguard the risk of electric shock caused by indirect contact, ie contact with metal normally at earth potential that has become 'live' because of a fault.

The main emphasis of this regulation is on the provision of earthing. However, it is also recognised that other techniques may be employed to achieve freedom from danger, eg double insulation, connection to a common voltage reference point on the system, equipotential bonding, use of safe voltages, earth-free non-conducting environments, current energy limitation, separated or isolated systems.

The defence provided by Regulation 29 is available.

Regulation 9 – integrity of referenced conductors

Again this regulation places an absolute duty subject to the defence provided by Regulation 29. It seeks to preserve the integrity of 'referenced conductors', these being the supply system neutral conductors which are required to be connected back to earth on the low voltage side of the distribution transformer.

The object of the regulation is to prevent referenced circuit conductors, which should be at or about the same potential as the reference point, from reaching significantly different potentials thereby giving rise to possible danger.

The defence provided by Regulation 29 is available.

Regulation 10 – connections

Regulation 10 places an absolute requirement that all joints and connections in a system be mechanically and electrically suitable for use. This requirement applies whether the installation be permanent or temporary.

The defence provided by Regulation 29 is available.

Regulation 11 – means for protecting from excess of current

This regulation requires the provision of efficient means, suitably located, to protect from excess of current every part of a system as may be necessary to prevent danger.

This is an absolute requirement and the defence provided by Regulation 29 is available.

Regulation 12 – means for cutting off the supply and for isolation

Where necessary, to prevent danger, suitable means (including, where appropriate, methods of identifying circuits) shall be available for:

- cutting off the supply of electrical energy to any electrical equipment and
- the isolation of any electrical equipment.

Isolation means the disconnection and separation of the electrical equipment from every source of electrical energy in such a way that this disconnection and separation is secure.

The requirements relating to isolation and separation do not apply to electrical equipment which is itself a source of electrical energy but, in such a case as is necessary, precautions shall be taken to prevent, so far as is reasonably practicable, danger.

Regulation 13 – precautions for work on equipment made dead

Adequate precautions be taken to prevent electrical equipment, which has been made dead in order to prevent danger while work is carried out on or near that equipment, from becoming electrically charged during that work if danger may thereby arise.

Mention is made in the Memorandum of Guidance on the need for formalisation of the isolation arrangements by the use of permit to work procedures.

Regulation 14 – work on or near live conductors

This regulation imposes an absolute duty not to carry out on or so near any live conductor (other than one suitably covered with insulating material so as to prevent danger) such that danger may arise unless:

- it is unreasonable in all the circumstances for it to be dead
- it is reasonable in all the circumstances for the person concerned to be at work on or near it while it is live and
- suitable precautions (including where necessary the provision of suitable protective equipment) are taken to prevent injury.

A written policy statement may be needed which establishes the need for live working to be permitted.

The defence provided by Regulation 29 is available.

It should be noted that Regulation 28 of the 1908 regulations imposed a duty that no person work unaccompanied when undertaking electrical work where danger may exist, eg from live conductors. The new regulations do not automatically require accompaniment for work of this nature but this matter must be considered in the general arrangements for achieving a safe system of work.

Regulation 15 – working space, access and lighting

There is a general requirement under this regulation for the provision of adequate working space, adequate means of access and adequate lighting at all electrical equipment on which or near which work is being done in circumstances which may give rise to danger.

Regulation 16 – persons to be competent to prevent danger and injury

This regulation clearly states that no person shall be engaged in any work activity where technical knowledge or experience is necessary to prevent danger or, where appropriate, injury, unless he possesses such knowledge or experience, or is under such degree of supervision as may be appropriate having regard to the nature of the work.

The need, therefore, to identify 'competent persons' for certain classes of electrical work is clear. Employers must also relate the level of competence to the degree of supervision necessary.

PART III – REGULATIONS APPLYING TO MINES ONLY

This part deals with specific regulations applying only to mines.

PART IV – MISCELLANEOUS AND GENERAL

Regulation 29 – defence

In any proceedings for an offence consisting of a contravention of regulations 4(4), 5, 8, 9, 10, 11, 12, 13, 14, 15, 16 or 25, it shall be a defence for any person to prove that he **took all reasonable precautions and exercised all due diligence** to avoid the commission of that offence.

Pressure vessels and pressure systems

PRESSURE VESSELS

A pressure vessel is generally taken to mean a closed vessel which operates at a pressure greater than atmospheric pressure, and within this definition are included steam boilers, steam receivers and air receivers.

PRESSURE SYSTEMS

This term is defined in the Pressure Systems and Transportable Gas Containers Regulations 1989 as:

- a system comprising one or more pressure vessels of rigid construction, and any associated pipework and protective devices
- the pipework with its protective devices to which a transportable gas container is, or is intended to be, connected or
- a pipeline and its protective devices.

CLASSIFICATION OF PRESSURE VESSELS (FACTORIES ACT 1961)

The Factories Act 1961 defines four types of pressure vessel.

Steam boiler

Any closed vessel in which for any purpose steam is generated under pressure greater than atmospheric and includes any economiser used to heat water being fed to any such vessel, and any superheater used for heating steam.

Steam receiver

Any vessel or apparatus, other than a steam boiler, steam container, steam pipe or coil, or part of a prime mover, used for containing steam under pressure greater than atmospheric pressure.

Steam container

Any vessel, other than a steam pipe or coil, constructed with a permanent outlet to atmosphere or into a space where pressure does not exceed atmospheric pressure, and through which steam is passed at atmospheric pressure, or at approximately that pressure, for the purpose of heating, boiling, drying, evaporating or other similar purpose.

Air receiver

- any vessel (other than a pipe or coil, or an accessory, fitting or part of a compressor) for containing compressed air and connected with an air-compressing plant or
- any fixed vessel for containing compressed air or compressed exhaust gases and used for the purpose of starting an internal combustion engine or
- any fixed or portable vessel (not being part of a spraying pistol) used for the purposes of spraying by means of compressed air any paint, varnish, lacquer or similar material or
- any vessel in which oil is stored and from which it is forced by compressed air.

Steam boilers

The purpose of a steam boiler or, more specifically, a steam generator, is to produce steam under pressure from the raw materials, fuel, air and water. The potential heat of the fuel is made available through combustion, and this is transmitted to and stored by water vapour in the form of sensible and latent heat. There are two principal types of steam boiler: the vertical boiler and the horizontal boiler.

The vertical boiler

In its simplest form the vertical boiler would be a metal cylinder containing water, with a firebox at the bottom and a flue passing up the centre to carry hot gases away. However, such a boiler would be inefficient, as there would be little opportunity for hot gases to give up their heat through the sides of the flue to the water. In order to ensure that more heat is transferred, a greater part of the metal surface must be exposed to hot gases. One way of achieving this is by means of water tubes located across the central flue, as in the vertical cross-tube boiler shown in Figure 6.1. In addition, extra exposed surface can be provided by the use of smoke tubes or fire tubes to carry the flue gases through water space, as in the fire-tube boiler shown in Figure 6.1(*b*). This latter is more efficient mainly because the firebox is shaped to expose a larger area to heat from fire. Vertical fire-tube boilers are used mainly in small factories where steam requirements are not excessive. They are moderately cheap and do not occupy a great deal of room.

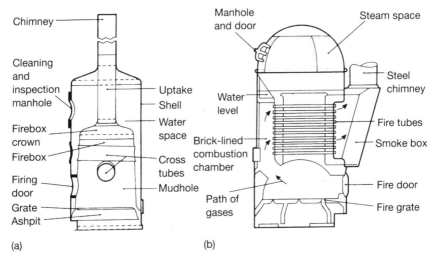

(a)   (b)

FIG 6.1   Vertical boilers (a) Vertical cross-tube boiler (b) Vertical fire-tube boiler with horizontal tubes

The horizontal boiler

This comprises a horizontal cylinder three-quarters full of water, with one or more furnace tubes passing through the water space. The fire is located at the front of the furnace tubes and hot gases travel through these tubes, heating the surrounding water prior to reaching the flue. The most common form of horizontal boiler is the economic boiler, shown in Figure 6.2. This boiler consists of a cylindrical shell with two flat end plates. One or more flue tubes are disposed between the end plates below the centre of the boiler, the grate or other fuel burning equipment, eg pressure jet oil burners, being arranged at the front end of these flues. The hot gases traverse the flue tubes to the back of the boiler where they enter a brick-lined combustion chamber in the case of a 'dry back' boiler or a water-cooled combustion chamber in the case of a 'wet back' boiler. Here the gas path is reversed and the gases travel to the front of the boiler through a bank of smoke tubes located above the flues. These tubes are normally about 8 cm in diameter and, by their use, the gas stream is broken up into a number of small elements, materially increasing the rate and efficiency and heat transfer. After passing through the smoke tubes, the gases are collected in a smoke box, whence they are led to atmosphere. This is the normal arrangement of a 'double pass' economic boiler. A

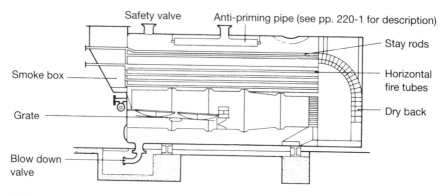

Safety valve — Anti-priming pipe (see pp. 220-1 for description)

Smoke box — Stay rods

Grate — Horizontal fire tubes

Blow down valve — Dry back

FIG 6.2 Economic boiler (solid fuel fired)

'treble pass' economic boiler has a second bank of tubes superimposed through which gases traverse the boiler from front to back, being finally collected in a smoke box, whence they are led to atmosphere.

THE TESTING OF PRESSURE VESSELS

A pressure vessel consists mainly of a series of sheets of metal suitably shaped and welded together. Most pressure vessel failures are associated with the blowing of a welded joint and, in order to ensure that a welded joint has properties comparable to those of the original materials and is metallurgically satisfactory, it is necessary for the actual physical properties of the weld to be investigated by destructive as well as non-destructive tests. Of course, the former cannot be carried out on the actual seams and it is undertaken using test plates. The normal system is to approve the manufacturer's procedures for the type of welding and the materials used in the vessel manufacture, as well as individual welders for certain classes of work, by the mechanical testing of separate test plates prepared by them before the actual production welding is commenced. Depending upon the requirements of the pressure vessel code used, the thickness of the materials, the difficulty in welding the materials selected, the future use of the vessel and the safety criteria used in the design code, non-destructive testing will be called for on the materials of construction and on the welding undertaken.

Although radiography has been used for non-destructive testing of pressure vessels for many years and produces a permanent record (radiograph), its effectiveness for identifying defects is dependent on the techniques used. Therefore, the radiograph should never be regarded as evidence of quality unless full details of the procedures are also known. Ultrasonic techniques are now also widely used, and in the construction of nuclear reactor vessels they are, on balance, more effective than radiography. There is, however, only limited scope for a permanent record of the results of the inspection.

As for inspection of boilers and other pressure vessels by non-destructive methods, it is essential to decide what defects require identification and to choose the particular method to suit. As the most serious defect likely to be encountered in a pressure vessel is a crack, it is important to recognise that radiography only discloses a fine crack if it is parallel to the direction of the radiation, ie approximately perpendicular to the X-ray film. Ultrasonic methods do not identify a crack in the direction of the ultrasonic beam, and dye penetrants only show a crack which breaks the surface. These limitations should be appreciated prior to testing.

PRESSURE VESSELS – FACTORS AFFECTING DESIGN

The initial, and probably most important, stage in the design of any pressure vessel is that of determining the conditions to which it is to be subjected. Such an assessment should take into account system fault and test conditions as well as normal working.

The main conditions likely to be encountered are:

- variations in pressure
- variations in temperature
- cyclic conditions of temperature and pressure which may cause fatigue failures
- the effects of the contents of the vessel
- the effect of induced loads from pipework, etc and
- the effects of weather – snow, wind, etc.

INSTALLATIONS AND FITTINGS – SAFETY REQUIREMENTS

To ensure maximum safety of operations, the following installations and fittings are recommended for all pressure vessels, in particular steam boilers:

- two water gauges
- two safety valves
- a pressure gauge
- a fusible plug or high and low water alarm
- a blow down valve
- a stop valve (steam)
- a feed check valve and
- an anti-priming pipe.

The functions of these installations and fittings are outlined below.

Water gauges

All boilers with an evaporative capacity exceeding 136kg of steam per hour should be fitted with two water gauges. For boiler pressures up to

4,400kg/cm² it is usual to fit tubular gauges which must be protected, protection usually consisting of a shield of specially toughened glass. Water gauges should be so situated that the water level can be easily seen by the operator and so arranged that the lowest visible section of the glass is higher than the minimum working level. It is good practice to test water gauges and cocks (a form of hand-operated tap or valve) once per shift by opening and closing the cocks in the prescribed manner.

Safety valves

Every boiler should have at least two safety valves, each capable of discharging the total peak evaporation of the boiler. The valves can be arranged on a single chest. This recommendation for two valves on each boiler is made on the assumption that if one valve fails to act, the other will function. However, this is not by itself a sufficient safeguard, and the safety valves should receive frequent attention and maintenance.

There are three types of safety valve – deadweight, lever arm or steelyard, and spring-loaded (see Figure 6.3 for the latter two).

A safety valve is fitted to open at a set pressure, higher than the normal working pressure but below the maximum working pressure established by the insurance company. Steam will be discharged until the pressure drops sufficiently for the valve to close again. Each type is manufactured in a variety of patterns (the more modern having means for locking and adjustment). Each valve is so arranged that no unauthorised person can tamper with its setting. Valves should be tested periodically to ensure their reliable operation, in accordance with boiler insurance requirements. Failure to comply with insurance requirements, although not in itself a breach of law, may wholly or partially invalidate cover, as it is an implied term of insurance contracts that the insured will take steps to mitigate loss, eg will take practical safety measures.

Pressure gauge

This must be connected to the steam space and indicate the pressure of steam in the boiler. The maximum permissible working pressure should be clearly marked on the gauge as the gauge glass.

Fusible plug, and high and low water alarm

A steam boiler must be equipped with either a fusible plug (if of the shell type) or a high and low water alarm, which makes a sound that can easily be recognised by the operator. A fusible plug is a plug of metal with a low melting point and is set into the boiler shell at low level. If the water level falls, and the boiler overheats, the plug melts, allowing the boiler water to escape and douse the fire.

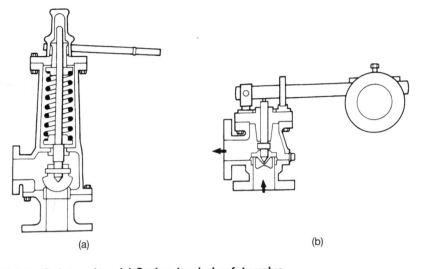

(a)   (b)

**FIG 6.3 Safety valves (a) Spring-loaded safety valve
(b) Lever arm safety valve**

There are two types of high and low water alarm, internal and external. The internal type of alarm consists of two floats, one at each end of a long arm suspended from the crown of the boiler shell. The arm is attached in such a manner as to pivot about an axis so that one float acts at a dangerously high level, the other at a dangerously low level. At correct levels of the water in the boiler the low-water float lies on the surface of the water, the high-water float being suspended clear of the surface, the system being maintained in equilibrium. When the water level falls, the low-level float drops and actuates a lever which operates a steam whistle. When the water level rises to the level of the top float, the upward movement of the bottom float being restricted, buoyancy occurs and causes the arm to tilt in the same direction as before so that the whistle again sounds.

The internal type of alarm is now being superseded by the external types: float and thermostatic. The first system, ie float, consists of chambers mounted at the normal working level of the water in the boiler and they are connected to the steam and water spaces. The floats respond to changes in the level of the water in the boiler and, at predetermined high and low positions, actuate a steam whistle, or two whistles of different notes, one for high-water conditions and the other for low. The thermostatic type, on the other hand, consists of rods that expand and contract according to whether they are in steam or water. When the water is at normal working level the upper rod is immersed in steam and lower one in water. If, through a rise in the water level, the upper rod becomes immersed in water, it contracts, and if the lower rod becomes immersed in steam, it expands. Either movement actuates an electric circuit which causes a bell to ring.

Blow down valve

A blow down valve has three important functions:

- deconcentration of the boiler water to prevent the solids content rising above prescribed limits
- ejection of sludge and solids precipitated from the boiler water which settle at the bottom of the boiler and
- for emptying the boiler prior to inspection or for other purposes.

Blow downs may be continuously or intermittently operated. The former method is more effective in deconcentrating the boiler to prevent priming or foaming. In many cases the blow down is located near the surface of the water in the boiler shell. The intermittent blow down valve is used for the systematic ejection of unwanted solid matter deposited from the boiler water, as well as for emptying the boiler. It is an essential fitting and must be of first-class structure. It is necessarily situated at the lowest part of the boiler. Consequently it may be in a position where it is not continuously under the eye of the attendant. Discharge from the valve should be piped to a place where it can easily be inspected, as undetected leakage can cause serious wastage of fuel, together with corrosion.

When two or more boilers discharge their blow downs into the same pipe, each valve should be operable by only one key that remains locked in position when the valve is open and is removable only when it is completely closed. In this way only one blow down in a bank of boilers can be operated at any one time.

Stop valve (steam)

This valve is located between the boiler and the steam pipe or outlet, and is used to control the flow of steam from the boiler.

Feed check valve

This valve is situated on the boiler shell or steam drum, usually just below the low water level. It is essentially a non-return valve to prevent water escaping from the boiler should the pressure in the feed line be less than that of the boiler. A stop valve must be inserted between this non-return valve and the boiler. This may be incorporated in the feed check valve but the arrangement should be such that when the stop valve is closed it will be possible to remove the non-return valve for inspection, adjustment or minor repair while the boiler continues in operation. When more than one boiler is being fed by a single pump, the stop valve can be manipulated to control the rate of feed to the boilers.

Anti-priming pipe

Priming is the phenomenon whereby water is carried over from one part of the boiler into another part, such as a superheater. The action is mainly siphonic in nature. To prevent the loss of water which would result, an anti-priming pipe is fitted to break this siphonic action.

HAZARDS ASSOCIATED WITH BOILER OPERATION

The two principal hazards are overheating caused by low water level, which is the most frequent cause of boiler explosions and other damage, and the long-term effects of corrosion, which often result in explosion but, more frequently boiler failure.

Overheating in boilers

The main causes of overheating incidents are:

- lack of testing and maintenance of controls and alarms, leading to malfunction
- occasional inadequate standards of control and
- (less frequently nowadays) isolation of control chambers.

The first two points above are associated with poor standards of boiler operation. Isolation of the control chambers (caused by the attendant closing and leaving closed either the water or the steam isolating valve, or both, and after closing the drain valve) has in the past resulted in cases of explosion and damage from overheating of the boiler brought about by the resulting low water level. This hazard has largely been eliminated through improved boiler design.

Boiler corrosion

The long-term effects of corrosion in boilers can be both explosions and boiler failure. The principal sites and causes of corrosion are as follows.

Vertical boilers (see Figure 6.1)

- external shell crown 'wastage' (loss of metal thickness, and therefore strength, due to corrosion) and internal and external uptake wastage, due to the effects of damp lagging and gases
- internal wastage of the upper firebox due to heat intensity, the effects of gases and ingress of water
- cross-tube wastage (gas side) due to the effects of gases and moisture
- lower firebox wastage caused by the excessive accumulation of ash in the ashpit which can be further accelerated by moisture
- wastage around the attachments of boiler mountings to the shell, in most cases due to leakage

- wastage at leaking mudhole doors, in many cases due to faulty or unsuitable jointing material; the lagging retains moisture and the wastage occurs unseen

- 'grooving', a form of mechanical corrosion, due to expansion and contraction, and accelerated by a build-up of solids, occurring at the junction of the firebox and shell

- grooving at the junction of the firebox and uptake due to pressure and temperature fluctuations and, possibly, continued forced firing of the boiler

- wastage on the water side of the uptake between high and low water levels due to ebullience at the water surface and oxygen release on the uptake surfaces

- wastage around the mudhole door and compensating ring caused by leakage or a badly fitting door to door joint

- grooving at the vertical lap joint of boiler shell plates due to steam pressure tending to improve the circular shell form; this is largely mechanical action which is localised at seam edges

- general wastage of the internal surfaces of the ashpit plating and wastage of rivet heads, largely caused by sulphur in ash deposits and moisture.

FIG 6.4 Corrosion in pressure vessels

Corrosion of a safety valve to a calorifier making it totally inoperable. The seat is completely corroded and the spring actually corroded away. In addition, this valve was not fitted with a test lever so that, without dismantling it at examination, no evaluation of the operational performance of the valve could be made

Horizontal boilers (see Figure 6.2)

- distorted chamber tube plates, a situation where the tubes have been allowed to develop excessive scale and push the plate inwards
- 'necked' stays – wastage of the stays or stay tubes at plate entry due to leakage at the thread; this is accelerated through the tensile forces acting
- shell wastage at the mountings due to leakage at the joints, especially under the lagging
- combustion chamber crown distortion resulting from overheating
- girder stay wastage caused by leakage at the entry of the stay into the plate
- stay tube leakage as a result of incorrect welding giving inadequate support
- fractured stays caused by forcing the boiler
- radial grooving around the stays, a mechanical action caused by varying expansion of the heating surfaces; this weakens and breaks down the material structure
- cracks from rivet holes to the plate edge due to overheating and subsequent corrosion
- front end plate grooving caused by cyclic variations in pressure; this accelerates with the age of the boiler
- front tube plate wastage due to leakage past defective tube ends; and sulphur attack from the slaking of ashes; this attacks most metal surfaces and will waste rivets away.

FIG 6.4 (cont'd)

The flues of a cast iron water-heating boiler showing evidence of extensive corrosion

FIG 6.4   (cont'd)

General corrosion in a cast-iron water-heating boiler can occur extremely rapidly. In this case the surveyor's hammer has gone through the shell where the cast iron had been corroded to paper thinness

6

FIG 6.4 (cont'd)

Primary to secondary leakage in heat exchangers results in loss of efficiency or in overpressure failure of the lower pressure side. The photograph shows the effect of a hydraulic test on the tube nest of a calorifier which indicated failure of one tube and prevented a more serious failure later

(Reproduced by courtesy of National Vulcan Engineering Insurance Group Ltd)

AUTOMATIC CONTROLS ON STEAM AND HOT WATER BOILERS

The majority of steam boilers are now automatically controlled, and the most common water level and firing controls are float-operated controls situated outside the boiler. The floats are housed in chambers which are connected to the steam and water spaces in the boiler so that the water level in the chambers will be approximately the same as that in the boiler. Water level controls, low-water alarms and firing controls may be incorporated in the same chamber, but an additional chamber, with an independent electrical control circuit and independently connected to the boiler, is required for overriding low-water alarm and fuel cut-off in the case of fully automatically controlled steam boilers.

Standards for automatic controls

Automatic water level controls are of two basis standards:

- controls to assist the boiler attendant who constantly supervises the boiler and

- controls intended to replace continuous supervision with occasional supervision.

The minimum recommended requirements for automatic controls for boilers not continuously supervised are as follows.

Automatic water level controls

These should be so arranged that they positively control the boiler or the feed pumps, or regulate the water supply to the boiler and effectively maintain the level of water in the boiler between certain predetermined limits.

Automatic firing controls

These should be so arranged that they effectively control the supply of fuel to the burners of oil- or gas-fired boilers, and shut off the supply in the event of any one or more of the following circumstances:

- flame/pilot flame failure on oil- or gas-fired boilers; the control should be of the lock-out type requiring manual resetting
- failure to ignite the fuel on oil- or gas-fired boilers within a predetermined time; the control should be of the lock-out type requiring manual resetting
- when a predetermined high pressure at or below the safety valve set pressure is reached
- when the water level falls to a predetermined point below the normal operating level; this control should also cause an audible alarm to sound and
- failure of forced or induced draught fans, or any automatic flue damper, when these are provided.

Independent overriding control

This control should cut off the fuel supply to oil- or gas-fired boilers or air to the mechanical stokers of solid fuel fired boilers and cause an alarm to sound when the water level in the boiler falls to a predetermined low water level. The control or its electrical circuit should be so arranged that it has to be reset manually before the boiler can be brought back into operation.

Electrical failure to safety

All electrical equipment for water level and firing controls should be so designed that faults in the circuits cause the fuel and air supply to the boiler to be automatically shut off. Positive means, requiring manual resetting, should be provided to cut off the fuel and air supplies to the boiler, should there be a failure of electrical supply to water level and firing control equipment. All electrical conductors and equipment in connection with water levels and firing controls should be of adequate size, properly insulated and protected to prevent danger and including, where necessary, adequate protection against the ingress of moisture or the effects of high temperature.

PRESSURE SYSTEMS AND TRANSPORTABLE GAS CONTAINERS REGULATIONS 1989

These regulations impose safety requirements with respect to pressure systems and transportable gas containers which are used or intended to be used at work. They further impose safety requirements with a view to preventing certain pressure vessels from becoming pressurised. The regulations replace the earlier relevant sections of the FA 1961 and are accompanied by an ACOP. The majority of duties are of an absolute nature.

Regulation 3 – interpretation

The regulations incorporate a number of definitions.

- **Pressure system** means:
  - a system comprising one or more pressure vessels of rigid construction, and associated pipework and protective devices
  - the pipework with its protective devices to which a transportable gas container is, or is intended to be, connected or
  - a pipeline and its devices.
- **Transportable gas container** (TGC) means a container, including any permanent fitting of such a container, which is used, or is intended to be used, to contain a relevant fluid and is:
  - designed to be transportable for the purpose of refilling and has an internal volume of at least 0.5 litres and not greater than 3,000 litres
  - a non-refillable container having an internal volume of at least 1.4 litres and not greater than 5 litres or
  - for the purposes of Regulation 17(3) only, a non-refillable container.
- **Competent person** means a competent individual person (other than an employee) or a competent body of persons corporate or unincorporate; and accordingly any reference in the Regulations to a competent person performing a function includes a reference to his performing it through his employees.
- **Danger** in relation to a pressure system means reasonably foreseeable danger to persons from a system failure, but (except in the case of steam) it does not mean danger from the hazardous characteristics of the relevant fluid other than from its pressure.
- **Design specification** means a specification for the design of one type of TGC.
- **Design standard** means a standard for the design of more than one type of TGC.

- **Examination** means a careful and critical scrutiny of a pressure system, part of a pressure system or TGC, in or out of service as appropriate, to assess:
  - its actual condition
  - whether, for the period up to the next examination, it will not cause danger when properly used if normal maintenance is carried out, and for this purpose **normal maintenance** means such maintenance as is reasonable to expect the user (in the case of an installed system) or owner (in the case of a mobile system or TGC) to ensure is carried out independently of any advice from the competent person making the examination.
- **Framework directive** means the Council Directive 76/767/EEC concerning the approximation of the laws of the Member States relating to common provisions for pressure vessels and methods of inspecting them.
- **Installed system** means a pressure system other than a mobile system.
- **Mobile system** means a pressure system which can be readily moved between and used in different locations, but it does not include a steam locomotive.
- **Owner** in relation to a pressure system or TGC means the employer or self-employed person who owns the pressure system or TGC or, if he does not have a place of business in Great Britain, his agent in Great Britain or, if there is no such agent, the user.
- **Pipeline** means a pipe or system of pipes used for the conveyance of relevant fluid across the boundaries of premises, together with any apparatus for inducing or facilitating the flow of relevant fluid through, or through a part of, the pipe or system, and any valves, valve chambers, pumps, compressors or similar works which are annexed to, or incorporated in the course of, the pipe or system.
- **Pipework** means a pipe or system of pipes together with associated valves, pumps, compressors and other pressure containing components and includes a hose or bellows, but does not include a pipeline or any protective device.
- **Relevant fluid** means:
  - steam
  - any fluid or mixture of fluids which is at a pressure greater than 0.5 bar above atmospheric pressure, and which fluid or mixture of fluids, is a gas, or a liquid which would have a vapour pressure greater than 0.5 bar above atmospheric pressure when in equilibrium with its vapour at either the actual temperature of the liquid or 17.5°C or
  - a gas dissolved under pressure in a solvent contained in a porous substance at ambient temperature and which could be released from the solvent without the application of heat.
- **Safe operating limits** means the operating limits (incorporating a suitable margin of safety) beyond which failure is liable to occur.

- **Scheme of examination** means the written scheme referred to in Regulation 8.
- **System failure** means the unintentional release of stored energy (other than from a pressure relief system) from a pressure system or TGC.

Part II of the regulations applies generally.

Regulation 4 – design, construction, repair and modification

This regulation imposes safety requirements on any person who designs, manufactures, imports or supplies any pressure system or TGC. In particular, they must ensure:

- that they are properly designed and properly constructed from suitable material
- they are so designed and constructed that all necessary examinations for preventing danger can be carried out
- where means of access to the interior of the system is incorporated, such access can be gained without danger and
- they are provided with such protection devices as may be necessary for preventing danger; and any such device designed to release contents shall do so safely, so far as is practicable.

The employer of a person who modifies or repairs a pressure system or TGC at work shall ensure that nothing about the way in which it is modified or repaired gives rise to danger or otherwise impairs the operation of any protective device or inspection facility.

Part III of the regulations deals specifically with pressure systems.

Regulation 5 – provision of information and marking

Regulation 5 requires designers and suppliers of pressure systems to provide sufficient information concerning the design, construction, examination, operation and maintenance of same as may reasonably foreseeably be needed to enable the provisions of the Regulations to be complied with. Similar requirements apply in the case of employers of persons who modify or repair such systems.

Manufacturers must mark pressure systems with specified information (see Schedule 4), and no person shall remove such a mark from or falsify any mark on a pressure system, or on a plate attached to it, relating to its design, construction, test or operation.

Regulation 6 – installation

The employer of a person who installs a pressure system at work shall ensure that nothing about the way in which it is installed give rise to danger or otherwise impairs the operation of any protective device or inspection facility.

Regulation 7 – safe operating limits

This regulation places specific duties on the users of installed systems and owners of mobile systems. They must not operate the system or allow it to be operated unless they have established the safe operating limits of that system.

Furthermore, the owner of a mobile system shall, if he is not also the user of it:

- supply the user with a written statement specifying the safe operating limits of that system or
- ensure that the system is legibly and durably marked with such safe operating limits and that the mark is clearly visible.

Regulation 8 – written scheme of examination

This regulation is, perhaps, the most important requirement. The user of an installed system and owner of a mobile system shall not operate the system or allow it to be operated unless he has a **written scheme for the periodic examination**, by a competent person, of the following parts of the system, namely:

- all protective devices
- every pressure vessel and every pipeline in which (in either case) a defect may give rise to danger and
- those parts of the pipework in which a defect may give rise to danger

and such parts of the system shall be identified in the scheme.
The user or owner shall:

- ensure that the scheme has been drawn up, or certified as being suitable, by a competent person
- ensure that:
  - the content of the scheme is reviewed at appropriate intervals by a competent person for the purpose of determining whether it is suitable in current conditions of use of the system and
  - the content of the scheme is modified in accordance with any recommendations made by that competent person arising out of that review.

No person shall certify or draw up a scheme of examination as above unless the scheme is suitable and:

- specifies the nature and frequency of examination
- specifies any measures necessary to prepare the pressure system for safe

examination other than those it would be reasonable to expect the user or owner respectively to take without specialist advice and

- where appropriate provides for an examination to be carried out before the pressure system is used for the first time.

References above to the suitability of the scheme are references to its suitability for the purposes of preventing danger from those parts of the pressure system included in the scheme.

Regulation 9 – examination in accordance with the written scheme

This regulation goes into considerable depth on the procedures to be followed in the examination of pressure systems.

(1) The user of an installed system and owner of a mobile system shall:
   (a) ensure that those parts of the system included in the scheme are examined by a competent person within the intervals specified and, where appropriate, before the system is used for the first time and
   (b) before each examination take all appropriate safety measures to prepare the system for examination, including any such measures as are specified in the scheme of examination.

(2) Where a competent person undertakes an examination for the purposes of paragraph (1) above, he shall carry out that examination properly and in accordance with the scheme of examination.

(3) Where a competent person undertakes an examination for the purposes of paragraph (1) above, he shall, subject to paragraph (4) and Regulation 13(4), make a **written report of examination**, sign or otherwise authenticate it, date it and send it to the user or owner respectively; and the said report shall be sent as soon as is practicable after completing the examination, and in any event to arrive:
   (a) within 28 days of the completion of the examination or
   (b) before the date specified in the report under paragraph (5)(b)
       whichever is the sooner.

(4) Where the competent person is the user or owner respectively, the requirement to send the report to the user or owner shall not apply, but he shall make the report by the time it would have been required to have been sent to him if he had not been the competent person.

(5) The report specified by paragraph (3) shall:
   (a) state which parts of the pressure system have been examined, the condition of those parts and the results of the examination
   (b) specify any repairs or modifications to, or changes in the established safe operating limits of, the parts examined which, in the opinion of the competent person, are necessary to prevent danger or to ensure

the continued effective working of the protective devices, and specify the date by which any such repairs or modifications must be completed or any such changes to the safe operating limits must be made

(c) specify the date within the limits set by the scheme of examination after which the pressure system may not be operated without a further examination under the scheme of examination and

(d) state whether in the opinion of the competent person the scheme of examination is suitable (for the purpose of preventing danger from those parts of the pressure system included in it) or should be modified, and if the latter, state the reasons.

(6) The user or owner respectively of a system which has been examined under this regulation shall ensure that the system is not operated, and no person shall supply such a mobile system for operation, after (in each case):

(a) the date specified under paragraph (5)(b), unless the repairs or modifications specified under that paragraph have been completed, and the changes in the safe operating limits so specified have been made or

(b) the date specified under paragraph (5)(c) (or if that date has been postponed under paragraph (7), the postponed date) unless a further examination has been carried out under the scheme of examination.

(7) The date specified in a report under paragraph (5)(c) may be postponed to a later date by agreement in writing between the competent person who made the report and the user or owner respectively if:

(a) any such postponement does not give rise to danger

(b) only one such postponement is made for any one examination and

(c) such postponement is notified by the user or owner in writing to the enforcing authority for the premises in which the pressure system is situated, before the date specified in the report under paragraph (5)(c).

(8) Where the competent person above is the user or owner respectively the reference to an agreement in writing shall not apply, but there shall be included in the notification under sub-paragraph (c) a declaration that the postponement will not give rise to danger.

(9) The owner of a mobile system shall ensure that the date specified under paragraph (5)(c) is legibly and durably marked on the mobile system and that the mark is clearly visible.

Regulation 10 – action in case of imminent danger

Where a competent person is of the opinion that the pressure system or part of the pressure system will give rise to imminent danger unless certain repairs or modifications have been carried out or unless suitable changes to the operating conditions have been made, then without prejudice to the requirements of Regulation 9, he shall forthwith make a written report to that effect identifying the system and specifying the repairs, modifications or changes concerned and give it:

(a) in the case of an installed system, to the user or
(b) in the case of a mobile system, to the owner and to the user, if any,

and the competent person shall within 14 days of the completion of the examination send a written report containing the same particulars to the enforcing authority for the premises at which the pressure system is situated.

Where a report is given in accordance with the above, the user or owner respectively shall ensure that the system is not operated until the repairs, modifications or changes have been carried out or made.

Regulation 11 – operation

The user or owner respectively shall provide for any person operating the system adequate and suitable instructions for:

(a) the safe operation of the system and
(b) the action to be taken in the event of an emergency.

The user of a pressure system shall ensure that it is not operated except in accordance with the instructions provided in respect of that system.

6

Regulation 12 – maintenance

This regulation places a duty on users and owners respectively to ensure that systems are properly maintained in good repair, so as to prevent danger.

Regulation 13 – keeping of records, etc

This regulation details the record keeping requirements in respect of installed and mobile systems. Such records must include:

(a) the last report by the competent person
(b) previous reports if they contain information which will materially assist in assessing whether:
   (i) the system is safe to operate or
   (ii) any repairs or modifications to the system can be carried out safely
(c) any documents provided pursuant to Regulation 5 which relate to those parts of the pressure system included in the written scheme of examination and
(d) any agreement made pursuant to Regulation 9(7), and, in a case to which Regulation 9(8) applies, a copy of the notification referred to in Regulation 9(7)(c), until a further examination has been carried out since that agreement or notification under the scheme of examination.

Part IV of the regulations covers the precautions to prevent pressurisation of certain vessels. Regulation 14 specifies such vessels as a vessel:

(a) which is constructed with a permanent outlet to the atmosphere or to a space where the pressure does not exceed atmospheric pressure and
(b) which could become a pressure vessel if that outlet were obstructed.

Regulation 15 – precautions to prevent pressurisation

Under Regulation 15 the user of a vessel to which Part IV applies shall ensure that the outlet referred to in Regulation 14(a) is at all times kept open and free from obstructions when the vessel is in use.

Part V of the regulations covers general and specific provisions for TGCs.

Regulation 16 – design standards, approval and certification

No person shall:

(a) supply for the first time
(b) import or
(c) manufacture and use

a TGC unless the conditions specified below have been met.

These conditions are as follows:

(a) the container has been verified (either by certificate in writing or by means of stamping the container) as conforming to a design standard or design specification approved by the HSE:
  (i) by a person or body of persons corporate or unincorporate approved by the HSE for the purposes of this paragraph, or
  (ii) in accordance with a quality assurance scheme approved by the HSE, or

(b) the container is an EEC-type cylinder, that is:
  (i) there is an EEC verification certificate in force in respect of it issued by an inspection body which, under the law of any member state, is authorised to grant such a certificate for the purposes of the framework directive and the separate directive relating to that type of cylinder, or, in the case of a cylinder not subject to EEC verification under any of the separate directives, it conforms to the requirements of the framework directive and the separate directive relating to that type of cylinder, and
  (ii) it bears all the marks and inscriptions required by the framework directive and the separate directive relating to that type of cylinder.

Any approval under this regulation shall be by a certificate in writing, may be made subject to conditions and may be revoked by a certificate in writing at any time.

Regulation 17 – filling of containers

The employer of a person who is to fill a TGC with a relevant fluid at work shall ensure that before it is filled that person:

(a) checks from the marks on the cylinder that:
    (i) it appears to have undergone proper examination at appropriate intervals by a competent person (unless the manufacturer's mark reveals that such an examination is not yet due), and
    (ii) it is suitable for containing that fluid, and
(b) makes all other appropriate safety checks.

The employer of a person who fills a TGC with a relevant fluid at work shall ensure that that person:

(a) checks that after filling it is within its safe operating limits
(b) checks that it is not overfilled and
(c) removes any excess fluid in a safe manner in the event of overfilling.

An employer shall ensure that no person employed by him refills at work a non-refillable container with a relevant fluid.

Regulation 18 – examination of containers

The owner of a TGC shall, for the purpose of determining whether it is safe, ensure that the container is examined at appropriate intervals by a competent person.
    Where a competent person undertakes such an examination, they shall carry out that examination properly, and if on completing the examination they are satisfied that the container is safe, he shall ensure that there is affixed to the container a mark showing the date of the examination.
    No person other than the competent person or person authorised by him shall affix to a TGC the above mark or a mark liable to be confused with it.

Regulation 19 – modification of containers

(1) Subject to paragraph (2):

(a) an employer shall ensure that no person employed by him modifies at work the body of a TGC:
    (i) of seamless construction or
    (ii) which has contained acetylene
(b) an employer shall ensure that no person employed by him modifies at work the body of another type of TGC if that modification would put the TGC outside the scope of the design standard or design specification to which it was originally constructed
(c) a person shall not supply any modified TGC for use unless following such

work a person or body of persons approved by the HSE has marked or certified it as being fit for use, or, in the case of an EEC-type cylinder, an inspection body has so marked or certified it.

(2) Paragraph (1) shall not apply to the remaking of a thread if this is done in accordance with a standard approved by the HSE.

Regulation 20 – repair work

An employer shall ensure that no person employed by him carries out at work any major repair on the body of a TGC:

(a) of seamless construction or
(b) which has contained acetylene.

An employer shall ensure that no person employed by him carries out at work any major repair on the body of any other type of TGC unless he is competent to do so.

No person shall supply a TGC which has undergone a major repair unless following such work a person or body of persons approved by the HSE has marked or certified it as being fit for use, or, in the case of an EEC-type cylinder, an inspection body has so marked or certified it.

In this regulation **major repair** means any repair involving hot work or welding on the body of the TGC but, except in the case of a TGC which has contained acetylene, it does not mean heat treatment applied for the purpose of restoring the metallurgical properties of the container.

Regulation 21 – re-rating

This regulation applies to the re-rating of a TGC, that is, the reassessment of its capability to contain compressed gas safely with a view to improving its capacity by means of an increase in the charging pressure (or in the case of liquefied gas, the filling ratio) from that originally assessed and marked on the container at the time of manufacture.

An employer shall ensure that no employee re-rates a TGC at work unless they are competent to do so and does it in accordance with suitable written procedures drawn up by the owner of the container.

No person shall supply a TGC which has been re-rated unless following the re-rating a person or body of persons approved by the HSE has certified it as being safe for use.

In this regulation **filling ratio** means the ratio of the volume of liquefied gas in the container to the total volume of the container.

Regulation 22 – records

The manufacturer, or their agent, or the importer of a TGC:

(a) made to an approved design specification, shall keep a copy of the said specification together with any certificate of conformity issued in accordance with Regulation 16(2)(a)

(b) made to an approved design standard, shall keep a copy of any certificate of conformity issued in accordance with Regulation 16(2)(a)

(c) which is an EEC-type cylinder, shall keep the EEC verification certificate referred to in Regulation 16(2)(b)(i) where one has been issued.

The owner of a hired out TGC:

(a) made to an approved design specification shall keep a copy of the said specification together with a copy of any certificate of conformity issued in accordance with Regulation 16(2)(a)

(b) made to an approved design standard, shall keep a copy of any certificate of conformity issued in accordance with Regulation 16(2)(a)

(c) which is an EEC-type cylinder, shall keep a copy of the EEC verification certificate referred to in Regulation 16(2)(b)(i) where one has been issued

(d) which:
    (i)   is a refillable container
    (ii) is used solely for containing liquefied petroleum gas and
    (iii) has a water capacity up to and including 6.5 litres

shall keep a copy of the design specification for the container.

The owner of a TGC for acetylene shall keep records of the tare weight of the container, including the porous substance and acetone or other solvent, the nature of the solvent and the maximum pressure allowed in the container.

Miscellaneous provisions of the regulations are covered in Part VI.

Regulation 23 – defence

(1) In any proceedings for an offence for a contravention of the provisions of these regulations, it shall, subject to paragraphs (2) and (3), be a defence for the person charged to prove:

(a) that the commission of the offence was due to **the act or default of another person** not being one of his employees (hereinafter called 'the other person') and

(b) that he took **all reasonable precautions** and exercised **all due diligence** to avoid the commission of the offence.

(2) The person charged shall not, without leave of the court, be entitled to rely on the above defence unless, within a period ending seven clear days before the hearing, they have served on the prosecutor a notice in writing giving such information of the other person as was then in their possession.

(3) For the purpose of enabling the other person to be charged with and convicted of the offence by virtue of section 36 of HSWA, a person who

establishes a defence under this regulation shall nevertheless be treated for the purposes of that section as having committed the offence.

Schedule 4 – marking of pressure vessels

The information referred to in Regulation 5(4) is as follows:

1. The manufacturer's name.

2. The serial number to identify the vessel.

3. The date of manufacture of the vessel.

4. The standard to which the vessel was built.

5. The maximum design pressure of the vessel.

6. The maximum design pressure of the vessel where it is other than atmospheric.

7. The design temperature.

CLASSIFICATION OF PRESSURE SYSTEMS

In the ACOP to the Pressure Systems and Transportable Gas Containers Regulations (PSTGCR) 1989, pressure systems are classified thus.

Minor systems

Minor systems include those containing steam, pressurised hot water, compressed air, inert gases or fluorocarbon refrigerants which are small and present few engineering problems. The pressure should be less than 20 bar (2.0 MPa) above atmospheric pressure (except for systems with a direct-fired heat source when it should be less than 2 bar (200 kPa)). The pressure-volume product for the largest vessel should be less than 2×10^5 bar litres (200 MPa/m³). The temperature in the system should be between –20°C and 250°C except in the case of smaller refrigeration systems operating at lower temperatures which will also fall into this category. No pipelines are included in this category.

Intermediate systems

These include the majority of storage systems and process systems which do not fall into either of the other two categories. Pipelines are included unless they come in the major system category.

Major systems

Major systems are those which because of size, complexity or hazardous contents require the highest level of expertise in determining their condition. They include steam generating systems where the individual capacities of the steam generators are more than 10MW, any pressure storage system where the pressure-volume product for the largest pressure vessel is more than 10^6 bar litres (100 MPa/m^3) and any manufacturing or chemical reaction system where the pressure volume product for the largest pressure vessel is more than 10^5 bar litres (10MPa/m^3). Pipelines are included if the contents make them major hazards (as defined in the Notification of Installations Handling Hazardous Substances Regulations 1982).

COMPETENT PERSONS

The term 'competent person' is not generally defined in law except in the PSTGCR and the Electricity at Work Regulations 1989. Therefore, the onus is on the employer to decide whether persons are competent to undertake these duties. An employer might do this by reference to the person's training, qualifications and experience. Broadly, a competent person *should have practical and theoretical knowledge as well as sufficient experience of the particular machinery, plant or procedure involved to enable him to identify defects or weaknesses during plant and machinery examinations, and to assess their importance in relation to the strength and function of that plant and machinery.* (**Brazier v Skipton Rock Company Ltd [1962] 1 AER 955**)

Under the PSTGCR, the term 'competent person' is used in connection with three distinct functions:

- advising the user on the scope of the written scheme of examination
- drawing up or certifying schemes of examination and
- carrying out examinations under the scheme.

The ACOP explains the position regarding the appointment of competent persons. It is the responsibility of users to select a competent person who is capable of carrying out his duties in a proper manner. In some cases the necessary expertise will lie within the user's own organisation, but small and medium size users are unlikely to have sufficient expertise and should use a properly qualified and experienced independent inspection body. In all cases users should ensure that the competent person has sufficient expertise in the particular type of system.

Pressure systems vary greatly in complexity and sophistication, and a competent person suitable for drawing up schemes of examination or examining a simple system may well not have the expertise to function adequately as a competent person for complex systems. For a number of systems, including the larger or more complex, no one individual will have sufficient knowledge and expertise to act on their own and a competent person should be chosen who has available a team of employees with the necessary breadth of knowledge and experience.

Any individual, when carrying out competent person duties, should be sufficiently independent from the interests of all other functions to ensure adequate segregation of accountabilities.

The competent person should act in an objective and professional manner, and advise users as to the scope of the written scheme, and draw up or certify written schemes, or carry out examinations solely on the basis of an impartial assessment of the nature and condition of the system under review.

Schemes of examination

The competent person should, through having staff with practical and theoretical knowledge and actual experience of relevant systems, access to specialist services, effective organisation, a proper degree of independence from those responsible for the operating function and proper standards of professional probity, have sufficient understanding of such systems as will enable it properly to draw up or certify as suitable schemes of examination under the regulations.

Different attributes are required depending upon the size and complexity of the system. For the purpose of indicating the level of attributes required in different circumstances systems are divided into three categories – major, intermediate and minor. (See **Classification of Pressure Systems**.) However, in practice there are no clear dividing lines and these categories should be taken as indicating the range of systems covered rather than being sharp divisions. Particular systems may in fact not justify the category in which they appear to fall and this is especially important where in fact additional attributes are needed in order adequately to understand the system.

SIMPLE PRESSURE VESSELS (SAFETY) REGULATIONS 1991

These regulations apply to:

- simple pressure vessels, ie welded vessels made of certain types of steel or aluminium, intended to contain air or nitrogen under pressure and manufactured in series and

- relevant assemblies, ie any assembly incorporating a pressure vessel.

The regulations incorporate a number of definitions, in particular:

Safe – means that when a vessel is properly installed and maintained and used for the purpose for which it is intended, there is no risk (apart from one reduced to a minimum) of its being the cause of or occasion of death, injury or damage to property (including domestic animals).

Manufacturer's instructions – are instructions issued by or on behalf of the manufacturer, and include the following information:

- manufacturer's name or mark
- the vessel type batch identification or other particulars identifying the vessel to which the instructions relate
- particulars of maximum working pressure in bar, maximum and minimum working temperature in °C and capacity in litres
- intended use of the vessel and
- maintenance and installation requirements for vessel safety and written in the official language of the member state accordingly.

Series manufacture – where more than one vessel of the same type if manufactured during a given period by the same continuous manufacturing process, in accordance with a common design.

Vessel – this means a simple pressure vessel, being a welded vessel intended to contain air or nitrogen at a gauge pressure greater than 0.5 bar, not intended for exposure to flame, and having the following characteristics:

- the components and assemblies contributing to the strength of the vessel under pressure are made either of non-alloy quality steel, or of non-alloy aluminium, or of non-age hardening aluminium alloy
- the vessel consists either:
  - of a cylindrical component with a circular cross-section, closed at each end, each end being outwardly dished or flat and being also co-axial with the cylindrical component or
  - of two co-axial outwardly dished ends
- the maximum working pressure (PS) is not more than 30 bar, and the PS.V not more than 10,000 bar litres
- the minimum working temperature is not lower than –50°C and the maximum working temperature is not higher than:

  300°C in the case of steel vessels and
  100°C in the case of aluminium or aluminium alloy vessels.

The regulations apply only to vessels manufactured in series. They do not apply to:

- vessels designed specifically for nuclear use, where vessel failure might or would result in an emission of radioactivity
- vessels specifically intended for installation in, or for use as part of the propulsive system of, a ship or aircraft or
- fire extinguishers.

Principal requirements of the regulations

1. Vessels with a stored energy of **over 50 bar litres** when supplied in the UK must:
   (a) meet the essential safety requirements, ie with regard to materials used

in construction, vessel design, manufacturing processes and placing in service of vessels

(b) have safety clearance, ie checks by an approved body

(c) bear the EC mark and other specified inscriptions

(d) be accompanied by manufacturer's instructions and

(e) be safe (as defined).

2. Vessels with a stored energy **up to 50 bar litres**, when supplied in the UK must:

(a) be manufactured in accordance with engineering practice recognised as sound in the Community country

(b) bear specific inscriptions (but not the EC mark) and

(c) be safe.

3. Similar requirements as above apply to such vessels when taken into service in the UK by a manufacturer or importer.

4. The regulations do not apply to exports to countries outside the Community, or, for a transitional period, to the supply and taking into service in the UK of vessels that comply with existing UK safety requirements.

5. Failure to comply with these requirements:

(a) means that the vessels cannot be sold legally and

(b) could result in penalties of a fine of up to £2,000 or, in some cases, of imprisonment for up to three months, or both.

Categories of vessels

Different provisions are made for different categories of vessels depending upon their stored energy expressed in terms of the product of the maximum working pressure in bar and its capacity in litres (PS.V).

Category A vessels

These are graded according to PS.V range thus:

- A.1 – 3,000 to 10,000 bar litres
- A.2 – 200 to 3,000 bar litres
- A.3 – 50 to 200 bar litres.

Category B vessels

These are vessels with a PS.V of 50 bar litres or less.

The safety requirements in each case are according to items 1 and 2 of the principal requirements. (See above.)

Safety clearance

A vessel in Category A has safety clearance once an approved body has issued an EC verification certificate or an EC certificate of conformity in respect of that vessel.

Approved bodies

These are bodies designated by member states, in the case of the UK, by the Secretary for Trade and Industry.

EC mark and other specified inscriptions

1. Where an approved body has issued an EC verification certificate, that approved body has responsibility for the application of the EC mark to every vessel covered by the certificate.

2. Where a manufacturer has obtained an EC certificate of conformity, he may apply the CE mark to any vessels covered by the certificate where he executes an EC declaration of conformity that they conform with a relevant national standard or the relevant prototype.

3. The EC mark must consist of the appropriate symbol, the last two digits of the year in which the mark is applied and, where appropriate, the distinguishing number assigned by the EC to the approved body responsible for EC verification or EC surveillance.

Other specified inscriptions to be applied to Category A and B vessels are:

- maximum working pressure in bar
- maximum working temperature in °C
- minimum working temperature in °C
- capacity of the vessel in litres
- name or mark of the manufacturer and
- type and serial or batch identification of the vessel.

EC surveillance

This implies surveillance by the approved body which issued a certificate. The approved body has the following powers with respect to surveillance:

- powers of entry:
  - to take samples
  - to acquire information and
  - to require additional information
- to compile reports on surveillance operations and
- to report to the Secretary of State cases of wrongful application, and failures by manufacturers to:
  - carry out their undertakings
  - authorise access and
  - provide other facilities.

Fire prevention and protection

Every year fire and its effects represent substantial losses to British industry. It is essential that everyone at work is familiar with fire procedures and the measures to prevent fire.

What is fire?

'Fire' can be defined in several ways:

- A spectacular example of a fast chemical reaction between a combustible substance and oxygen accompanied by the evolution of heat.
- A mixture in gaseous form of a combustible substance and oxygen with sufficient energy put into the mixture to start a fire.
- An unexpected combustion generating sufficient heat or smoke resulting in damage to plant, equipment, goods and/or buildings.

PRINCIPLES OF COMBUSTION

In order to appreciate the principles of fire prevention, it is necessary to have a broad understanding of the principles of combustion. The three requirements for a fire to start and continue are the presence of fuel to burn, an ignition source of sufficient energy to set the fuel alight and air or oxygen to maintain combustion. If one of these three components is removed, combustion cannot take place.

Elements of fire

Oxygen/air

A fire always requires oxygen for it to take place or, having commenced, to continue. The chief source of oxygen is air, which is a mixture of gases comprising nitrogen (78 per cent) and oxygen (21 per cent). The remaining one per cent is made up of water vapour, carbon dioxide, argon and other gases. A number of substances can be a source of oxygen in a fire, eg oxidising agents. These are substances which contain oxygen that is readily available under fire conditions and include sodium chlorate, hydrogen peroxide, nitric acid and organic peroxides. A third source of oxygen is the combustible substance itself, eg ammonium nitrate.

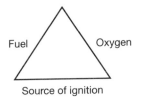

Fuel

Oxygen

Source of ignition

FIG 7.1 The fire triangle

Combustible substance

This is the second requirement for fire and includes a large group of organic substances, ie those with carbon in the molecule, eg natural gas (methane), butane, petrol, plastics, natural and artificial fibres, wood, paper, coal and living matter. Inorganic substances, ie those not containing carbon in the molecule, are also combustible, eg hydrogen, sulphur, sodium, phosphorus, magnesium and ammonium nitrate.

Ignition source

This is the energy that has to be applied to the oxygen/fuel mixture to start the fire. Usually this energy is in the form of heat, but not necessarily. The heat can simply be that contained in the combustible substance. This is often the source of ignition energy when hot fuel leaks from a pipe and fires, but it can be generated by friction, such as striking a match against sandpaper or a hot bearing in a machine. Electrical energy in the lightning of a thunder storm, or when an electrical contact, such as a switch, is made or broken, would also qualify.

CHEMISTRY OF COMBUSTION

Combustion chemistry is an example of a larger group of chemical reactions known as oxidation reactions. Other examples are the rusting of iron and the process of breathing. Chemically the process can be written as:

Fuel + Oxygen produces **Products of combustion + Heat**

If the fuel is natural gases, ie methane, the reaction is written as:

$$CH_4 \quad + \quad 2O_2 \quad \longrightarrow \quad CO_2 \quad + \quad 2H_2O \quad + \quad Heat$$

Methane   **Oxygen**   **Carbon dioxide**   **Water**

If the fuel were hydrogen, the equation would be:

$$2H_2 \quad + \quad O_2 \quad \longrightarrow \quad 2H_2 \quad + \quad Heat$$
$$\text{Hydrogen} \quad \text{Oxygen} \quad \text{Water}$$

Or if it were sulphur, it would be:

$$S \quad + \quad O_2 \quad \longrightarrow \quad SO_2 \quad + \quad Heat$$
$$\text{Sulphur} \quad \text{Oxygen} \quad \text{Sulphur dioxide}$$

However, for ammonium nitrate, which has its own source of oxygen, the equation is:

$$NH_4\,NO_3 + \quad \longrightarrow \quad N_2O \quad + \quad 2H_2O \quad Heat$$
$$\text{Ammonium nitrate} \quad \text{Nitrous Oxide} \quad \text{Water}$$

Generally, the carbon in the fuel is oxidised to carbon dioxide and hydrogen to water. The other elements will be oxidised to a variety of substances.

Initiation energy

When the chemical reaction

$$2H_2 \quad + \quad O_2 \quad \longrightarrow \quad 2H_2O \quad + \quad Heat$$

is taking place, it can be thought of as molecules hitting one another and sometimes bouncing off like balls or otherwise mutually breaking up into different molecules. In the latter case, a chemical reaction has occurred. Characteristic of the 'ball' theory (more properly known as the Kinetic Theory of Gases) is that kinetic energy possessed by the balls, ie. their speed, is a function of the temperature of the gas. In particular, the higher the temperature the higher the kinetic energy of the molecules. The reaction may be described as one where the energy of the collision has to be greater than some value for the molecules to hit and break up into different molecules. If the collision energy is below this value the molecules will just bounce off one another and no reaction will take place. **Collision energy** is the physical representation of the initiation energy required for a fire to start. It is usually heat, ie increasing the temperature of the combustion mixture, but it can be electrical energy from a spark.

The final feature of all combustion reactions is that they emit energy. These reactions are known as **exothermic reactions**.

Table 7.1 shows the heat of combustion in kilocalories per molecular weight of the substance when combustion takes place at atmospheric pressure and 20°C. Table 7.2 gives the minimum ignition energy of substances in millijoules.

Table 7.1   Standardised values of heat output

Fuel	kcal
Acetone	126.8
Benzene	782.3
Carbon disulphide	246.6
Cyclohexane	937.8
Dimethyl ether	347.6
Ethane	368.8
Ethyl alcohol	327.6
n-Hexane	989.6
Hydrogen	58.3
Methane	210.8
Methyl alcohol	170.9
Propane	526.3

Table 7.2   The fire process

Minimum ignition energy	mJ
Benzene	0.22
Carbon disulphide	0.01–0.02
Ethane	0.24
n-Hexane	0.25
Hydrogen	0.019
Methane	0.39
Propane	0.25

7

THE FIRE PROCESS – A SUMMARY

A fire may be described as a mixture in gaseous form of a combustible substance and oxygen, with sufficient energy being put into the mixture to start the fire. Once started, the energy output from the fire provides a continuous source of energy for it to be sustained and excess is given off as sensible heat. (See Table 7.2.) For all practical purposes, fire takes place in the gaseous state and division of fires into those of solids (eg wood), liquid (eg petrol) and gas (eg a gas flame is convenient but not accurate). This can be seen with burning wood and liquid where close observation reveals that the flame burns at a small distance from the wood or liquid.

Ignition energy – liquids and gases

Ignition energy of liquids and gases can be measured, and is expressed in different ways. The three measures are:

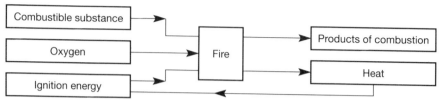

FIG 7.2   The fire process

Flash point

The flash point is the minimum liquid temperature at which sufficient vapour is given off to form a mixture with air capable of ignition under prescribed test conditions. There are two sets of prescribed conditions, the **Abel** and **Pensky-Martin**. The former usually yields slightly lower results. It is necessary to cite the method used when quoting flash point values.

Fire point

This is the lowest temperature at which the heat from combustion of a burning vapour is capable of producing sufficient vapour to sustain combustion.

Spontaneous ignition temperature or ignition temperature

This is the lowest temperature at which the substance will ignite spontaneously.

Usually for a given combustible substance the flash point is less than the fire point, which is less than the ignition temperature. Since energy is measured by temperature and two effects are being studied, the evaporation of the liquid and combustion of evaporated vapour, the ignition temperature must be the highest value because the whole of the required energy comes from the heat, ie the temperature of the liquid. The flash point must be the lowest because the source of ignition is external to the evaporation of the liquid.

Hitherto it has been assumed that a mixture will only react if sufficient energy is put into it. This is not always the case. Consider an oxygen and methane mixture. If there are very few methane molecules in the mixture these will react very quickly and the fire stops. As the concentration of methane increases, a point will be reached when the heat output from the fire will eventually be sufficient to provide the source of ignition for the rest of the methane and the fire is sustained. Similar conditions apply if the oxygen/methane mixture is rich in methane and weak in oxygen. Here it is the oxygen, however, that is instantaneously used up until only sufficient oxygen is present for the heat output to sustain combustion. These two concentration values which exist for all gaseous combustible substances and oxygen are known as the **lower** and **upper flammability limits**.

Lower flammable limit

The lower flammable limit (or lower explosive limit) is the smallest concentration of flammable gas or vapour which, when mixed with air, is capable of ignition and subsequent flame propagation under prescribed test conditions.

Upper flammable limit

The upper flammable limit (or upper explosive limit) is the highest concentration of gas or vapour which, when mixed with air, is capable of ignition and subsequent flame propagation under prescribed test conditions. Table 7.3 gives values of flammable limits for some common substances.

Table 7.3   Properties of some flammable substances

Substance	Flash point (°C)	Ignition temperature (°C)	Flammable range (% v/v in air)
Acetic acid	40	485	4–17
Acetone	–18	535	2.1–13
Acetylene	–18	305	1.5–80
Ammonia	Gas	630	1.5–27
Benzene	–17	560	1.2–8
n-Butane	–60	365	1.5–8.5
Carbon disulphide	–30	100	1–60
Carbon monoxide	Gas	605	12.5–74.2
Cyclohexane	–20	259	1.2–8.3
Ether	–45	170	1.9–48
Ethanol	12	425	3.3–19
Ethylene	Gas	425	2.7–34
Hydrogen	Gas	560	4.1–74
Methane	Gas	538	5–15
Toluene	4	508	1.2–7
Vinyl chloride	–78	472	3.6–33

Spontaneous combustion

This is the final combustion characteristic. Sometimes materials burst into flames without apparent means of ignition. Typical examples are haystacks, rags soaked in linseed oil and oil-soaked lagging. This property is known as spontaneous ignition. It is clear from the mechanism of fire that there must be a source of ignition but the source itself is not obvious. Some organic substances, when exposed to oxygen, undergo slow oxidation, a process similar to fire, releasing little sensible heat. Slow oxidation does not result in carbon dioxide and water but other substances chemically smaller and more easily combustible that the original substance. In effect, the original substance is being made more combustible by oxidation and, in consequence, little heat is generated. When reduction in combustibility and heat output match, a fire occurs. The source of ignition is the heat of oxidation.

HEAT TRANSMISSION

Heat may be transmitted or transferred by the process of convection, conduction and radiation.

Convection

When matter is heated the range of vibration of its molecules increases and the matter expands. In a solid this has little significance, but in a fluid, where the particles are free to move throughout the substance, it gives rise to a **convection current** in the body of the fluid.

These currents are produced due to the fact that the unheated particles of a fluid are more dense than the newly heated particles and thus gravitate to the lowest point of the body of fluid. In doing so they upwardly displace the hot particles. These hot particles, whether of liquid or gas, have no specific ability to rise. They rise simply because they are displaced from beneath, and the difference in weight between hot and cold particles is the sole force operating. The greater the difference in temperature between the hottest and coldest particles, the more vigorous will be the convection current produced. If the source of heat is maintained, the cooler particles, already in motion as a result of their greater weight, become heated in turn, whilst the previously heated particles, having been displaced from the heat source, lose some of their heat to the surroundings and become cooler. A convection current is thus continuous and is described as a **circulation** within the body of the fluid.

Gases are also fluids and act in the same way as fluids. For instance, systems of natural ventilation in buildings operate on the basic of convection currents being established and maintained. Hot air rises and cold air sinks.

Conduction

With solids the increased molecular vibration due to an increase in temperature of one part is imparted by contact to adjoining molecules. Thus if a length of metal wire is heated at one end it would, by the process of conduction, ultimately reach uniform temperature through its entire length, but for the fact that some of the heat is lost to the air from its exposed surface. This method of transmission is called **conduction** and is confined largely to solids because of their rigid structure.

Solids are generally classed as good or bad conductors according to their ability or otherwise to conduct heat. Metals are good conductors, whereas wood is a bad conductor.

Conduction also takes place in liquids and gases. In any normal body of liquid or gas the particles are displaced by convection before any appreciable transfer of heat by conduction can take place. Generally, liquids are poor conductors and gases even worse.

Radiation

In **convection** heat is transferred from one point to another by the relative movement of particles. In **conduction** transference is between adjoining particles which do not move relative to each other. In **radiation** the molecular heat motion of a body causes to be emitted or radiated into space rays or waves travelling in straight lines, in all directions from the source, and at a speed of about 186,400 miles per second.

All hot bodies emit waves; the larger and hotter the body the more intense the waves. These are waves of energy which, when directed on to a body, produce sensible heat in the body. Heat radiation travels best through empty space but can also travel through a variety of media.

Heat radiation is subject to the **Inverse Square Law**. This law states that the intensity of heat produced by radiation is inversely proportional to the square of the distance from the source.

$$\text{Intensity} = \frac{1}{\text{Distance}^2}$$

Thus if the distance from the source is doubled, the same amount of radiation affects four times the area and the intensity is thus one quarter. The same law applies in the case of light emission.

THE MAIN CAUSES OF FIRE AND FIRE SPREAD

Various studies by the Fire Protection Association of a range of industrial fires have indicated the following as the principal sources of fire in production and storage areas.

Production areas

- heat-producing plant and equipment
- frictional heat and sparks
- refrigeration plant
- electrical equipment

setting fire to:

- materials being processed
- dust
- waste and packing materials.

Storage areas

- intruders, including children
- cigarettes and matches

- refuse burning
- electrical equipment

setting fire to:

- stored goods
- packing materials.

Ignition temperature

Generally, fire is spread by a range or combination of factors, namely through heat transmission, direct contact and/or through the release of flammable gases or vapours. In all cases, some form of ignition source must be present which is sufficient to create the energy necessary to raise a volume of combustible material to its **ignition temperature**. This is the temperature at which a small amount of combustible material (fuel) will spontaneously ignite in a given atmosphere and continue to burn without any further input of heat. There must be specific conditions present for ignition to take place, as seen with the fire triangle, namely the appropriate temperature, the right source of ignition and an appropriate mixture of combustible material and oxygen.

Sources of ignition

Classic sources of ignition in both domestic and industrial premises include:

- **Electrical equipment** – arcing, which results in the production of sparks, incorrectly located lights and hot surfaces produced by defective electrical equipment, is a common source of ignition.
- **Spontaneous ignition** – when some liquids are heated or sprayed on to a very hot surface, they may ignite spontaneously without an ignition source actually present.
- **Spontaneous combustion** – when materials react with oxygen an **exothermic reaction** takes place, ie one emitting heat, and with materials which readily oxidise, there may be some degree of heat accumulation which eventually causes the material to ignite or burst into flames.
- In many work situations, **smoking** by employees and others can be a source of fire, principally from discarded cigarette ends and matches, but also from smoking in areas where flammable materials are stored or where flammable vapours may be present.
- Sparks, sufficient to act as a source of ignition, can be created by **friction** between surfaces, for instance, where the moving part of a machine comes into contact with a fixed part, or two moving surfaces may rub or slide together during routine machine operation.
- **Hot work**, such as welding, soldering, hot cutting and brazing, can be a

source of ignition, particularly where flammable vapours may be present; the operation of a permit to work system may be necessary in high risk situations.

- In situations where electrostatic charging is produced by induction or friction, the charge, in the form of **static electricity**, can be carried away from the point of origin and, in the event of accumulation of charge, sparks can be produced.
- In vehicle maintenance and parking areas, diesel and petrol-operated **engines, vehicle emissions and hot surfaces** or, for instance, exhaust systems, can be a source of ignition.
- Many **open flame sources** are encountered in workplaces, eg boilers, furnaces, portable heating appliances and pilot lights to same.
- In limited cases, **lightning** can be a source of ignition and this may require the installation of lightning protection by direct earthing.

THE SECONDARY EFFECTS OF FIRE

7

Whilst the primary effects of fire, in most cases, can cause loss of life and substantial damage, the secondary effects must also be considered in any fire protection strategy. These secondary effects can include:

- 'smoke-logging' of buildings, which may make them uninhabitable for a period of time
- some reduction in structural stability of adjacent buildings
- damage to services, including engineering, electrical systems, pressure systems, pipework and ancillary systems
- deterioration of wall and ceiling surfaces which may require subsequent redecoration
- deterioration in the condition of stored final products which may render such products unsaleable and
- dust explosions in certain types of industrial plant, such as spray drying plant, milling and grinding plant.

THE EFFECTS OF FIRE ON STRUCTURAL ELEMENTS

The structural elements of a typical building include stone, bricks, concrete, timber, glass, steel, plastics, plaster, plasterboard, asbestos-cement products and a range of surface coatings. The effects of fire on all or some of these materials, combined together to form a structure, are complicated and, in some cases, unpredictable. The majority of these elements, other than timber and plastics, are of an incombustible nature. However, all substances respond to heat with different results.

Stone, brick and concrete items

Stone and brick tend to be unaffected by fire other than flaking of the surface. Concrete, on the other hand, suffers dehydration and tends to shrink within around 400 °C, with breaking down of the cement and total disintegration of the concrete at around 800 °C.

Glass items

Glass expands on heating resulting in initial cracking and subsequent bursting out of items, such as windows and glass panelled doors. At around 800 °C, glass will actually melt.

Plastic items

These include pipework of various types, coatings to windows and doors, and various forms of internal finish. Much will depend upon the type of plastic as to the effect, but all plastics will burn. Burning droplets of plastic falling from, for instance, a roof of a building to another can rapidly spread fire to other areas below.

Steel structural items

Steel is an excellent conductor of heat. It rapidly expands and will become ductile at between 550–650 °C. The expansion can result in distortion of other structural items, such as concrete floors and walls, thereby increasing the rate at which a structure becomes unstable.

Timber members

All timber burns, the rate of burning depending on the type of timber, that is, hardwood or softwood, the intensity of heat applied and whether on a continuous basis. The ash formed on the surface acts as an insulating barrier and can slow down the rate of burning.

Surface coatings

Coatings to internal walls, ceilings and floors vary considerably in their combustibility. Several layers of gloss paint on a wall, for instance, burn well once the right temperature has been reached. This causes softening of the paint surface and allows the fire to spread more rapidly across the painted surface.

Roof coverings

Typical roof coverings are slates, tiles, asbestos cement sheetings and bitumen felt. Slates and tiles tend to withstand high levels of temperature. Asbestos cement sheeting becomes friable and disintegrates noisily in a fire as a result of the rapid decomposition of the cement binder. Bitumen-impregnated felt burns rapidly and, as with plastics, burning droplets can rapidly spread the fire to other parts of the building.

PRINCIPLES OF FIRE SPREAD CONTROL

Any fire will continue to spread under the right conditions, that is:

- the presence of combustible fuel to burn
- sufficient air with an appropriate oxygen content and
- a continuing source of ignition from the existing fire.

Fire spread control, therefore, is directed at eliminating one or more of the above elements which maintain the fire. The ultimate objective is the extinction of the fire, using one or more of the following:

Starvation

There are three ways that starvation can be achieved:

- take the fuel away from the fire
- take the fire away from the fuel and
- reduce the quantity or bulk of the fuel.

The first is achieved every day on a gas hob when the tap is turned off. For industrial installations this means isolating the fuel feed at the remote isolation valve. Examples of taking the fire away from the fuel include breaking down stacks and dragging away the burning debris. Breaking down a fire into smaller units is an example of reducing the quantity or bulk of the fuel.

Smothering

Smothering can be achieved by:

- allowing the fire to consume the oxygen while preventing the inward flow of more oxygen and
- adding an inert gas to the burning mixture.

Wrapping a person, whose clothing is on fire, in a blanket is an example of smothering. Other examples include pouring foam on top of a burning pool of oil or putting sand on a small fire. A danger inherent in extinguishing fires by smothering occurs when the fire is out but everything is still hot. Any inrush of oxygen, caused by disturbing the foam layer or by opening the door to a room, could result in reignition as there may still be sufficient energy in the form of sensible heat present.

If an inert gas is to be used as an extinguisher, carbon dioxide or halogenated hydrocarbons, such as BCF, are suitable. Alternatively, nitrogen can be used, and is in fact more common for petrochemical plant fires. If a flammable gas pipeline leaks and the escaping gas ignites, nitrogen blanketing can be achieved by injecting nitrogen into the gas downstream of the release. Smothering is only effective when the source of oxygen is air. It is totally ineffective when the burning substance contains oxygen, such as ammonium nitrate.

Cooling

This is the most common means of fighting a fire, water being the most effective and cheapest medium. For a fire to be sustained, some of the heat output from the combustion is returned to the fuel, providing a continuous source of ignition energy. When water is added to a fire, the heat output serves to heat and vaporise the water, that is, the water provides an alternative heat sink. Ultimately, insufficient heat is added to the fuel and continuous ignition ceases. In order to assist rapid absorption of heat, water is applied to the fire as a spray rather than a jet, the spray droplets being more efficient in absorbing heat than the stream of water in a jet.

Another example of heat absorption is provided by dry chemical extinguishers. These are fine powders which rapidly absorb heat. Dry powders can also be used for the smothering method.

CLASSIFICATION OF FIRES

Fires are commonly classified into four categories according to the fuel type and means of extinction.

Class A

Fires involving solid materials, normally of organic nature, in which the combustion occurs with the formation of glowing embers, eg wood, paper, coal and natural fibres. Water applied as a jet or spray is the most effective way of achieving extinction.

Class B

Fires involving:

- liquids
- liquefiable solids.

Liquids fall into two groups:

- **miscile with water** – methanol, acetone, acetic acid and
- **immiscible with water** – petrol, benzene, fats and waxes.

Foam, light water, vaporising liquids, carbon dioxide and dry powder can be used on all Class B fires. Water spray can be used on liquids but not on liquefiable solids. There may also be some restriction on the type of foam which can be used because some foams break down on contact with alcohols. In all cases, extinction is mainly achieved by smothering. However, water on a fire involving liquids also acts by cooling, and by removal of the fuel in that the fuel dissolves in the water.

Class C

Fires involving gases or liquefied gases, eg methane, propane and butane. Both foam and dry chemicals can be used on small liquefied gas spillage fires, particularly when backed up by water to cool the leaking container or spillage collector. A fire from a gas leak can be extinguished either by isolating the fuel remotely or by injecting an inert gas into the gas stream. Direct flame extinguishment is difficult and may be counterproductive in that if the leak continues there may be reignition, often in the form of an explosion. Extinguishers used on liquid gas spillage fires work by smothering.

Class D

Fires involving metals, eg magnesium and aluminium. They can only be extinguished by use of dry powders which include talc, soda ash, limestone and dry sand. All these extinguishers work by smothering.

'Electrical fires'

This is now an obsolete classification. Fires which involve electrical equipment must always be tackled by first isolating the electricity supply and then by the use of carbon dioxide, vaporising liquid or dry powder. The use of these agents minimises damage to equipment.

PORTABLE FIRE-FIGHTING APPLIANCES

These are appliances designed to be carried and operated by hand. They contain an extinguishing medium which can be expelled by action of internal pressure and directed on to a fire. This pressure may be stored, or obtained by chemical reaction or by release of gas from a cartridge. The maximum mass of a portable extinguisher in working order is 23kg. Portable extinguishers are grouped and coded as shown in Table 7.4.

Water-containing extinguishers

There are three kinds, namely soda acid, gas cartridge and stored pressure.

Soda acid

This is the original form of water-containing extinguisher, and is gradually

Table 7.4   Grouping and coding of fire appliances

Extinguisher	Colour code
Water	Red
Foam	Cream
Carbon dioxide	Black
Dry chemical powder	Blue
Vaporising liquid	Green

being replaced by the gas cartridge and stored pressure types. Two common types are shown in Figure 7.3. Gas is generated in the cylinder when the acid phial is broken, and this expels all the water through the discharge tube.

Gas cartridge

With this type, carbon dioxide is held in a small pressure cylinder, the seal being broken by a plunger. The gas so released expels the water through the nozzle (see Figure 7.4).

Stored pressure

This appliance contains carbon dioxide under pressure. Water is expelled when the trigger is pulled, and closing the trigger stops the water flow (see Figure 7.5).

Precautions for water-containing extinguishers

It must be recognised that all water extinguishers are pressure vessels. They must, therefore, be maintained regularly in accordance with the manufacturer's instructions. The interior of the vessel must be protected against corrosion and the water contained in it may need the addition of anti-freeze. It must be operated in the upright position in order to discharge water and not gas.

Water extinguishers are ideal for small Class A fires and are effective for Class B(i). They must not be used, however, on Class B(ii), C or D, and certainly not on live electric wiring and appliances.

Foam extinguishers

Of the four types of foam extinguisher (see Figures 7.6–7.9), three contain foam solution which is expelled by carbon dioxide. With the fourth, namely the gas cartridge type, foam is generated at the exit by carbon dioxide.

Chemical foam

The cylinder contains two solutions which are mixed on inversion, namely aluminium sulphate and sodium bicarbonate. The cylinder itself is filled with sodium bicarbonate solution containing about three per cent of a stabiliser, such as saponin, liquorice or turkey red oil. The inner compartment contains 13 per cent of aluminium sulphate. The foaming mixture is expelled in the inverted position by carbon dioxide generated in the chemical reaction. In some chemical foam extinguishers, the inner cylinder is sealed and has to be broken with a plunger before inversion (see Figure 7.6).

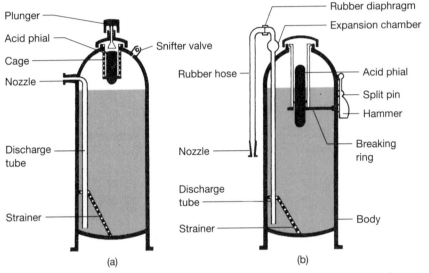

FIG 7.3 Sections through a soda acid extinguisher (a) with plunger at the top; (b) with hammer at side
(Source Home Office, Manual of Firemanship)

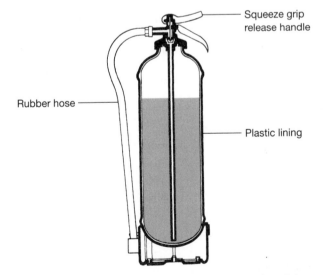

FIG 7.4 Section through a water (gas cartridge) type extinguisher
(Source Home Office, Manual of Firemanship)

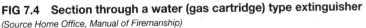

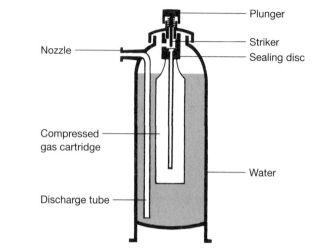

FIG 7.5   Section through a stored pressure type of water extinguisher
(Source Home Office, Manual of Firemanship)

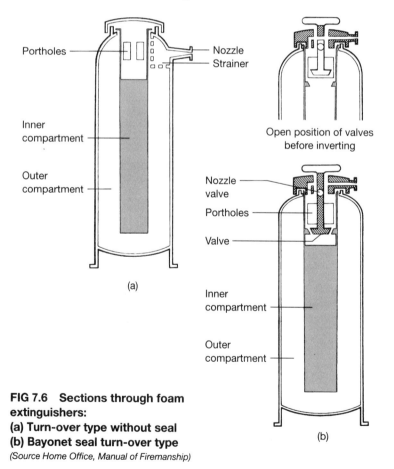

FIG 7.6   Sections through foam extinguishers:
(a) Turn-over type without seal
(b) Bayonet seal turn-over type
(Source Home Office, Manual of Firemanship)

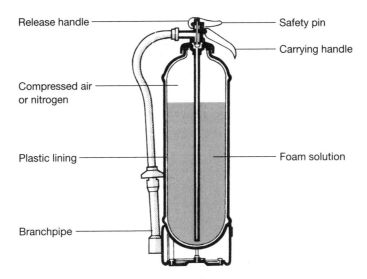

FIG 7.7 Foam extinguisher (stored pressure) type
(Source Home Office, Manual of Firemanship)

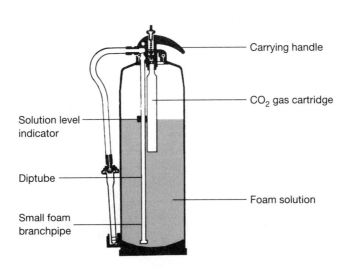

FIG 7.8 Gas cartridge foam solution type of foam extinguisher
(Source Home Office, Manual of Firemanship)

Stored pressure

The alternative to the chemical foam extinguisher is the self-aspirating type. Here the cylinder contains foam concentrate which is expelled wither by types pressure or by gas cartridge. There are four types of foam concentrate – protein, fluor-protein, fluor-chemical and synthetic. In a stored pressure foam extinguisher the cylinder is filled with foam concentrate and pressurised to 10 bar with air or nitrogen. Operation of the trigger valve allows the pressure to expel the foam concentrate through the exit pipe where foam is generated at the end of the hose (see Figure 7.7).

In the gas cartridge extinguisher the foam concentrate is expelled by breaking a seal on a carbon dioxide cartridge (see Figure 7.8). Alternatively, the cylinder can be filled with water, the foam concentrate being contained in a plastic bag which surrounds the gas cartridge (see Figure 7.9). Breaking the seal on the cartridge releases the carbon dioxide which then bursts the plastic bag. Pressure expels the foam concentrate through the exit hose, releasing foam at the exit.

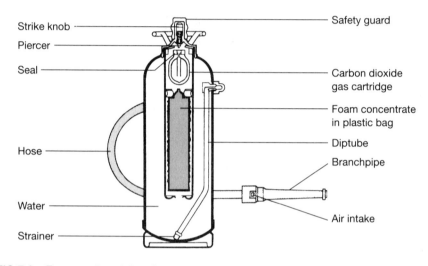

FIG 7.9 Foam extinguisher (gas cartridge) type
(Source Home Office, Manual of Firemanship)

Precautions relating to foam extinguishers

The cylinders of foam extinguishers are pressure vessels and so must be maintained in accordance with the manufacturer's instructions and protected against internal corrosion. Because chemical foam extinguishers operate by inversion, they must always be completely discharged. The self-aspirating types can be stopped simply by releasing the trigger.

Foam extinguishers are best used in Class B(ii) fires, but can also be used on Classes A and B(i). In the latter case, however, foam must be compatible with the burning liquid. When in use on a contained liquid fire, the foam should be directed to the back or side of containers and allowed to spread over the fire. On a liquid spillage, the foam should be directed to the front and spread over the fire with a side-to-side movement until the fire is covered.

Carbon dioxide extinguishers

This extinguisher consists of a pressure cylinder filled with liquid carbon dioxide. A trigger allows the liquid to be discharged through a horn under its own pressure. On discharge the liquid is converted into carbon dioxide snow in the nozzle which is converted to gas in the fire. It is noisy on discharge and the horn can become very cold (see Figure 7.10).

Carbon dioxide can be used on both Class A and Class B fires and on fires involving electrical equipment. On Class A fires it is less efficient than water because of its limited cooling effect, and on Class B fires it is less efficient than vaporising liquid. A second extinguisher should always be available because of the limited cooling effect. It should be recognised that carbon dioxide is an asphyxiant and is heavier than air. It can collect in pits and hollows where it may create a risk to people entering the premises.

Dry chemical powder

There are two types – stored pressure and gas cartridge. In both cases the cylinder is fed with dry powder, but in the stored pressure type the cylinder is pressurised to 10 bar with dry air or nitrogen. Operating the trigger allows the pressure to expel the dry powder through the hose. With the gas cartridge type, the seal on the cartridge is broken by a plunger and the flow of powder is controlled by a trigger valve on the hose (see Figure 7.11).

Precautions relating to dry powder extinguishers

The cylinder is a pressure vessel so it needs to be maintained in accordance with the manufacturer's instructions. Dry powder has a tendency to cake

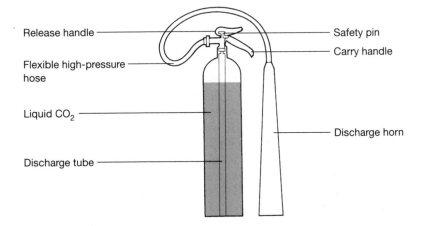

Release handle

Flexible high-pressure hose

Liquid CO_2

Discharge tube

Safety pin

Carry handle

Discharge horn

FIG 7.10 A carbon dioxide extinguisher showing the piercing mechanism, control valve and discharge horn
(Source Home Office, Manual of Firemanship)

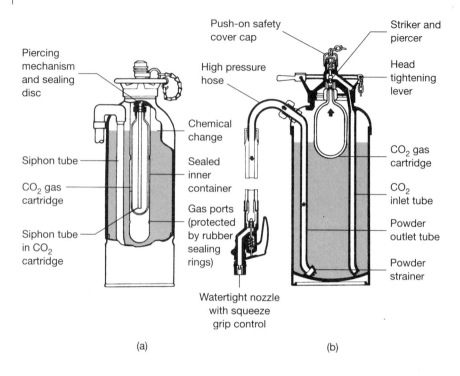

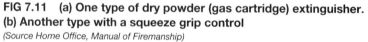

(a)   (b)

**FIG 7.11   (a) One type of dry powder (gas cartridge) extinguisher.
(b) Another type with a squeeze grip control**
(Source Home Office, Manual of Firemanship)

during prolonged storage in the cylinder. Moreover, after discharge, the trigger end of the hose can become blocked, necessitating thorough cleaning.

These extinguishers can be used on Class A and Class B fires provided that they contain general purpose powder.

Vaporising liquid

All vaporising liquid extinguishers consist of a cylinder containing the liquid which is pressurised to 10 bar with dry carbon dioxide or nitrogen. Striking a knob allows the pressure to expel the liquid (see Figure 7.12).

These extinguishers are useful for dealing with Class A and B fires and with small or incipient fires involving burning liquids. They are less efficient than foam on large liquid fires because the heat dissipates the vaporising liquid, and less efficient than water on Class A fires as they have a lower cooling effect. With fires involving electrical equipment they are particularly effective because they are non-conducting and do not cause damage to the equipment. Vaporising liquids should not be used in a confined space as the liquids and their combustion products are toxic. Discharge should be started at one edge of the fire, then swept across the surface of the burning material to concentrate on the heart of the fire.

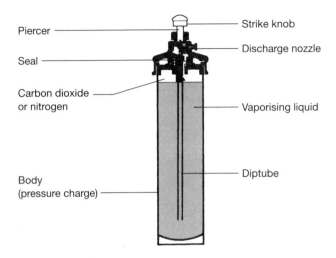

Piercer

Strike knob

Discharge nozzle

Seal

Carbon dioxide
or nitrogen

Vaporising liquid

Diptube

Body
(pressure charge)

FIG 7.12   Section through vaporising liquid (stored pressure) extinguisher
(Source Home Office, Manual of Firemanship)

FIRE-FIGHTING EQUIPMENT

Portable fire extinguishers

Portable extinguishers provide first aid fire fighting for Class A and Class B fires, but not in general for Class C and Class D fires. They are only useful, however, if sufficient appliances are provided of the right type, in the right place, if they are properly maintained and if people are available who have been trained in their use. They should be located in conspicuous positions, identified by an approved sign, usually on exit routes by doors in corridors or on landings. In multi-storey buildings they should be stored in the same position on each floor, to be available for use at all times. They must be easily accessible at all times and free from obstruction. The travel distance from a possible fire to the nearest extinguisher should not be more than 30 metres. It is important to recognise that no one should have to make a choice regarding the specific extinguisher necessary for a particular type of fire. On this basis, appropriate fire extinguishers should be provided (see Table 7.5).

Where a fire can occur in a confined space, extinguishers should be kept outside and be suitable for use in a confined space. All extinguishers should be protected against excessive heat and cold. Storage in easily opened containers will provide some protection against external corrosion.

A monthly inspection routine should be undertaken for all extinguishers and the manufacturer's instructions followed for all routine and non-routine maintenance. Maintenance and internal replacement should be undertaken by trained personnel and accurate records kept of all inspections and maintenance of extinguishers.

Table 7.5 Classification of fires which can be controlled by portable extinguishers

Class of fire	Description	Appropriate extinguisher
A	Solid materials, usually organic, with glowing embers	Water, foam, dry powder, vaporising liquid, carbon dioxide
B	Liquids and liquefiable solids:	
(i)	miscible with water, eg methanol, acetone	Water, foam (but must be stable on miscible solvents), carbon dioxide, dry powder
(ii)	immiscible with water, eg petrol, benzene, fats, waxes	Foam, dry powder, vaporising liquid, carbon dioxide

Hose reels

These are a form of fire-fighting installation and consist of a coil of 25mm internal diameter flexible hose directly connected to a rising main. They should be located in a recess so as not to obtrude into an access way, each hose reel container being marked with the standard notice. The complete fixed installation, with the hose reel as the terminal point, consists of either a wet or a dry rising main and a landing valve or fire hydrant. The main consists of heavy quality wrought steel pipe of not less than 100mm internal diameter.

A wet rising main should be full of water and connected directly into the fire main with the water at fire main pressure, whereas with a dry rising main the pipe has to be charged with water prior to use. This can be done either by opening out the main to the fire main or by charging the main via a water pump. Wet rising mains are subject to frost damage if not suitably protected. The inlet to a dry rising main must be in a convenient position for the fire brigade to gain access to it, and it must be provided with a hard standing for pumps. The inlet must be suitably identified and kept free for access at all times. In addition to hose reels, rising mains are fitted with landing valves which allow the connection of a standard fire hose. Both landing valves and hose reels must be kept free from obstruction at all times and should be sited not more than 30 metres from a possible fire location.

Sprinkler systems

Sprinkler systems are a passive form of fire fighting system and provide an automatic means of both detecting and extinguishing or controlling a fire in its early stages. The system consists of an overhead pipe installation on which sprinkler heads are fitted at suitable intervals. The installation is supplied with water from a header tank and/or water main. Each sprinkler head acts as a valve which is preset to open at a given temperature and release water on to the fire. For the system to be effective, the water supply must be automatic, reliable and not subject to freezing or drought. As each head is temperature operated only, those heads nearest the fire open and are not subject to smoke or fume. Being located in an overhead position, they do not block or restrict access routes and can be arranged to operate an alarm on releasing water.

FIRE DETECTION AND ALARM SYSTEMS

Fire detection systems

Fire can be detected in one of three main ways:

- by sensing heat – actual temperature or the rate of temperature rise
- by detecting the presence of smoke or
- by detecting flame.

Heat detectors

Heat detectors are of two kinds – fusion and expansion.

With **fusion heat detectors**, a metal melts completing an electrical circuit and releasing water. Alternatively, the expansion of a solid, liquid or gas activates some other device. The simplest form of fusion detector consists of an electrical circuit containing a switch held in either the open or closed position by a piece of low melting alloy. In the heat of the fire the alloy melts, the switch is released, and the circuit conditions change (see Figure 7.13).

The simplest form of **thermal expansion heat detector** consists of a bimetallic strip which expands in a circular mode under the influence of heat, closing off an electrical circuit. Gases and liquids have greater coefficients of heat expansion than metals and, as such, are potentially more sensitive than metals as heat detectors. The most common use of liquid expansion occurs in the quartzite bulb used in sprinkler systems. The final 'valve' consists of a quartzite bulb filled with liquid and, on contact with the fire, the liquid expands. At a predetermined temperature the bulb bursts and water is released.

The flame of a fire emits not only visible light but ultra violet and infra red radiation. Each of these forms of radiation can be used to detect the presence of fire. Although visible radiation is obscured by smoke, ultra violet and infra red radiation remain unaffected. **Flame detectors** operate on the principle of detecting either or both of these forms of radiation. The disadvantages of these forms of detector is that they react to any source of ultra violet or infra red radiation, such as the sun or the moon. Hence they can be subject to spurious alarms as well as circuit failure.

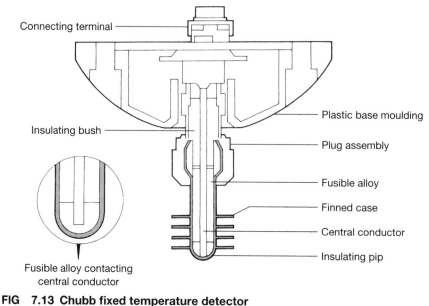

Connecting terminal

Insulating bush

Plastic base moulding

Plug assembly

Fusible alloy

Finned case

Central conductor

Insulating pip

Fusible alloy contacting
central conductor

FIG   7.13 Chubb fixed temperature detector
(Source Home Office, Manual of Firemanship)

Smoke detectors

These are of three principal types operating on the basis of ionising radiation, light scatter and light obscuration.

Ionising detectors utilise a small radioactive source which maintains a level of ionisation in two chambers, one of which is open to the atmosphere. When smoke enters the chamber, the smoke particles absorb some of the ionisation, causing an electrical imbalance detected by the instrument.

Light scatter detectors work on the easily observed fact that smoke scatters light. A photo-electric cell is fitted in a chamber at right angles to the source of light. In a fire-free condition, the cell would receive no light, but when smoke enters the chamber, light is scattered and detected by the cell.

With **light obscuration detectors** a photo-electric cell is mounted opposite a light source in a chamber so, when smoke enters, some of the light is obscured. The cell detects decreases in light intensity.

Flammable gas detectors

Technically, a flammable gas detector is not a fire detector since it operates on the pre-fire condition, measuring the concentration of flammable gas in the atmosphere and actuating an alarm when the concentration reaches a predetermined fraction of the lower explosive limit. The gas mixture is drawn over catalytic surface on which the flammable gas is oxidised. In turn, the heat of oxidation raises the temperature of the catalyst surface and the device responds to the rise in temperature dependent on the concentration of the air/flammable gas mixture passing over it. These detectors must be calibrated to take into account the different gases to which they will be exposed. For instance, different calibrations are required for propane and petrol.

Fire alarm systems

The most effective fire alarm system is the human voice, but this can be very expensive when 24-hour coverage is needed. Routine patrols of premises, carried out diligently and in a disciplined way, will detect most fires before they become a serious risk. The alarm should be raised by telephoning a local centre or the local fire brigade.

A fire can also be detected by any of the detection systems outlined above. Each device can be made to operate an alarm system which alerts occupants or an in-house fire brigade. Some detection devices will automatically start to fight the fire through the operation of sprinkler systems, where the flow of water sets off the alarm.

The major disadvantage of all automatic alarms is the frequency of false alarms. All systems suffer from this problem and should be tuned to deal with the local situation.

A method of giving warning of fire is required in commercial, industrial and public buildings. The purpose of a fire alarm is to give an early warning of a fire in a building.

- to increase the safety of occupants by encouraging them to escape to a place of safety
- to increase the possibility of early extinction of the fire thus reducing the loss of or damage to the property.

BS 5839: Part 1:1988 lays down guidelines to be followed for the installation of fire alarm systems.

In larger buildings this may take the form of a mains operated system with breakglass alarm call points, an automatic control unit and electrically-operated bells or sirens.

In small buildings it would be reasonable to accept a manually operated, dry battery or compressed air-operated gong, klaxon or bell. To avoid the alarm point being close to the seat of a fire, duplicate facilities are necessary.

STORAGE AND USE OF FLAMMABLE SUBSTANCES

Under Schedule 1 of the Chemicals (Hazard Information and Packaging for Supply) (CHIP) Regulations 1994, flammable substances are classified as 'extremely flammable', 'highly flammable' and 'flammable'. These terms are defined below.

Extremely flammable

Liquid substances and preparations having an extremely low flash point and a low boiling point and gaseous substances and preparations which are flammable in contact with air at ambient temperature and pressure.

Highly flammable

The following substances and preparations, namely:

- substances and preparations which may become hot and finally catch fire in contact with air at ambient temperature without any application of energy
- solid substances and preparations which may readily catch fire after brief contact with a source of ignition and which continue to burn or to be consumed after removal of the source of ignition
- liquid substances and preparations having a very low flash point or
- substances and preparations which, in contact with water or damp air, evolve highly flammable gases in dangerous quantities.

Flammable

Liquid substances and preparations having a low flash point.

General precautions

Precautionary measures necessary will depend upon whether the flammable substance is in an uncompressed or compressed state, that is, contained in a cylinder under pressure.

Compressed gases

Compressed gases have numerous uses both commercially and domestically. In addition to their inherent flammable, toxic or corrosive properties, they are potentially dangerous as a consequence of their physical properties. Leakage from cylinders into an open room or workshop can give rise to dangerous concentrations resulting in fire, explosion, gassing incidents or oxygen depletion. The relative force with which the contents of a cylinder can be ejected can result in death, physical injury, damage to property and plant, and even the propulsion of the cylinder, like a rocket, across a working area.

Precautions with cylinders

One of the principal causes of accidents is incorrect storage of cylinders, resulting in incompatible reactions taking place between different gases leaking into the storage area. For this reason alone, the following precautions should be taken in the design of storage facilities:

- cylinders should be stored outside the main buildings in a purpose-built store
- the store should be a detached structure and well segregated from buildings frequently occupied
- storage should incorporate separate compartments for individual gases or groups of compatible gases
- the structure should be of weather-proof lightweight construction, eg single skin brick or lightweight concrete block walls and partitions providing a notional period of fire resistance of at least one hour – and should have a sloping roof
- high- and low-level ventilation by air bricks should be located in the end and back walls and
- each compartment should be provided with a lockable mesh door of mesh size within the range XM21 to XM26 or XM41 to XM43 (see BS 405:1945).

Only compatible gases should be stored in individual storage compartments. A typical arrangement is:

Compartment A – arcton, freon, argon, nitrogen, helium, hydrogen
Compartment B – propane, butane
Compartment C – oxygen, compressed air
Compartment D – ammonia
Compartment E – chlorine (this compartment should incorporate a lockable louvred door)

(see Figure 7.14 on p. 272).

Other storage design features include:

- concrete floor with slight fall to facilitate trolley loading; no drainage should be incorporated in the floor
- total prohibition of the installation of electrical or heating equipment
- marking of the store with approved signs indicating the contents and prohibiting smoking and the use of naked flames
- racking, incorporating restraining chains, for cylinder storage; racking is not necessary where cylinders are of freestanding design
- water supply through a 20mm hose reel installation adjacent to the store, but well away from the chlorine cylinder storage compartment
- artificial lighting to a minimum illuminance level of 150 lux, remote from the store but directed into the store and door openings and
- fire appliances, eg dry powder, of adequate size, located at a specific point.

Storage buildings should be so spaced that the distance between any aperture in the wall and the nearest point of any other building, boundary or ignition source is:

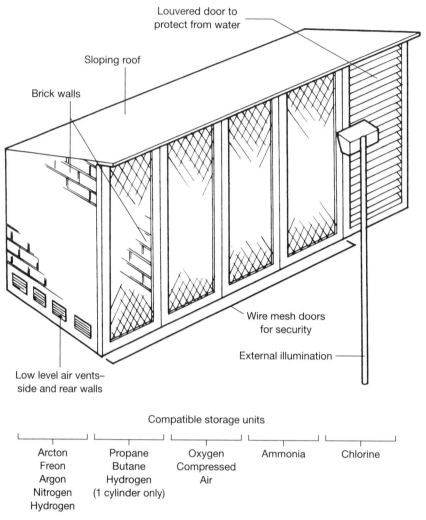

FIG 7.14 Liquefied and pressurised gas cylinder store

- not less than 3 m for storage up to 1,000kg, and
- not less than 6 m for storage over 1,000kg.

Where the above standard is not practicable, it may be possible to locate the store against an existing building wall. However, there should be:

- no opening lights in the wall above the store, and any fixed lights should be glazed with georgian wired glass
- no adjacent apertures – ie windows, doors – within three metres of the store and

- no ventilation intake above or immediately adjacent to the store.

Empty cylinders should be treated in the same manner as full or partially full cylinders, and the valves maintained closed. 'Full' and 'empty' cylinder racks within each compartment should be conspicuously marked.

Handling of cylinders

- Cylinders should not be dropped or allowed to come into contact with one another or with any hard object.
- Cylinders should be treated with extreme care; they are a potential source of energy.
- When transported, cylinders should be strapped in properly designed trolleys.
- Cylinders used for lecturing and training purposes should be handled in a fume cupboard and stood in a suitable rack.
- Improperly labelled cylinders should not be accepted. The colour code on the cylinder is only a secondary guide.

Use of cylinders

Cylinders should be stored and used in an upright position with the valve uppermost.

- A regulator should be used to maintain the outlet pressure at a correct and uniform value.
- Cylinders should **not** be used as rollers for moving heavy objects.
- Valves and fittings should not be lubricated.
- Cylinders and valves should be kept clean.
- Cylinders with damaged threads or valves should immediately be labelled '*defective*' and returned to the supplier.
- When exchanging cylinders, the valves should be closed before the connections are transferred.
- After remaking a connection, the valve should be opened carefully in order to detect any leakage. In the event of leakage, the cylinder should be moved into the open air.
- Cylinder keys should not be extended to give greater leverage as valve spindles may be damaged.
- Leak detectors and alarms may be necessary when very dangerous gases are stored.
- Only the appropriate regulator should be used for each type of cylinder. Regulators should be examined at 6-monthly intervals and labelled for use with one specific gas.

Dangerous gases – special precautions

These gases, especially flammable gases, should be housed in a suitably ventilated compartment outside the building and the gas piped in to the working area. Cylinders must:

- be fitted with automatic shut-off valves operable from inside the working area, eg laboratory
- be fitted with flash-back arrestors in the line
- have cylinder keys captive to the cylinder by non-ferrous chains and
- have their lines examined for leaks on commencement of work and on change of cylinder.

When cylinders are not in use:

- cylinder and bench valves must be closed tightly and
- protective caps screwed down over the valves.

Transportable gas containers

These are defined in the Pressure Systems and Transportable Gas Containers Regulations 1989 as meaning a container, including any permanent fitting of such a container, which is used, or, is intended to be used, to contain a relevant fluid and is:

- designed to be transportable for the purposes of refilling and has an internal volume of at least 0.5 litres and not greater than 3,000 litres
- a non-refillable container having an internal volume of at least 1.4 litres and not greater than 5 litres or
- for the purposes of Regulation 17(3) only, a non-refillable container.

Specific provisions relating to transportable gas containers are covered in Part V of the Regulations (Regulations 16–22). The regulations prohibit a person from supplying for the first time, importing or manufacturing and using such a container unless it has either been verified (by a person or in accordance with a quality assurance scheme approved by the HSE) as conforming to a design standard or design specification so approved, or been verified under or conforms with specified Council Directives (Regulation 16). Schedule 5 contains provisions with respect to fees for such approvals.

These regulations require specified checks to be made when transportable gas containers are filled and prohibit the filling of non-refillable containers. They also require containers to be examined at appropriate intervals by a competent person and to be marked with the date of the examination. Specific requirements with respect to modification and repair of containers are laid down (Regulations 19 and 20), and with respect to re-rating. The regulations require specified documents to be kept (Regulation 22).

An ACOP 'Safety of transportable gas containers' gives guidance on compliance with Part V of the regulations.

Dust explosions

Many solid particulates, particularly organic materials, in the right combination with air, will form an explosive mixture. Some particulates are relatively harmless in their traditional form, but when reduced to dust by grinding, sanding or other forms of size reduction or refining they can become highly explosive. In fact, some of the most serious dust explosions have been associated with dusts created during the processing of tea, sugar, starch and potato as well as metals such as zinc and aluminium. Other materials such as coal, wood, cork, grain and many plastics can form explosive dust clouds.

Although an intimate mixture of flammable dust and air may burn with explosive violence, not all mixtures will do so. There is a range of concentrations of the dust and air within which the mixture can explode, but above or below this range an explosion will not take place. The lowest concentration of dust capable of exploding is referred to as the lower explosive limit and the concentration above which an explosion will not take place as the upper explosive limit. Furthermore, the range of the explosive concentrations of a dust cloud is not solely a function of the chemical composition of the dust. The limits vary, inter alia, with the size and shape of the particles in the dust cloud.

For an explosion to take place there must be some form of ignition source available. This can be a hot surface, electrical spark, frictional spark or direct flame. The ignition temperature for sugar is 350 °C, coal 610 °C, wood 430 °C, zinc 600 °C, polystyrene 490 °C and magnesium 520 °C. The lower explosive concentration for sugar is 350 mg/m^3, coal 550 mg/m^3, wood 400 mg/m^3, zinc 4,800 mg/m^3, polystyrene 150 mg/m^3 and magnesium 200 mg/m^3.

There are several clearly defined stages of a typical factory dust explosion. The preliminary stage, similar to the situation where fine coal dust is thrown onto an open fire, is the typical 'flare up', where there is a sudden release of flame for an instant. This can, however, be sufficient to raise locally deposited dust into suspension in air and cause a localised explosion. This primary explosion stage may not result in a great degree of damage but is sufficient to send pressure waves in all directions, causing further liberation into the air of deposited dust. The secondary explosion stage, which is much more devastating than the primary stage, follows quickly, resulting in extensive damage and often loss of life. Depending upon the layout of the premises and the presence of walls, which may act as temporary baffles, the secondary stage may take place as one great explosion or a series of lesser explosions in different parts of the premises.

Most dust explosions take place, however, in specific items of plant such as spray driers, cyclones, settling chambers, powder silos, pneumatic conveying equipment, grinding plant, disintegrators, milling plant and dust collection systems.

Precautions against dust explosions

The frequent removal of deposited dust by industrial vacuum cleaners is one of the most important strategies in preventing dust explosions. Moreover, dust-producing plant should be checked frequently for leakages. Items of plant such as evaporator driers, storage silos and bins, grain elevators, fluid beds and cyclones should be fitted with explosion reliefs, which minimise the devastation by relieving the explosive pressure to a safe area or to atmosphere. Explosion reliefs (vents) may take the form of lightweight panels installed at the top of evaporator driers, elevators and silos. The size of the explosion relief is related to the volume of the installation and its mechanical strength. There are several methods for calculating the size of explosion relief according to the type of installation and particulate under consideration.

In general, any explosion of a flammable mixture, whether dust or gaseous, which, when ignited in a confined space, reaches its maximum pressure in not less than 40 milliseconds, can be brought under control by methods which include suppression, venting, advance inheriting, isolation and automatic plant shutdown.

As a dust explosion is not an instantaneous occurrence but requires a definite time for the development of maximum pressure, it is possible, by the introduction of a suppressant, to arrest the rise of pressure before it reaches dangerous levels. The explosion suppression system in its simplest form consists of a detector, an electrical power unit and a number of suppressors (see Figure 7.15).

An explosion detector and the associated electrical equipment may also be used to open detonator-operated bursting discs, to close high-speed isolation valves, to inert automatically parts of the plant remote from the seat of the explosion and to shut down the plant immediately an explosion occurs. These methods may be used individually but more often are used in combination, depending upon the type and construction of plant and its operating conditions.

Although the fitting of explosion reliefs may prevent devastation of plant by an explosion this may not be sufficient to stop flame or smouldering material from spreading elsewhere through rotary valves, worms, conveyors or other inlets or outlets for the plant. The use of an explosion detector to initiate inerting and isolating arrangements coupled with automatic plant shutdown, therefore, offers an important additional degree of safety which it is often difficult, if not impossible, to achieve in any other way (see Figure 7.16).

Other precautions include the installation of baffle walls in processing areas to prevent the spread of explosion, regular damping down of dusty areas, enclosure of processes and the use of dust arrestment plant appropriate to the type of dust produced.

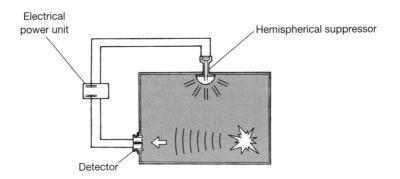

FIG 7.15 Explosion suppression using an explosion detector, electrical power unit and a hemispherical suppressor

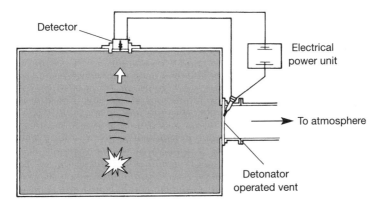

FIG 7.16 Explosion venting using a detonator operated bursting disc

FIRE SAFETY LEGISLATION

The Fire Precautions Act 1971 (FPA), as amended by the Fire Safety and Safety of Places of Sport Act 1987 (FSSPSA), applies to all premises actually in use – industrial, commercial or public – and is enforced by the various fire authorities. Where premises incorporate intrinsically hazardous substances eg storage of flammable substances and explosives, control is exercised by the HSE. Fire safety legislation is principally concerned with ensuring the provision of:

- means of escape in the event of fire and
- the means for fighting fire

and this is implemented through a process of fire certification.

The FPA required that a fire certificate be issued for certain classes of factory and commercial premises, based on the concept of **designated use**. The

FSSPSA in effect deregulated many premises which formerly required certification under the FPA. These include:

- factories, offices and shops where:
  - more than 20 persons are employed at any one time
  - more than 10 persons are employed at any one time elsewhere than on the ground floor
  - buildings containing two or more factory and/or office premises, where the aggregate of persons employed in all of them at any one time is more than 20
  - buildings containing two or more factory and/or office premises, where the aggregate of persons employed at any one time in all of them, elsewhere than on the ground floor, is more than 10
  - factories where explosive or highly flammable materials are stored, or used in or under the premises, unless, in the opinion of the fire authority, there was no serious risk to employees from fire and

- hotels and boarding houses where sleeping accommodation:
  - for six or more persons or
  - at basement level or
  - above the first floor;

  was provided for either guests or staff.

The effect of this deregulation was to exempt certain low risk premises from the certification requirements. Thus the FSSPSA empowers local fire authorities to grant exemptions in respect of certain medium-risk and low-risk premises which were previously 'designated use' premises. The exemption certificate must, however, specify the maximum number of persons who can safely be in or on the premises at any one time. Furthermore, the exemption can be withdrawn by the fire authority without prior inspection and by service of notice of withdrawal, where the degree of risk associated with the premises increases.

FIRE PRECAUTIONS ACT 1971

Section 5 – application for fire certificates

Premises will require a fire certificate where they have not been granted an exemption under the FSSPSA. An application for a fire certificate should normally be made to the local fire authority on Form FP1 by the occupier in the case of factories, offices and shops. In certain cases, however, it must be made by the owner, thus:

- premises consisting of part of a building, all parts of which are owned by the same persons, ie multi-occupied buildings in single ownership

- premises consisting of part of a building, the different parts being owned by different persons, ie multi-occupied buildings with plural ownership.

An application must specify the premises concerned, the use to be covered and, if required by the fire authority, be supported within a specified time by plans of the premises. Before a fire certificate is issued, inspection of the premises is essential under the FPA. Where following an inspection, the fire authority does not consider the premises safe against fire, they will normally require the occupier to carry out improvements before issuing a certificate.

Section 6 – fire certificates

A fire certificate specifies:

- the particular use or uses of the premises which it covers
- the means of escape in case of fire indicated in a plan of the premises
- the means for securing that the means of escape can be safely and effectively used at all relevant times
- the means for fighting fire for use by persons in the premises
- the means for giving warnings in the case of fire and
- particulars as to explosive or highly flammable liquids stored and used on the premises.

The fire certificate may also impose requirements relating to:

- the maintenance of the means of escape and keeping it free from obstruction
- the maintenance of other fire precautions outlined in the certificate
- the training of employees as to action in the event of fire and the maintenance of suitable records of such training
- limiting the number of persons who at any one time may be on the premises and
- any other relevant fire precautions.

A fire certificate, or a copy of same, must be kept in the building concerned.

Section 8 – inspection of premises

So long as a fire certificate is in force for any premises, the fire authority may cause inspections to be made from time to time to ascertain whether the requirements of the certificate are being maintained or are becoming inadequate.

Before cárrying out any structural alterations or any material internal alterations to premises requiring a fire certificate, it is necessary first to notify the fire authority, or in the case of 'special premises', the HSE of the proposed changes. Similar requirements apply in the case of proposed alterations to equipment or furniture on the premises. Following notification, the premises will be inspected before the alteration work can go ahead. Failure to follow this procedure is an offence under the FPA.

FIRE SAFETY AND SAFETY OF PLACES OF SPORT ACT 1987 (FSSPSA)

Legal requirements relating to the fire certification of premises, as contained in the FPA, were modified by the FSSPSA. One of the main general purposes of the FSSPSA was to concentrate effort on high fire risk premises, at the same time reducing the need for certification in the case of low risk premises. The FSSPSA is, therefore, a de-regulating measure. It empowers fire authorities to grant exemptions in respect of low risk premises which were previously 'designated use' premises under the FPA and which required a fire certificate. An occupier does not have to formally apply for such exemption. It may be granted either on application for a fire certificate or whilst a fire certificate is in force. Generally, however, premises would not be exempted unless they had been inspected within the previous 12 months. The consequence of this is that if an exemption is granted:

- on application for a fire certificate, it disposes of the application
- whilst the certificate is in force, the certificate no longer has any effect.

The **exemption certificate** must, however, specify the maximum number of persons who can safely be in or on the premises at any one time. Depending on the relative degree of fire risk, the exemption can be withdrawn by the fire authority without prior inspection, on notice being given to the occupier of such withdrawal.

Section 5 – means of escape in case of fire

Although low or medium risk premises may be exempt from certification under the FSSPSA, occupiers must still provide a means of escape and fire fighting equipment. **Escape** is defined in the Act as *'escape from premises to some place of safety beyond the building, which constitutes or comprises the premises, and any area enclosed by it or within it; accordingly, conditions or requirements can be imposed as respects any place or thing by means of which a person escapes from premises to a place of safety'*.

Section 8 – alterations to exempted premises

An occupier who intends to carry out any material alterations to a premises whilst an exemption order is in force must first notify the fire authority of the proposed alterations. Failure to notify is an offence under the Act.

Notification is particularly necessary in the following cases where:

- – the proposed extension of, and/or structural alterations to premises may affect the means of escape
  – any alteration to the interior of the premises, in furniture or equipment, may affect the means of escape
- the proposed storage of explosive or highly flammable material in or on the premises in quantities/aggregate quantities is greater than that specified by the current certificate
- it is proposed that a greater number of persons be on the premises than specified by the certificate.

Enforcement provisions of the FSSPSA

Section 9 – improvement notices

Where a fire authority is of the opinion that an occupier has not fulfilled their duty with regard to the provision of:

- means of escape in case of fire and/or
- means for fighting fire

the authority may serve on the occupier an **improvement notice** detailing the steps that should be taken by way of improvements, alterations and other measures to remedy this breach of the act. The occupier must normally undertake remedial work within 21 days unless they submit an appeal against the notice. Such an appeal must be lodged within 21 days from the date of service of the notice, and has the effect of suspending the operation of the notice. Where such an appeal fails, the occupier must undertake the remedial work specified in the improvement notice. Failure to do so can result in a fine on summary conviction, and on conviction on indictment, an indefinite fine or imprisonment for up to two years, or both.

Section 10 – prohibition notices

Where there is considered to be a **serious risk of injury to employees and visitors** from fire on premises, the fire authority can serve on the occupier a **prohibition notice** requiring to have remedial work carried out in the interests of fire safety or, alternatively, have his premises closed down. The power to serve prohibition notices applies to all former 'designated use' premises but not places of public religious worship or single private dwellings.

A prohibition notice may be served on the following types of premises:

- providing sleeping accommodation, eg hotels
- providing treatment/care, eg nursing homes

- for the purposes of entertainment, recreation or instruction, or for a club, society or association
- for teaching, training or research
- providing access to members of the public, whether for payment or otherwise and
- places of work.

A prohibition notice is most likely to be served where means of escape are inadequate or non-existent, or where there is a need to improve means of escape. As with a prohibition notice under the HSWA, such a notice can be served with immediate effect or deferred. An appeal does not suspend the operation of a prohibition notice.

Places of sport

The FSSPSA extends the existing Safety of Sports Grounds Act (SSGA) 1975 which only applied to sports stadia, ie sports grounds where the accommodation for spectators wholly or substantially surrounds the activity taking place, to all forms of sports ground.

The legal situation relating to sports grounds under the FSSPSA is as follows:

- a **general safety certificate** is required in respect of any sports ground
- the SSGA is extended to any sports ground which the Secretary of State considers appropriate
- validity of safety certificates no longer requires the provision at a sports ground of a police presence, unless consent has been given by a chief constable or chief police officer and
- there is provision for the service of prohibition notices in the case of serious risk of injury to spectators, prohibiting or restricting the admission of spectators in general or on specified occasions.

Prohibition notices

A prohibition notice may specify steps which must be taken to reduce risk, particularly from a fire, to a reasonable level, including structural alterations (irrespective of whether this may contravene the terms of a safety certificate for the ground issued by the local authority, or for any stand at the ground). (See later in this chapter **Safety Certificates**.) Where a prohibition notice requires provision of a police force, such requirements cannot be specified without the consent of the chief constable or chief police officer.

Under section 23 of the FSSPSA, a prohibition notice may be served on any of the following persons:

- the holder of a general safety certificate

- the holder of a **specific safety certificate**, ie a safety certificate for a specific sporting activity or occasion
- where no safety certificate is in operation, the management of the sports ground
- in the case of a specific sporting activity for which no safety certificate is in operation, the organisers of the activity
- where a general safety certificate is in operation for a stand at a ground, the holder of same and
- where a specific safety certificate is in operation for a stand, the holder of the certificate.

Under section 25 of the FSSPSA sports grounds must be inspected at least once per annum.

Safety certificates

Where a sports ground provides covered accommodation in stands for spectators, a safety certificate, issued by the local authority, is required for each stand providing covered accommodation for 500 or more spectators, ie a **regulated stand**. In certain cases, safety certificates may be required for stands accommodating smaller numbers.

7

Records

Section 27 of the Act gives the local authority power to require the keeping of the following records in the case of stands at sports grounds:

- the number of spectators in covered accommodation and
- procedures relating to the maintenance of safety in the stand.

Sports grounds with regulated stands must be inspected periodically.

Offences under the FSSPSA

The principal criminal offences under the Act are committed in respect of regulated stands. Where:

- spectators are admitted to a regulated stand at a sports ground on an occasion when a safety certificate should be, but is not, in operation or
- any term or condition of a safety certificate for a regulated stand at a sports ground is contravened

both the management of the sports ground and, in the second case, the holder of the certificate, are guilty of an offence. (Section 36)

Under section 36 of the FSSPSA, a number of defences are available, namely:

- that either:

- – the spectators were admitted with no safety certificate in operation or
- – the contravention of the safety certificate occurred without his/her consent AND
- that he/she took all reasonable precautions and exercised all due care to avoid the commission of the offence him/herself or by other persons under their control.

Where a person or corporate body is charged with an offence under section 36, ie no safety certificate in respect of a regulated stand, the defendant may plead that they did not know that the stand had been determined to be a regulated stand.

Construction activities

The construction industry, by virtue of the nature of the work and the effect of weather conditions, has always ranked as one of the more dangerous industries. Major construction project work is now regulated by the Construction (Design and Management) (CONDAM) Regulations 1994 (see later in this chapter).

THE PRINCIPAL HAZARDS

These are commonly associated with the following:

Ladders

- workers falling from ladders
- ladders slipping outwards at the base or falling away at the top (the 1 out: 4 up rule should always be used)
- use of defective ladders
- over-reaching situations.

Falls from working platforms

- unfenced or inadequately fenced working platforms
- inadequate boarding to scaffolds
- defective boarding
- absence of toe boards.

Falls of materials

- small objects, such as bricks or hand tools, dropped from a height
- poor standards of housekeeping on working platforms
- inadequate or absent toe boards and barriers

- incorrect assembly of gin wheels for raising and lowering materials
- incorrect or careless hooking and slinging of loads
- failure to install catching platforms (fans) for falling debris
- demolition materials being thrown to the ground.

Falls from pitched roofs and through fragile roofs

- unsafe working practices
- inappropriate footwear
- failure to provide eaves protection and verge protection
- failure to use crawl boards
- stacking of materials on fragile roofs.

Falls through openings in flat roofs and floors

- failure to cover openings or provide edge protection
- failure to replace after use
- covers not clearly marked to show their presence.

Collapses of excavations

- failure to support trench excavations
- inadequate timbering and shoring
- shifting sand situations
- presence of water in large quantities, eg flash floods
- timbering collapses due to materials stacked too close to the edge of the excavation
- defective and inadequate shoring materials
- failure to reinstate shoring after damage.

Transport

- men falling off vehicles not designed to carry passengers, eg dumper trucks
- men being run over or crushed by reversing lorries and trucks
- poor maintenance of site vehicles, eg braking and reversing systems
- operation of vehicles and machinery, particularly lifting appliances, such as cranes, hoists and winches, by inexperienced and incompetent persons
- overloading of passenger-carrying vehicles
- poor standards of driving on site roads
- mud on roads

- poor housekeeping on roads causing skidding and obstruction to vehicles.

Machinery and powered hand tools

- failure to adequately guard all moving parts of machinery, eg power take-offs, cooling fans and belt drives
- dangerous woodworking machinery, particularly circular saws
- portable hand powered tools with exposed rotating heads
- defective or uninsulated electric hand tools.

Housekeeping

- poor housekeeping levels
- trips and falls over debris that can accumulate during construction.

Fire

- poor fire protection measures, often associated with poor site supervision.

Personal protective equipment

- failure to provide and to enforce the wearing and use of personal protective equipment, eg safety helmets, safety boots, gloves, overalls, full-face protection, goggles, etc.

Competent persons

The expression 'competent person' occurs frequently in construction safety legislation. For example under the CGPR and the Construction (Working Places) Regulations (CWPR), certain inspections, examinations, operations and supervisory duties must be undertaken by competent persons. 'Competent person', however, is not defined under the regulations and the onus is on the employer to decide whether persons are competent to undertake these duties. It is necessary to look to case law for the definition of same. Broadly, a competent person should have practical and theoretical knowledge as well as sufficient experience of the particular machinery, plant or procedure involved to enable him to identify defects or weaknesses during plant and machinery examinations, and to assess their importance in relation to the strength and function of that plant and machinery. (**Brazier v Skipton Rock Company Ltd. [1962] 1 AER 955**)

Competent persons are used in the following construction-related activities:

- supervision of demolition work
- supervision of the handling and use of explosives

Table 8.1   Fatal injuries to employees and the self-employed in the construction sector as reported to the HSE's field operations division inspectorates 1993–94

Type of accident	*Number of fatalities*	*Percentage of total*
Falls from a height		
Ladders (all types)	9	
Scaffolding (all types)	8	
Fragile roofs	8	
Roof edges or holes in roofs	6	
Structural steelwork	4	
Temporary work platform	3	
Parts of floors/surfaces not		
listed above	4	
Other	1	
Total	**43**	**56%**
Trapped by something collapsing or overturning		
Buildings/structures (or parts of)	7	
Earth, rocks, eg trench collapse	3	
Plant including lifting machinery	1	
Scaffolding collapse	1	
Vehicles falling from supports/		
overturning	3	
Other	1	
Total	**16**	**21%**
Struck by a moving vehicle		
Bulldozer	1	
Excavator	2	
Private vehicle	1	
Road tanker	1	
Trailer	1	
Other	2	
Total	**8**	**10%**
Contact with electricity or an electrical discharge		
Domestic type equipment	1	
Hand tools or hand lamps	1	
Overhead lines	2	
Total	**4**	**5%**
Struck by falling/flying object during machine lifting of materials		
Total	**3**	**4%**
Contact with moving machinery or material being machined		
Conveyor belt	1	
Hoist	1	
Total	**2**	**3%**
Exposure to a hot or harmful substance		
Total	**1**	**1%**

- inspection of scaffold materials prior to erection of a scaffold
- supervision of erection of, substantial alterations or additions to, and dismantling of scaffolds
- inspections of scaffolds every seven days, and after adverse weather conditions which could affect the strength and stability of a scaffold, or cause displacement of any part
- inspections of excavations on a daily basis
- supervision of the erection of cranes
- testing of cranes after erection, re-erection and any removal or adjustment involving changes of anchorage or ballasting and
- examination of appliances for anchorage or ballasting prior to crane erection.

A competent person, therefore, must be able to discover defects. He must also be able to understand and act upon the possible outcome of such defects.

General and specific requirements of the CWPR

It should be appreciated that the majority of the duties of employers under the CWPR are of an absolute nature.

Safe working conditions

Places at which persons are habitually working must be covered so as to give protection against any falling material.

Temporary structures must be of good construction, sound material, adequate strength and stability, free from patent defect and adequately maintained.

Suitable and sufficient safe access and egress must be maintained for every working position.

All workplaces must be made and kept safe for any person working there.

Scaffolds or, if appropriate, ladders or other suitable means of support, must be provided and properly maintained where work cannot be done safely on or from the ground or from part of a building or other permanent structure.

Openings, corners, breaks or edges in floors, walls and roofs must be fenced.

Safety sheets or nets, or safety belts, must be used when other legal requirements designed to prevent falls cannot be complied with.

All practicable steps must be taken to prevent danger from live electric cables or apparatus.

Scaffolding

Erection of scaffolds

A competent person must inspect scaffold materials before each occasion on which they are put into use.

Any erection, substantial alterations or additions to, and dismantling of a scaffold must be under the immediate supervision of a competent person. Competent and experienced workmen must be employed, so far as is possible, for the erection, substantial alterations or additions to, and dismantling of scaffolds.

Every part of a scaffold must be so fixed, secured or placed as to prevent accidental displacement as far as is practicable.

Scaffolds must be constructed of suitable and sound material and of adequate strength.

They must be rigidly connected to the building or other structure unless designed and constructed as an independent scaffold. Scaffolds must be securely supported or suspended and strutted or braced where necessary.

Parts of buildings or other structures must not be used to support scaffolds unless they are of sound material and sufficiently strong and stable.

Gutters must not be used as supports unless they are suitable for the purpose and of adequate strength. Overhanging eaves gutters must not be so used unless designed as walkways. Loose bricks and other rubble must not be used as supports except for certain low platforms.

Inspection and maintenance of scaffolds

All scaffolds used must have been inspected by a competent person within the preceding seven days unless no part has been erected for over seven days. Scaffolds must be inspected after being exposed to weather conditions likely to affect the strength or stability of the scaffold or to have displaced any part. The results of inspections of scaffolds must be entered in or attached to the prescribed register (except for ladder scaffolds, trestle scaffolds and scaffolds from which persons cannot fall more than two metres.)

Each employer whose men use a scaffold must satisfy himself that it complies with the regulations, whether or not his own men have erected it.

All scaffolds must be properly maintained. Platforms, gangways, runs and stairs must be kept clear of unnecessary obstructions, materials or rubbish and from projecting nails. Slippery platforms, gangways, runs and stairs must be sanded, cleaned or otherwise remedied as soon as is practicable.

Scaffolds must never be overloaded. Materials must not be kept on scaffolds unless needed within a reasonable time. Movement of materials on or on to scaffolds must be carried out without causing any violent shock. Loads on scaffolds must be evenly distributed as far as is practicable.

Partly erected or dismantled scaffolds must either comply with the regulations even in their incomplete state, or else have prominent warning notices to indicate that they must not be used or have access to them blocked as far as is reasonably practicable.

Ladders

Construction

Any ladder must be of good construction, suitable and sound material, adequate strength and properly maintained. Ladders with missing or defective rungs must not be used. Wooden stiles and rungs must be used with the grain of the wood running lengthwise. Wooden ladders must not be painted or treated in such a way that defects in the timber may be concealed. Wooden ladders must have reinforcing ties if the tenon joints are not secured by wedges.

Use

Ladders not standing on a base must be securely, equally and properly suspended by each stile and must be secured where necessary to prevent undue swinging or swaying. Ladders standing on a base must be equally and properly supported on each stile.

A ladder standing on a base must be securely fixed near its upper resting place (or its upper end, if vertical). If such fixing is impracticable, the ladder must be fixed at or near its lower end. If this is also impracticable, a person must be stationed at the foot of the ladder to prevent it from slipping.

Except where there are equal handholds, ladders must rise to a height of at least 3´6˝ (1.07m) above the landing place or above the highest rung reached by the feet of a person using the ladder. The space at each rung of a ladder must be sufficient to provide an adequate foothold. Landing places of adequate size must be provided if practicable every 30´0˝ (9.14m) of vertical distance, or more often. Landing places from which persons are liable to fall more than 6´6˝ (2m) must have handrails to a height of between 3´0˝ (920mm) and 3´9˝ (1.15m) and also toe boards or other barriers to a height of at least 6˝ (155mm). The space between the toe board and the nearest guard rail must not be more than 2´6˝ (760mm). Openings in landings through which ladders pass must be as small as practicable.

Folding ladders must have a level and firm footing and not stand on loose bricks or other loose packing.

Excavations

Materials and equipment

An adequate supply of timber or other suitable material must be provided. Any machinery in use must have any dangerous parts securely fenced (unless safe by position or construction).

Fencing

Barriers must be provided around excavations, shafts, pits and openings into which persons can fall a vertical distance of more than 6´6˝ (1.98m), and such barriers must be as close as practicable to the edge of the excavation, etc. Barriers must be maintained in position except when necessarily removed for the access of persons or materials.

Timbering

Adequate and suitable materials must be used to prevent danger from falls or dislodgement of the sides of any excavation, etc or materials adjacent to it.

Timbering must be undertaken as early as practicable in the course of the work, and persons engaged in timbering must be protected as far as possible from danger.

Timbering or other supports must be of good construction, sound materials, free from patent defect, and of adequate strength for the purpose. Struts and braces must be properly and adequately secured to prevent accidental displacement or fall.

A competent person must be employed to direct the erection and dismantling of all timbering and other supports, as well as any subsequent alterations or additions to same. Experienced workmen must further be employed, as far as possible, for the erection, dismantling, etc of timbering and other supports.

Inspections and examinations

Material for timbering and other supports must be inspected by a competent person before being taken into use. Every part of any excavation, shaft, earthwork or tunnel must be inspected by a competent person at least once during every day that persons are employed there. The face of every tunnel and base or crown of every shaft must be inspected by a competent person at the beginning of every shift. The working end of every trench more than 6′6″ (1.98m) must be inspected by a competent person before the beginning of every shift. No person must work in any excavation, etc after explosives have been used in or near it, in a manner likely to affect stability, until a thorough examination has been made by a competent person. No person must work in any excavation, etc unless it has been thoroughly examined by a competent person within the previous seven days. No person must work in any excavation, etc after an unexpected fall of rock, earth or other material, or after substantial damage to timber or other supports, unless the part concerned has been thoroughly examined by a competent person. Reports of such examinations must be made on the day of examination, in the form prescribed by the Construction (General Provisions) Reports Order 1962.

Other precautions

Excavations and the approaches to same must be well-lit.

Materials must not be placed near the edge of any excavation, etc so as to endanger persons below.

If the excavation is likely to affect the security of another structure (permanent or temporary) steps must be taken to safeguard persons employed from possible collapse of that structure.

Means of reaching a place of safety must be provided, as far as practicable, when there may be danger from rising water or irruption of water or material.

Means to prevent overrunning must be provided when a vehicle is used to tip material into a pit or excavation or over the edge of any embankment or earthwork.

The atmosphere in an excavation must be well-ventilated and free from dust, fumes, etc.

Lifting appliances and lifting gear

Packing or other means must be used to prevent the edges of a load from coming into contact with slings, ropes or chains, if this would cause danger.

The angle between the legs of multiple slings must not be so great that the safe working load is exceeded.

Every part of a load must be securely suspended and supported and secured to prevent displacement or slipping. Slings must be securely attached to the appliance and in a way not likely to damage the slings of any lifting gear.

The hoisting mechanism of a crane must be used only for vertical raising or lowering, unless it can be used otherwise without imposing undue stress or endangering stability and is so used under the supervision of a competent person. The safe working load of the appliance must not be exceeded.

The radius of the load must not exceed the maximum working radius of the jib.

Where a load is equal to, or nearly equal to the safe working load, lifting must be halted for a moment after the load has been raised for a short distance.

All practicable measures must be taken to prevent a load coming into contact with, and displacing, any other object.

No load must be left suspended unless a competent person is actually in charge of the lifting appliance.

Loads being lowered on to a scaffold must be deposited without causing any violent shock to the scaffold.

Where more than one appliance is used for a lift, work must be so arranged that no appliance is overloaded or rendered unstable, and the operation must be supervised by a competent person.

Lifting appliances must not be used on soft or uneven surfaces nor on a slope unless precautions are taken to ensure stability.

No crane must be used for raising or lowering unless it is either securely anchored or adequately weighted with ballast properly placed and secured. (Rails on which cranes are mounted must not be used as anchorages.)

Only trained and competent persons must operate a lifting appliance. No person under the age of 18 years must operate any lifting appliance driven by mechanical power, or give signals to a driver of a power-operated lifting appliance.

ROOF WORK AND WORK AT HIGH LEVEL

General requirements for safe working

1. A safe system of work should be established, eg method statement, before work commences. This should include all contractors and

sub-contractors involved, and should incorporate the provision of scaffolding, barriers, gin wheels, hoists, etc, the maintenance of a safe place of work and records of inspection of the plant, equipment, access arrangement and working positions.

Roofing

2. Where a properly erected scaffold is not used, a rigid roof-edge barrier, incorporating guard rail and toe boards, must be provided before work commences. This arrangement must stay in position until work is completed.

3. Any roof opening left as work progresses must be suitably guarded or secured and marked 'Hole Below'.

4. Suitable crawling boards must be used for access and working areas on pitched roofs, when working on fragile roofs or roofs which may become slippery, and in every case where roofs have a pitch greater than 30°.

5. Precautions must be taken against adverse weather conditions, including the arrangements for storage of equipment and materials on roofs.

6. Dry powder fire appliances must be provided when fires are used to heat mastics. Distances between boilers not being heated and the fires in use must be not less than 10 feet (3.3m).

7. Care must be taken not to overload partially completed roofs or roof trusses.

8. Where excessive loading is anticipated, purpose-designed loading towers should be used.

9. Satisfactory access must be provided to the working position.

10. The method of lifting or storage of materials must be established with a safe place of work to operate from.

11. The collection of all roof material off-cuts must be closely controlled.

Cladding operations

12. The method of lifting or storage of materials must be established with a safe place of work to operate from.

13. A suitable scaffold working platform may be required.

14. The method of tying in the scaffold must be satisfactory.

15. Mobile access towers must have appropriate base dimensions and good ground conditions.

16. Satisfactory access and means of lifting materials must be provided.

WORK ABOVE GROUND

Work above ground generally entails the use of scaffolds, mobile access equipment and/or ladders. The following factors need consideration to ensure safe working practices for this type of work.

Basic scaffolding requirements

1. Suitable and sufficient means of access to the working platform and egress from same must be provided.

2. As far as practicable, all workplaces must be kept safe.

3. Scaffolds must be provided at working heights exceeding two metres above ground/floor level.

4. Toeboards and handrails must be fitted on scaffolds exceeding two metres above ground/floor level.

5. Scaffolds must be adequately lit.

6. Materials must not be thrown or tipped from working platforms.

7. Scaffolds must be constructed using approved materials, in sound condition, and free from excessive rust, etc.

8. Scaffolds must be rigid, every part so fixed, secured or placed as to prevent accidental displacement, and erected on a sound foundation.

9. Standards must be vertical, or lean towards the structure, and be securely fixed and braced.

10. Ledgers and transoms must be horizontal and securely fixed so as to prevent movement.

11. Putlogs must be straight, provided with flat ends, and securely fixed into the structure.

12. A scaffold board must not project beyond its support more than four times its thickness.

13. The minimum width for gangways provided at heights exceeding two metres above floor/ground level is 0.44m (17˝).

14. Stairs must be provided throughout their length with handrails or other accepted safety measures in order to prevent the fall of workmen and materials. The fitting of toe boards is necessary on landings but not on stairs.

15. Minimum permitted widths for scaffolds are:

- general – 0.64m (25˝) except where used for special tasks
- for men and materials – 0.87m (34˝)

- for supporting another platform – 1.07m (42″)
- for the side of a sloping roof – 0.44m (17″).

16. Partly erected/dismantled scaffolds must display appropriate warning notices and access blocked.

17. When dismantling scaffolds, tubes and fittings must be lowered to the ground, not thrown.

18. Competent person to inspect scaffold materials before each occasion on which they are put into use.

19. Erection, substantial alterations or additions to, and dismantling of scaffolds to be carried out under the immediate supervision of a competent person.

20. Competent and experienced workmen to be employed, so far as is practicable, for the erection, substantial alterations or additions to, and dismantling of scaffolds.

21. Scaffolds to be rigidly connected to the building or other structures unless designed and constructed as an independent scaffold.

22. Scaffolds to be securely supported or suspended and strutted or braced where necessary.

23. Parts of buildings or other structures not to be used to support scaffolds unless they are of sound material and sufficiently strong and stable.

24. Gutters not to be used as supports unless they are suitable for the purpose and of adequate strength.

25. Overhanging eaves gutters not to be so used unless designed as walkways.

Inspection and maintenance

1. All scaffolds in use must have been inspected by a competent person within the preceding seven days unless no part has been erected for over seven days.

2. Scaffolds must be inspected after being exposed to adverse weather conditions likely to affect strength or stability or displacement of any part.

3. Results of inspections to be entered in or attached to the prescribed register (except for ladder scaffolds, trestle scaffolds, and scaffolds from which persons cannot fall more than 6′6″ (2m)).

4. Each employer whose staff use a scaffold must satisfy themselves that it complies with the Construction (Working Places) Regulations 1966, whether or not his own staff have erected it.

5. All scaffolds must be properly maintained.

6. Platforms, gangways, runs and stairs to be kept clear of unnecessary obstructions, material or rubbish and from projecting nails.

7. Slippery platforms, gangways, runs and stairs to be sanded, cleaned or otherwise remedied as soon as is practicable.

8. Movement of materials on or onto scaffolds to be done without causing any violent shock.

9. Loads on scaffolds to be evenly distributed so far as is practicable.

Movable access equipment

This type of equipment, which takes the form of an access tower, may take several forms:

- a movable tower formed from scaffold tubes or
- a similar movable tower but constructed from pre-formed frames which interlock together.

In each case, the tower incorporates a working platform, access by means of an externally fixed ladder or a series of internally-placed raking ladders, and castor wheels at the base which permit the tower to be moved with ease. As such, this form of equipment is very adaptable, being used for a wide range of activities on both construction sites or in routine maintenance tasks in all types of premises. They are commonly used for:

- high level maintenance work
- painting inner roof surfaces and walls and
- small-scale building operations.

The following precautions should be taken in their use:

1. Working platforms should be fitted with guard rails and toeboards.

2. The platform should be secure and completely boarded.

3. The height of the working platform must not exceed three times the smaller base dimension, and no tower should have a base dimension of less than four feet.

4. In certain cases, eg when working in windy conditions, outriggers should be fitted to increase stability.

5. Rigidity of the tower should be increased by the use of diagonal bracing on all four elevations and horizontally.

6. Castors used with the tower should be fixed at the extreme corners of the tower in such a manner that they cannot fall out when the tower is moved. Castors should be fitted with an effective wheel brake.

7. Towers should be moved with great care, and under no circumstances should they be moved whilst a person is present on the working platform. All equipment and materials should be removed from the platform prior to moving the tower.

8. The tower should be moved by pulling or pushing at base level.

Further information is incorporated by BS 5973: 1981 'Code of practice for the access and working scaffolds and special scaffold structures in steel'.

Ladders

Construction

1. All ladders should be of good construction, suitable and sound material, adequate strength and properly maintained.

2. Ladders with missing or defective rungs, split stiles or other forms of defect should not be used.

3. Wooden stiles and rungs should have the grain running lengthwise.

4. Wooden ladders should not be painted or treated in such a way that defects in the timber may be concealed. (Wooden ladders may, however, be treated with clear preservative.)

5. Wooden ladders should be fitted with reinforcing ties if tenon joints are not secured by wedges.

Use

6. Ladders not standing on a base should be securely, equally and properly suspended by each stile and secured where necessary to prevent undue swinging or swaying.

7. Ladders standing on a base to be equally and properly supported on each stile.

8. A ladder standing on a base to be securely fixed near its upper resting place (or its upper end, if vertical). If such fixing is impracticable, the ladder must be fixed at or near its lower end.

Where this is also impracticable, a person must be stationed at the foot of the ladder to prevent it from slipping.

9. Except where there are adequate handholds, ladders must rise to a height of at least 3′6″ (1m) above the landing place or above the highest rung reached by the feet of a person using the ladder.

10. The space at each rung must be sufficient to provide an adequate foothold.

11. Landing places of adequate size to be provided if practicable every 30′0″ (9.14m) of vertical distance, or more frequently.

12. Landing placed from which persons are liable to fall more than 6′6″ (1.98m) to have handrails to a height of between 3′0″ (0.92m) and 3′9″ (1.15m), and also toeboards or other barriers to a height of at least 6″ (0.155m). The space between the toeboard and the nearest guard rail must be not more than 2′6″ (0.76m).

13. Openings in landings through which ladders pass must be as small as practicable.

14. Folding step ladders must have a level and firm footing and must not be stood on loose bricks or other loose packing.

WORK BELOW GROUND

Excavation work and other forms of work below ground can be particularly dangerous due to the risk of collapse of such excavations, flooding of same or people, materials and vehicles falling in to the excavation.

General safety requirements

The methods of supporting the sides of excavations vary widely in design, the method of placing materials and the materials used.

For larger excavations the support will be based on the anticipated soil and structural pressures, taking into account the various stages during construction when the support will be installed and subsequently dismantled.

For smaller excavations, one of three systems shown in the illustrations are generally used. Where timber runners or boards are shown, these could equally well be replaced by steel trench sheeting. Similarly timber struts could be replaced by adjustable steel struts or hand-operated hydraulic shoring. Much will depend upon:

- the nature of the subsoil
- projected life of the excavation
- work to be undertaken, including equipment used
- the possibility of flooding from ground water and heavy rain
- the depth of the excavation and
- the number of people using the excavation at any one time.

Examples of skeleton timbering, close timbering and sheet piling are illustrated.

Excavations

Materials and equipment
1. An adequate supply of timber or other materials should be provided.

2. Any dangerous parts to machinery must be securely fenced, unless safe by position or construction.

Fencing

3. Barriers must be provided around excavations, shafts, pits and openings into which persons can fall to a vertical distance of more than 6′6″ (1.98m).

4. Barriers must be as close as practicable to the edge of the excavation.

5. Barriers must be maintained in position except when necessarily removed for the access of persons or materials.

Timbering

6. Adequate and suitable material must be used to prevent danger from falls or dislodgement of the sides of the excavation, etc or materials adjacent to it.

7. Timbering should be completed as early as practicable in the course of the work.

8. Persons engaged in timbering must be protected as far as possible from danger.

9. Timbering or other supports must be of good construction, sound material, free from patent defect and of adequate strength for the purpose.

10. Struts and braces must be properly and adequately secured to prevent accidental displacement or fall.

11. A competent person must direct the erection and dismantling of all timbering and other supports, as well as any subsequent alterations or additions to same.

12. Experienced workmen should be employed, as far as possible, for the erection, dismantling, etc of timbering and other supports.

Inspection and examination

13. Material for timbering and other supports to be inspected by a competent person before being taken into use.

14. Every part of any excavation, shaft, earthwork or tunnel must be inspected by a competent person at least once every day that persons are employed there.

15. The face of every tunnel and base or crown of every shaft must be inspected by a competent person at the beginning of every shift.

16. The working end of every trench more than 6′6″ deep (1.98m) must be inspected by a competent person before the beginning of every shift.

17. No person must work in any excavation, shaft, earthwork or tunnel:
    - after explosives have been used in or near it, in a manner likely to affect stability, until a thorough examination has been made by a competent person
    - unless it has been thoroughly examined by a competent person within the previous seven days and
    - after an unexpected fall of rock, earth or other material, or after substantial damage to timber or other supports, unless the part concerned has been thoroughly examined by a competent person.

18. A report of each examination must be made on the day of the examination in the form prescribed by the Construction (General Provisions) Reports Order 1962.

Other precautions

19. Excavations and approaches must be well-lit.

20. Materials must not be placed near to the edge of any excavation etc so as to endanger persons below.

21. Where an excavation is likely to affect the security of another structure (permanent or temporary), steps must be taken to safeguard persons employed from possible collapse of that structure.

22. Means of reaching a place of safety must be provided, as far as practicable when there may be a danger of rising water or irruption of water or material.

23. Means to prevent overrunning to be taken when a vehicle is used to tip material into a pit or excavation or over the edge of an embankment or earthwork.

24. The atmosphere must be well-ventilated and free from dust, fumes, etc.

DEMOLITION OPERATIONS

Demolition is probably the most hazardous operation undertaken in the construction industry. The principal hazards are:

- falls of men, falls of materials, flying materials, dust and debris, resulting in a wide range of injuries and conditions, some of which are of a fatal nature
- collapse of a building or structure, either deliberately or unplanned
- overloading of floors or the structure with debris, resulting in floor and/or building collapse
- the use of incorrect or unsafe demolition techniques

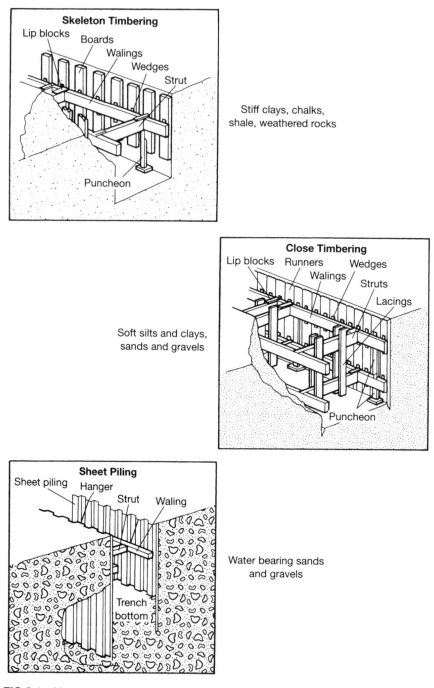

FIG 8.1 Methods of supporting excavations

- explosions in tanks or other confined spaces
- the presence of live electric cables and gas mains
- the presence of dusty, corrosive and poisonous materials and/or atmospheres and
- projecting nails in timber, broken glass and cast iron fragments which can penetrate the hands, feet and other parts of the body.

In addition to these hazards, the ever-present risk of **asbestos** inhalation must be considered. The presence or otherwise of asbestos should be assessed in any pre-demolition survey undertaken.

Management of the demolition process

Principal features of this process include a pre-demolition survey, the action necessary prior to demolition, the action whilst demolition is in progress and the procedures to ensure close supervision of demolition sites.

Pre-demolition survey

Prior to demolition commencing, a safe system of work must be established. In most cases, this would be done through a written method statement. Such a system will be determined following a pre-demolition survey undertaken by a competent person and, where possible, perusal of the plans of the building.

The use of the **demolition hazard checklist** (see Figure 8.2) is recommended, together with Table 8.2 'Guide to typical methods of demolition' of BS 6187:1982 (Code of Practice for Demolition).

The pre-demolition survey should identify:

- the nature and method of construction of the building or structure
- the arrangement of buildings adjacent to that for demolition and the condition of such adjoining property
- the location of underground services, eg water mains, electricity cables, gas pipes, drains, sewers and telephone cables
- the previous use of the premises, which could be significant
- the presence of dangerous substances inherent in the structure, eg asbestos, or stored internally
- the method of bonding of the main load-bearing walls
- the system of shoring or the provision of other support necessary during demolition
- the presence of cantilevered structures, their form of construction and the nature of any dangers from same
- the presence of basements, cellars, vaults or other spaces affecting the structure of adjoining properties

- the presence of storage tanks below ground, and the nature of their contents or previous contents and

- the actual sequence of operations for demolition, which should generally take place in the reverse order of erection of the building.

Table 8.2 Guide to typical methods of demolition (see Note 1)

Type of structure	Type of construction	Method of demolition			
		Detached building isolated site	Detached building confined site	Attached building isolated site	Attached building confined site
Small and medium two-storey buildings	Loadbearing walls	ABCDM	ABDM	ABDM	ADM
Large buildings three storeys and over	Loadbearing walls	ABDM	ABDM	ABDM	AD
	Loadbearing walls with wrought iron and cast iron members	ABDM	AM	AM	AM
Framed structures	Structural steel	ACM	AM	AM	AM
	In situ reinforced concrete	ADM	ADM	ADM	AM
	Precast reinforced concrete	ADM	ADM	ADM	AM
	Prestressed reinforced concrete				
	Composite (structural steel and reinforced concrete)	ADM	ADM	ADM	AM
	Timber	ABCDM	ABDM	ABDM	ABDM
Independent cantilevers (canopies, balconies and staircases)		ADM	ADM	ADM	ADM
Bridges		ABCDM	ABCDM	AM	AM
Masonry arches		ACDM	ACDM	ACDM	ACDM
Chimneys	Brick or masonry	ACD	A	ACD	A
	Steel	AC	A	A	A
	In situ and precast reinforced concrete	AD	A	AD	A
	Reinforced plastics	AC	A	A	A
Spires		ACD	A	A	A
Pylons and masts		AC	A	A	A
Petroleum tanks (underground) Above ground storage tanks Chemical works and similar establishments Basements Special structures					

Note 1. This table is a general guide to the methods of demolition usually adopted in particular circumstances. In addition, subject to local restraints, explosives may be used by experienced personnel in many of the circumstances listed. This table should be read in conjunction with the main text. The indication of a particular method does not necessarily preclude the use of another method, or the use of several methods in combination

Note 2. *Legend*
  A denotes hand demolition
  B denotes mechanical demolition by pusher arm
  C denotes mechanical demolition by deliberate collapse
  D denotes mechanical demolition by demolition ball

Demolition work should be undertaken in accordance with the BS Code of Practice for Demolition by registered demolition contractors listed in the Demolition and Dismantling Industry Register.

Action prior to demolition

Prior to demolition, a number of actions must be taken, in particular:

- Form 10 (Notification of Project) must be submitted to the local office of the HSE (See **CONDAM Regulations** later in this chapter.)

SERVICES	Gas	☐	Electricity	☐	Water	☐	
	Telephone	☐	Sewers	☐	Others	☐	
GLASS	Doors/windows	☐	Partitions	☐	Sky lights	☐	
ROOF	Fragile	☐	weak	☐			
BASEMENT	Sumps/wells	☐	Extensions under pavements/ other buildings	☐			
STRUCTURAL TIMBER	Decayed	☐	Damaged	☐			
ADJACENT BUILDINGS	Bracing or shoring required	☐	Weather-proofing required	☐			
INDUSTRIAL PLANT	Carboniferous dust deposits	☐	Gas test required required	☐			
AFTER-EFFECTS OF FIRE, FLOODING, BLASTING	Bracing or shoring required	☐	Gas test required required	☐			

FIG 8.2 Demolition hazard checklist

- local authorities, statutory undertakings and owners of adjacent properties must be notified and consulted
- services, such as gas, water and electricity, must be isolated
- a **competent supervisor**, with knowledge and experience of this type of

work, must be appointed to take charge of the operation, and all persons on the site briefed

- all dangerous areas, particularly those affecting members of the public, must be fenced off or barricaded, and appropriate warning notices displayed
- 'fans' or catching platforms should be installed not more than 20′0″ (6m) below the working level when there is a risk to the public and
- operators must be briefed that personal protective equipment, including safety helmets with chin straps, goggles, heavy duty gloves and safety boots with steel insoles, must be provided and worn during the total period when demolition is in progress; respiratory protective equipment, together with safety belts and/or harnesses, may also be necessary.

Action during demolition

The following precautions are necessary during the demolition process:

1 Demolition should, wherever possible, be carried out in the reverse order of erection of the building.

2 No isolated freestanding wall should be left on its own unless judged to be secure by the competent person in charge.

3 Scaffold working platforms should be used, all refuse and debris being removed from these temporary structures on a regular basis to avoid overloading, together with debris which has accumulated behind walls.

4 Support for members of framed structures must be provided before gutting, along with temporary props, bracing or guys to restrain remaining parts of the building.

5 On no account must operators work on the floor being demolished, and site control must ensure that all operators are kept at a safe distance from the scene of operations when pulling arrangements, demolition ball, pusher arm and/or explosives are being used.

6 Entrances, passages, stairs and ladder runs should be kept clear of all material and debris and, where necessary, be so protected as to safeguard any person using them from falling materials.

7 Disturbed staircases, particularly stone staircases, should not be used.

8 Accumulated debris and piled materials should not be used by operators for the performance of their work; every employee should be provided with a safe footing in the form of safe planking or flooring.

9 Access to areas where flooring has been removed, or where there are dangerous holes or openings, such as lift shafts, should be barricaded, barred against entry or protected by means of a guard rail and toe boards.

10 Where work cannot be done safely from the ground, or from a sound part of the structure, close-boarded scaffolds, ladders or other means of support should be provided.

11 All openings, corners, breaks and edges from which or through which a person could fall a distance of more than 6´6˝ (2m) should be securely covered or provided with guard rails and toeboards; material used to cover holes should be securely fixed in position and clearly marked; where such measures are impracticable, safety nets or sheets should be provided below openings and at corners, etc; where the use of safety nets is impracticable, safety belts should be provided and worn.

12 Employees should not be permitted to work on, above or pass across open joisting, through which they could fall a distance of more than 6´6˝ (2m) unless such joisting is covered by boards or other temporary covering.

13 Timber with protruding nails should have the nails removed or knocked down or, alternatively, stacked where it cannot be a source of danger.

14 Glass in partitions, doors, roofs and windows should be removed separately prior to demolition activities commencing.

15 Adequate and suitable lighting should be provided for all working places, approaches, dangerous openings and places where lifting or lowering is taking place.

8

Supervision of demolition sites

A high degree of supervision and control is required in demolition activities. The following requirements must be implemented:

1 Before any demolition work is commenced, a **competent supervisor**, with knowledge and experience of the type of work to be undertaken, should be appointed in writing.

2 All work should be carried out under the immediate supervision of a supervisor or by fully-experienced men working under the direction of a **competent foreman**.

3 When work is under the immediate supervision of the appointed supervisor, he must give clear instructions and ensure that they are correctly understood. He must not pass instructions through an intermediary, but give them direct to the men concerned.

4 During demolition, continuing inspections must be made as work progresses to detect any hazards to operators resulting from weakened or overloaded floors, or loosened materials.

5 Express measures must be taken by shoring or other means to prevent premature collapse.

6   Where mechanical plant is used for demolition purposes, the drivers/operators of the machines, together with the banksmen, should be fully trained and experienced in the type of work being undertaken. Lookouts should be posted at a safe distance to prevent persons, including members of the public, approaching the danger area.

SAFETY METHOD STATEMENTS

A safety method statement is a formally written safe system of work, or series of integrating safe systems of work, agreed between client/occupier and contractor or between main contractor and sub-contractor, and produced where work with a foreseeably high hazard content is to be undertaken.

It should specify the operations to be undertaken on a stage-by-stage basis and indicate the precautions necessary to protect site operators, staff occupying the premises where the work is undertaken and members of the public who may be affected by the work.

It may incorporate information and specific requirements stipulated by occupiers of premises, employers, health and safety advisers, enforcement officers, the police, site surveyor and the manufacturers and suppliers of plant, equipment and substances used during the work. In certain cases, it may identify training needs, eg under the Control of Substances Hazardous to Health (COSHH) Regulations, Electricity at Work Regulations, or the use of specifically-trained operators.

The use of safety method statements

A safety method statement is necessary to ensure safe working in activities involving:

- the use of hazardous substances, eg toxic, corrosive, harmful, irritant, flammable, etc substances
- the use of explosives
- lifting operations
- potential fire risk situations
- electrical hazards
- the use of sources of radiation
- the risk of dust explosions or inhalation of hazardous dusts, gases, fumes, vapours, etc
- certain types of excavation adjacent to existing structures
- demolition work and

the removal of asbestos from existing buildings.

Contents of the safety method statement

The following features should be incorporated in a safety method statement:

- techniques to be used
- access provisions
- safeguarding of existing work locations and positions
- structural stability requirements, eg shoring
- procedures to ensure the safety of others, eg members of the public
- health precautions, including the use of local exhaust ventilation systems and personal protective equipment
- plant and equipment to be used
- procedures to prevent area pollution
- segregation of certain areas
- procedures for disposal of toxic wastes
- procedures to ensure compliance with specific legislation, eg Environmental Protection Act, Control of Substances Hazardous to Health (COSHH) Regulations, Noise at Work Regulations, Control of Asbestos at Work Regulations.

Asbestos

In addition to the above recommendations, the following features should be incorporated in a specific safety method statement where work entails the removal or stripping of asbestos:

- the specific safe system of work
- procedures for segregation of the asbestos stripping area
- personal protective equipment requirements
- welfare amenity provisions – hand washing, showers, separation of protective clothing from personal clothing, sanitation arrangements, catering facilities, drinking water provision
- ventilation requirements and arrangements for the working area
- personal hygiene requirements for operators
- supervision requirements and arrangements
- atmospheric monitoring procedures, including action to be taken following unsatisfactory results of air samples taken and notification requirements under the Control of Asbestos at Work Regulations 1987.

The need for safety method statements

The need for contractors to produce safety method statements prior to high risk operations should be raised in any pre-contract discussions between occupier and main contractor.

In certain cases, a standard form of safety method statement is agreed, used and signed by the main contractor as an indication of his intention to follow that particular safe system of work which has been agreed between himself and the occupier.

Further guidance on safety method statements is provided in 'A guide to managing health and safety in construction' prepared by the Construction Industry Advisory Committee (CONIAC) in consultation with the HSE. (HSE Books: 1995)

THE CONSTRUCTION REGULATIONS

Employers in the construction industry and related operations must comply with the general provisions of HSWA and with specific regulations relating to construction made under the FA. The 'Construction Regulations' comprise four sets of regulations:

- Construction (General Provisions) Regulations 1961
- Construction (Lifting Operations) Regulations 1961
- Construction (Working Places) Regulations 1966
- Construction (Health and Welfare) Regulations 1966

which were made under the FA. To facilitate understanding of these regulations, their various provisions are covered on a safety topic basis, sooner than on an individual set of regulations basis.

These regulations apply to **building operations** and to **works of engineering construction** undertaken by way of trade or business, or for the purpose of any industrial or commercial undertaking, or by or on behalf of the Crown or any municipal or other public authority and to any line or siding (not being part of a railway or tramway) used in connection with them.

Section 176 of the FA defines a **building operation** as the construction, structural alteration, repair or maintenance of a building (including repointing, redecorating, and external cleaning of the structure), the demolition of a building, and the preparation for and laying the foundation of an intended building, but does not include works of engineering construction.

Works of engineering construction are defined as the construction of any railway line or siding otherwise than on an existing railway, and the construction, structural alteration, repair (including repointing and repainting) or demolition of any dock, harbour, inland navigation, tunnel, bridge, viaduct, waterworks reservoir, pipeline, aqueduct, sewer, sewage works, or gasholder, except where carried on upon a railway or tramway.

The term also covers the following operations except when carried on in a factory, electricity station, railway or tramway, namely the construction, structural alteration, repair, repointing, repainting or demolition of any steel or reinforced concrete structure other than a building, and any road, airfield, sea defence works or river works, and any other civil or constructional engineering works of a similar nature. This part of the definition was added by the Engineering Construction (Extension of Definition) Regulations 1960.

Duties of contractors, employees, safety supervisors and competent persons

Contractors

The duties imposed by the regulations are directed to the contractor or 'employer of workmen'. This is because, in many cases, construction workers are not technically employees but self-employed operators under a contract for service.

Generally, the employer must comply with the regulations in so far as they are relevant to the nature of the work being carried out, eg excavations, roof work. Certain regulations must, however, be complied with whatever the work, eg the duty to appoint a safety supervisor.

Employees

Employees are also under a duty to comply with the provisions of the regulations. This means they must operate in accordance with the regulations and co-operate with the employer in ensuring safety requirements are met. They must report any defect in plant or equipment to their employer of the safety supervisor without delay.

CONSTRUCTION (DESIGN AND MANAGEMENT) REGULATIONS 1994

These regulations impose requirements and prohibitions with respect to design and management aspects of **construction work** as defined. They give effect to Council Directive 92/57/EEC on **the implementation of minimum safety and health requirements at temporary or mobile construction sites**.

Regulation 2 – interpretation

1 The more significant definitions in the regulations are given below:

Agent in relation to any client means any person who acts as agent for a client in connection with the carrying on by the person of a trade, business or other undertaking (whether for profit or not).

Cleaning work means the cleaning of any window or any transparent or translucent wall, ceiling or roof in or on a structure where such cleaning involves a risk of a person falling more than two metres.

Client means any person for whom a project is carried out, whether it is carried out by another person or carried out in-house.

Construction phase means the period of time starting when construction work in any project starts and ending when construction work in that project is completed.

Construction work means the carrying out of any building, civil engineering or engineering construction work and includes any of the following:

(a) the construction, alteration, conversion, fitting out, commissioning, renovation, repair, upkeep, redecoration or other maintenance (including cleaning) which involves the use of water or an abrasive at high pressure or the use of substances classified as corrosive or toxic for the purpose of Regulation 7 of the Chemicals (Hazard Information and Packaging for Supply) Regulations 1994, decommissioning, demolition or dismantling of a structure

(b) the preparation for an intended structure, including site clearance, exploration, investigation (but not site survey) and excavation, and laying or installing the foundations of the structure

(c) the assembly of prefabricated elements to form a structure or the disassembly of prefabricated elements which, immediately before such disassembly, formed a structure

(d) the removal of a structure or part of a structure or of any product or waste resulting from demolition or dismantling of a structure or from disassembly of prefabricated elements which, immediately before such disassembly, formed a structure

(e) the installation, commissioning, maintenance, repair or removal of mechanical, electrical, gas, compressed air, hydraulic, telecommunications, computer or similar services which are normally fixed within or to a structure

but does **not** include the exploration for or extraction of mineral resources or activities preparatory thereto carried out at a place where such exploration or extraction is carried out.

Contractor means any person who carried on a trade or business or other undertaking (whether for profit or not) in connection with which they:

(a) undertake to or do carry out or manage construction work

(b) arrange for any person at work under their control (including where they are an employer, an employee of theirs) to carry out or manage construction work.

Design in relation to any structure includes drawing, design details, specification and bill of quantities (including specification of articles or substances) in relation to the structure.

Designer means any person who carries on a trade, business or other undertaking in connection with which he:

(a) prepares a design or

(b) arranges for any person under his control (including, where he is an employer, any employee of his) to prepare a design relating to a structure or part of a structure.

Domestic client means a client for whom a project is carried out not being a project carried out in connection with the carrying on by the client of a trade, business or other undertaking (whether for profit or not).

Project means a project which includes or is intended to include construction work.

Structure means:

(a) any building, steel or reinforced concrete structure (not being a building), railway line or siding, tramway line, dock, harbour, inland navigation, tunnel, shaft, bridge, viaduct, waterworks, reservoir, pipe or pipe-line (whatever, in either case, it contains or is intended to contain), cable, aqueduct, sewer, sewage works, gasholder, road, airfield, sea defence works, river works, drainage works, earthworks, lagoon, dam, wall, caisson, mast, tower, pylon, underground tank, earth retaining structure, or structure designed to preserve or alter any natural feature, and any other structure similar to the foregoing or

(b) any formwork, falsework, scaffold or other structure designed or used to provide support or means of access during construction work or

(c) any fixed plant in respect of work which is installation, commissioning, de-commissioning or dismantling and where any such work involves a risk of a person falling more than two metres.

2 In determining whether any person **arranges** for a person (the **relevant person**) to prepare a design or to carry out or manage construction work, regard shall be had to the following, namely:

(a) a person **does arrange** for the relevant person to do a thing where:
   (i) they specify in or in connection with any arrangement with a third person what the relevant person shall do that thing (whether by nominating the relevant person as a sub-contractor to the third person or otherwise) or
   (ii) being an employer, it is done by any of their employees in-house.

(b) a person **does not arrange** for the relevant person to do a thing where:
   (i) being a **self-employed person**, they do it themselves or, being in **partnership** it is done by any of their partners
   (ii) being an **employer**, it is done by any of their employees otherwise than in-house

(iii) being a **firm** carrying on its business anywhere in Great Britain whose principal place of business is in Scotland, it is done by any partner in the firm or

(iv) having arranged for a **third person** to do the thing, they do not object to the third person arranging for it to be done by the relevant person

and the expressions **arrange** and **arranges** shall be construed accordingly.

3 For the purpose of these regulations:

(a) **a project is carried out in-house** where any employer arranges for the project to be carried out by an employee of theirs who acts, or by a group of employees who act, in either case, in relation to such a project as a separate part of the undertaking of the employer distinct from the part for which the project is carried out

(b) **construction work is carried out or managed in-house** where an employer arranges for the construction work to be carried out or managed by an employee of theirs who acts or by a group of employees who act, in either case, in relation to such construction work as a separate part of the undertaking of the employer distinct from the part for which the construction work is carried out or managed or

(c) **a design is prepared in-house** where any employer arranges for the design to be prepared by an employee of theirs who acts, or by a group of employees who act, in either case, in relation to such design as a separate part of the undertaking of the employer distinct from the part for which the design is prepared.

4 For the purposes of these regulations, a project is **notifiable** if the construction phase:

(a) **will be longer than 30 days** or

(b) **will involve more than 500 person days of construction work**

and the term **notifiable** shall be construed accordingly.

5 Any reference in these regulations to a person being **reasonably satisfied**:

(a) as to another person's **competence** is a reference to that person being satisfied after the taking of such steps as it is reasonable for that person to take (including making reasonable enquiries or seeking advice where necessary) to satisfy himself as to such competence

(b) as to whether another person has allocated or will allocate **adequate resources** is a reference to that person being satisfied that after the taking of such steps as is reasonable for that person to take (including making reasonable enquiries or seeking advice necessary):

(i) to ascertain what resources have been or are intended to be so allocated and

(ii) to establish whether the resources so allocated or intended to be allocated are adequate.

Regulation 3 – application of regulations

1 Subject to the following paragraphs of this regulation, these regulations shall apply to and in relation to construction work.

2 Subject to paragraph 3, regulations 4 to 12 and 14 to 19 **shall not** apply to or in relation to construction work included in a project where the client has **reasonable grounds** for believing that:
   (a) the project is not notifiable and
   (b) the largest number of persons at work **at any one time** carrying out construction work included in the project will be, or as the case may be, less than five.

3 These regulations **shall apply** to and in relation to construction work which is the **demolition or dismantling of a structure** notwithstanding paragraph 2.

4 These regulations **shall not apply** to or in relation to construction work in respect of which the **local authority** within the meaning of regulation 2(1) of the Health and Safety (Enforcing Authority) Regulations 1989 is the **enforcing authority**.

5 Regulation 14(b) (co-operation between designers) **shall not apply** to projects in which **no more than one designer** is involved.

6 Regulation 16(1) (co-operation between all contractors) **shall not apply** to projects in which **no more than one contractor** is involved.

7 Where construction work is carried out or managed in-house or a design is prepared in-house, then, for the purpose of paragraphs 5 and 6, each part of the undertaking shall be treated as a person and shall be counted as a designer, or as the case may be, contractor, accordingly.

8 Except where regulation 5 (requirements on developers) applies, regulations 4, 6, 8 to 12 and 14 to 19, **shall not apply** to or in relation to construction work included or intended to be included in a project carried out for a **domestic client**.

Regulation 4 – clients and agents of clients

1 A client may appoint an **agent** or another client to act as the only client in respect to a project and where such an appointment is made the provisions of paragraph 2 shall apply.

2 No client shall appoint any person as his agent unless the client is reasonably satisfied that the person he intends to appoint has the **competence** to perform the duties imposed on a client by these regulations.

3 Where the person appointed under paragraph 1 makes a **declaration** in accordance with paragraph 4, from the date of receipt of the declaration by the Executive (HSE), such requirements and prohibitions as are imposed upon a client shall apply to the person so appointed (so long as he remains as such) as if he were the only client in respect of that project.

4 A **declaration** in accordance with this paragraph:
   (a) is a declaration **in writing**, signed by or on behalf of the person referred to in paragraph 3, to the effect that the client or agent who makes it will act as client for the purposes of these regulations and
   (b) shall include the name of the person by or on behalf of whom it is made, the address where documents may be served on that person and the address of the construction site and
   (c) shall be sent to the HSE.

5 Where the HSE receives a declaration in accordance with paragraph 4, it shall give **notice** to the person by or on behalf of whom the declaration is made and the notice shall include the date the declaration was received by the HSE.

6 Where the person referred to in paragraph 3 does **not** make a declaration in accordance with paragraph 4, any requirement or prohibition imposed by these regulations on a client shall also be imposed on him but only to the extent it relates to any matter within his authority.

Regulation 5 – requirements on developer

1 This regulation applies where the project is carried out for a **domestic client** and the client enters into an arrangement with a person (**the developer**) who carries on a trade, business or other undertaking (whether for profit or not) in connection with which:
   (a) land or an interest in land is **granted or transferred** to the client and
   (b) the developer undertakes that construction work will be carried out on the land and
   (c) following the construction work, the land will include premises which, as intended by the client, will be occupied as a **residence**.

2 Where this regulation applies, with effect from the time the client enters into the arrangement referred to in paragraph 1, the requirements of regulations 6 and 8 to 12 shall apply to the developer as if he were the client.

Regulation 6 – appointments of planning supervisor and principal contractor

1 Subject to paragraph 6(b), every client **shall** appoint:
   (a) a planning supervisor and
   (b) a principal contractor
      in respect of each other.

2 The client shall **not** appoint as principal contractor any person who is not a contractor.

3 The **planning supervisor** shall be appointed as soon as is practicable after the client has such information about the project and the construction work involved in it as will enable him to comply with the requirements imposed on him by regulations 8(1) and 9(1).

4 The **principal contractor** shall be appointed as soon as is practicable after the client has such information about the project and the construction work involved in it as will enable him to comply with the requirements imposed on him by regulations 8(3) and 9(3) when making an arrangement with a contractor where such arrangement consists of the appointment of the principal contractor.

5 The appointments mentioned in paragraph 1 shall be **terminated, changed or renewed** as necessary to ensure that those appointments remain filled at all times until the end of the **construction phase**.

6 Paragraph 1 does not prevent:
   (a) the appointment of the **same person** as planning supervisor or as principal contractor provided that person is competent to carry out the functions under these regulations of both appointments or
   (b) the appointment of the client as planning supervisor or as principal contractor or as both, provided the client is competent to perform the relevant functions under these regulations.

Regulation 7 – notification of project

1 The planning supervisor shall ensure that **notice of the project** in respect of which he is appointed is given to the HSE in accordance with paragraphs 2 and 4 unless the planning supervisor has reasonable grounds for believing that the project is not notifiable.

2 Any **notice** required by paragraph 1 shall be **in writing** or in such other manner as the HSE may from time to time approve in writing and shall contain the **particulars** specified in paragraph 3 or, where applicable, paragraph 4 and shall be given at the times specified in those paragraphs.

3 Notice containing such of the particulars specified in **Schedule 1** as are known or can reasonably be ascertained shall be given as soon as is practicable after the appointment of the planning supervisor.

4 Where any particulars specified in Schedule 1 have not been notified under paragraph 3, notice of such particulars shall be given as soon as is practicable after the appointment of the principal contractor and, in any event, before the start of construction work.

5 Where a project is carried out for a **domestic client** then, except where regulation 5 applies, every contractor shall ensure that notice of the project is given to the HSE in accordance with paragraph 6 unless the contractor has reasonable grounds for believing that the project is not notifiable.

Regulation 8 – competence of planning supervisor, designers and contractors

1 No client shall appoint any person as **planning supervisor** in respect of a project unless the client is reasonably satisfied that the person he intends to appoint has the competence to perform the functions of planning supervisor under the regulations in respect of that project.

2 No person shall arrange for a **designer** to prepare the design unless he is reasonably satisfied that the designer has the competence to prepare that design.

3 No person shall arrange for a **contractor** to carry out or manage construction work unless he is reasonably satisfied that the contractor has the competence to carry out or, as the case may be, manage, that construction work.

4 Any reference in this regulation to a person having **competence** shall extend only to his competence:
(a) to perform any requirement and
(b) to conduct his undertaking without contravening any prohibition imposed on him by or under any of the **relevant statutory provisions**.

Regulation 9 – provision for health and safety

1 No person shall appoint any person as **planning supervisor** in respect of a project unless the client is reasonably satisfied that the person he intends to appoint has allocated or, as appropriate, will allocate **adequate resources** to enable him to perform the functions of planning supervisor under these regulations in respect of that project.

2 No person shall arrange for a **designer** to prepare a design unless he is reasonably satisfied that the designer has the **competence** to prepare that design.

3 No person shall arrange for a **contractor** to carry out or manage construction work unless he is reasonably satisfied that the contractor has allocated or, as appropriate, will allocate, **adequate resources** to enable the contractor to comply with the requirements and prohibitions imposed upon him by or under the relevant statutory provisions.

HSE
Health & Safety
Executive

Notification of project

Note
1. This form can be used to notify any project covered by the Construction (Design and Management) Regulations 1994 which will last longer than 30 days or 500 person days. It can also be used to provide additional details that were not available at the time of initial notification of such projects. (Any day on which construction work is carried out (including holidays and weekends) should be counted, even if the work on that day is of short duration. A person day is one individual, including supervisors and specialists, carrying out construction work for one normal working shift.)
2. The form should be completed and sent to the HSE area office covering the site where construction work is to take place. You should sent it as soon as possible after the planning supervisor is appointed to the project.
3. The form can be used by contractors working for domestic clients. In this case only parts 4–8 and 11 need to be filled in.

HSE – For official use only

Client	V	PV	NV	Planning supervisor	V	PV	NV
Focus serial number				Principal contractor	V	PV	NV

1 Is this the initial notification of this project or are you providing additional information that was not previously available

Initial notification ☐   Additional notification ☐

2 Client: name, full address, postcode and telephone number (*if more than one client, please attach details on separate sheet*)

Name:	Telephone number:
Address:	
Postcode:	

3 Planning Supervisor: name, full address, postcode and telephone number

Name:	Telephone number:
Address:	
Postcode:	

4 Principal Contractor (or contractor when project for a domestic client) name, full address, postcode and telephone number

Name:	Telephone number:
Address:	
Postcode:	

5 Address of site: where construction work is to be carried out

Address:
Postcode

F10 (rev 03.95)

FIG 8.3 Notification of a project

6 Local Authority: name of the local government district council or island council within whose district the operations are to be carried out

7 Please give your estimates on the following: Please indicate if these estimates are

original ☐ revised ☐ (*tick relevant box*)

a. The planned date for the commencement of the construction work

b. How long the construction work is expected to take (*in weeks*)

c. The maximum number of people carrying out construction work on site at any one time

d. The number of contractors expected to work on site

8 Construction work: give brief details of the type of construction work that will be carried out

9 Contractors: name, full address and postcode of those who have been chosen to work on the project (*if required continue on a separate sheet). (Note this information is only required when it is known at the time notification is first made to HSE. An update is not required)*

Declaration of planning supervisor

10 I hereby declare that .... (*name of organisation*) has been appointed as planning supervisor for the project

Signed by or on behalf of the organisation...(*print name*).......................................

Date ....

Declaration of principal contractor

11 I hereby declare that .... (*name of principal contractor*) has been appointed as principal contractor for the project, (*or contractor undertaking project for domestic client*)

Signed by or on behalf of the organisation...(*print name*).......................................

Date ....

FIG 8.3   (Continued)

Regulation 10 – start of construction phase

Every client shall ensure, so far as is reasonably practicable, that the construction phase of any project does not start unless a **health and safety plan** complying with regulation 15(4) has been prepared in respect of that project.

Regulation 11 – client to ensure information is available

1 Every client shall ensure that the planning supervisor for any project carried out for the client is provided (as soon as is reasonably practicable but in any event before the commencement of the work to which the information relates) with **all information** mentioned in paragraph 2 about the **state or condition of any premises** at or on which construction work included or intended to be included in the project is or is intended to be carried out.

2 The information required to be provided by paragraph 1 is information which is relevant to the functions of the planning supervisor under these regulations and which the client has or could ascertain by making enquiries which it is reasonable for a person in his position to make.

Regulation 12 – client to ensure health and safety file is available for inspection

1 Every client shall take such steps as it is reasonable for a person in his position to take to ensure that the information in any **health and safety file** which has been delivered to him is kept available for inspection by any person who may need information in the file for the purpose of complying with the requirements and prohibitions imposed upon him by or under the relevant statutory provisions.

2 It shall be sufficient compliance with paragraph 1 by a client who **disposes of his entire interest** in the property of the structure if he delivers the health and safety file for the structure to the person who acquires his interest in the property of the structure and ensures such person is aware of the nature and purpose of the health and safety file.

Regulation 13 – requirements on designer

1 Except where a design is prepared in-house, no employer shall cause or permit any employee of his to prepare, and no self-employed person shall prepare, a design in respect of any project unless he has taken reasonable steps to ensure that the client for that project is aware of the duties to which the client is subject by virtue of these regulations and of any practical guidance issued from time to time by the HSC with respect to the requirements of these regulations.

2 Every designer **shall**:

(a) ensure that any design he prepares and which he is aware will be used for the purposes of construction work includes among the **design considerations** adequate regard to the need:

    (i)   to **avoid foreseeable risks** to the health and safety of any person at work carrying out construction work or cleaning work in or on the structure at any time, or of any person who may be affected by the work of such a person at work

    (ii) to **combat at source** risks to health and safety of any person at work carrying out construction work or cleaning work in or on the structure at any time, or of any person who may be affected by the work of such a person at work and

    (iii) to **give priority to measures which will protect all persons at work** who may carry out construction work or cleaning work at any time and all persons who may be affected by the work of such persons over measures which only protect each person carrying out such work

(b) ensure that the design includes **adequate information** about any aspect of the project or structure or materials (including articles or substances) which might affect the health or safety of any person at work carrying out construction work or cleaning work in or on the structure at any time or of any person who may be affected by the work of such a person at work and

(c) **co-operate** with the planning supervisor and with any other designer who is preparing any design in connection with the same project or structure so far as is necessary to enable each of them to comply with the requirements and prohibitions placed on him in relation to the project by or under the relevant statutory provisions.

3 Sub-paragraphs (a) and (b) of paragraph 2 shall require the design to include only the matters referred to therein to the extent that it is reasonable to expect the designer to address them at the time the design is prepared and to the extent that it is otherwise reasonably practicable to do so.

Regulation 14 – requirements on planning supervisor

The planning supervisor appointed for any project **shall**:

(a) ensure, so far as is reasonably practicable, that the **design** of any structure comprised in the project:

    (i) includes among the design considerations adequate regards to the needs specified in heads (i) to (iii) of regulations 13(2)(a) and

    (ii) includes information as specified in regulation 13(2)(b)

(b) take such steps as it is reasonable for a person in his position to take to ensure **co-operation between designers** so far as is necessary to enable each designer to comply with the requirements placed on him by regulation 13

(c) be in a position to give **adequate advice** to:

(i) any client and any contractor with a view to enabling each of them to comply with regulations 8(2) and 9(2) and to

(ii) any client with a view to enabling him to comply with regulations 8(3), 9(3) and 10

(d) ensure that a **health and safety file** is prepared in respect of each structure comprised in the project containing:

(i) information included with the design by virtue of regulation 13(2)(b)

(ii) any other information relating to the project which it is reasonably foreseeable will be necessary to ensure the health and safety of any person at work who is carrying out or will carry out construction work or cleaning work in or on the structure of or any persons who may be affected by the work of such a person at work

(e) **review, amend or add to** health and safety file prepared by virtue of sub-paragraph (d) of this regulation as necessary to ensure that it contains the information mentioned in that sub-paragraph when it is delivered to the client in accordance with sub-paragraph (f) of this regulation and

(f) ensure that, **on the completion of construction work** on each structure comprised in the project, the health and safety file in respect of that structure is delivered to the client.

Regulation 15 – requirements relating to the health and safety plan

1 The **planning supervisor** appointed for any project shall ensure that a **health and safety plan** in respect of the project has been prepared no later than the time specified in paragraph 2 and contains the information specified in paragraph 3.

2 The **information** required by paragraph 1 to be contained in the health and safety plan is:

(a) a **general description** of the construction work comprised in the project

(b) details of the **time** within which it is intended that the project, and any intermediate stages, will be completed

(c) details of the **risks to health and safety** of any person carrying out the construction work so far as such risks are known to the planning supervisor or are reasonably foreseeable

(d) any **other information** which the planning supervisor knows or could ascertain by making reasonable enquiries and which it would be necessary for any contractor to have if he wished to show:

(i) that he has the **competence** on which any person is required to be reasonably satisfied by regulation 8 or

(ii) that he has allocated or, as appropriate, will allocate, **adequate resources** on which any person is required to be reasonably satisfied by regulation 9

(e) such **information** as the planning supervisor knows or could ascertain by making reasonable enquiries and which it is reasonable for the planning supervisor to expect the **principal contractor** to need in order for him to comply with the requirement imposed on him by paragraph 4 and

(f) such **information** as the planning supervisor knows or could ascertain by making reasonable enquiries and which it would be reasonable for any **contractor** to know in order to understand how he can comply with any requirements placed upon him in respect of **welfare** by or under the relevant statutory provisions.

4   The principal contractor shall take such measures as it is reasonable for a person in his position to take to ensure that the **health and safety plan** contains until the end of the construction phase the following features:

(a) **arrangements for the project** (including where necessary, for management of construction work and monitoring of compliance with the relevant statutory provisions) which will ensure, so far as is reasonably practicable, the health and safety of all persons at work carrying out the construction work and of all persons who may be affected by the work of such persons at work, taking account of:

(i) **risks** involved in the construction work

(ii) any **activity specified in paragraph 5** and

(b) sufficient **information** about arrangements for the **welfare** of persons at work by virtue of the project to enable any contractor to understand how he can comply with any requirements placed upon him in respect of welfare by or under the relevant statutory provisions.

5   Any **activity** is an activity referred to in paragraph 4(a)(ii) if:

(a) it is an activity of **persons at work**

(b) it is carried out **in or on premises where construction work is or will be carried out** and

(c) either:

(i) the activity may affect the health or safety of persons at work carrying out the construction work or persons who may be affected by the work of such persons at work; or

(ii) the health or safety of the persons at work carrying out the activity may be affected by the work of persons at work carrying out the construction work.

Regulation 16 – requirements on and powers of principal contractor

1   The principal contractor appointed for any project shall:

(a) take reasonable steps to ensure **co-operation between all contractors** (whether they are sharing the construction site for the purpose of regulation 9 of the Management of Health and Safety at Work Regulations 1992 or otherwise) so far as is necessary to enable each of those contractors to comply with the requirements and prohibitions imposed on him by or under the relevant statutory provisions relating to construction work

(b) ensure, so far as is reasonably practicable, that every contractor, and every employee at work in connection with the project complies with any **rules contained in the health and safety plan**

(c) takes reasonable steps to ensure that only **authorised persons** are allowed into any premises or part of premises where construction work is being carried out

(d) ensure that any **particulars** required to be in any **notice** given under regulation 7 are **displayed** in readable condition in a position where they can be read by any person at work on construction work in connection with the project and

(e) promptly provide the planning supervisor with any **information** which:
  (i) is in the possession of the principal contractor or which he could ascertain by making reasonable enquiries of a contractor and
  (ii) it is reasonable to believe the planning supervisor would include in the health and safety file in order to comply with the requirements imposed upon him in respect thereof in regulation 14 and
  (iii) is not in the possession of the planning supervisor.

8

2 The principal contractor may:
  (a) give **reasonable directions** to any contractor so far as is necessary to enable the principal contractor to comply with his duties under these regulations
  (b) include in the health and safety plan **rules for the management of the construction work** which are reasonably required for the purposes of health and safety.

3 Any **rules** contained in the health and safety plan shall be in writing and shall be brought to the attention of persons who may be affected by them.

Regulation 17 – information and training

1 The **principal contractor** appointed for any project shall ensure, so far as is reasonably practicable, that every contractor is provided with **comprehensible information** on the risks to the health or safety of that contractor or of any employees or other persons under the control of that contractor arising out of or in connection with the construction work.

2 The **principal contractor** shall ensure, so far as is reasonably practicable, that **every contractor who is an employer** provides any of his employees at work carrying out the construction work with:
  (a) any **information** which the employer is required to provide to those employees in respect of that work by virtue of regulation 8 of the Management of Health and Safety at Work Regulations 1992 and
  (b) any **health and safety training** which the employer is required to

provide to those employees in respect of that work by virtue of regulation 11(2)(b) of the Management of Health and Safety at Work Regulations 1992.

Regulation 18 – advice from, and views of, persons at work

The **principal contractor** shall:

(a) ensure that employees and self-employed persons at work on the construction work are able to **discuss, and offer advice to him on,** matters connected with the project which it can reasonably be foreseen will affect their health or safety and

(b) ensure that there are **arrangements for the co-ordination of the views of employees** at work on construction work, or of their representatives, where necessary for reasons of health and safety having regard to the nature of the construction work and the size of the premises where the construction work is carried out.

Regulation 19 – requirements and prohibitions on contractors

1 Every contractor shall, in relation to the project:

(a) **co-operate** with the principal contractor so far as is necessary to enable each of them to comply with his duties under the relevant statutory provisions

(b) so far as is reasonably practicable, promptly provide the principal contractor with any **information** (including any relevant part of any **risk assessment** made by virtue of the Management of Health and Safety at Work Regulations 1992) which might affect the health or safety of any person at work carrying out the construction work or of any person who may be affected or which might justify a review of the health and safety plan

(c) comply with any **directions** of the principal contractor given to him under the regulation 16(2)

(d) comply with any **rules** applicable to him in the health and safety plan

(e) promptly provide the principal contractor with the **information in relation to any injury, death, condition or dangerous occurrence** which the contractor is required to notify under the Reporting of Injuries, Diseases and Dangerous Occurrences Regulations 1985 and

(f) promptly provide the principal contractor with any **information** which:

(i) is in the possession of the contractor or which he could ascertain by making reasonable enquiries of persons under his control and

(ii) it is reasonable to believe the principal contractor would provide to the planning supervisor in order to comply with the requirements imposed on the principal contractor in respect thereof by regulation 16(1)(e) and

(iii) which is not in the possession of the principal contractor.

2 No employer shall cause or permit any employee of his to work on construction work unless the employer has been provided with the information mentioned in paragraph 4.

3 No self-employed person shall work on construction work unless he has been provided with the information mentioned in paragraph 4.

4 The information referred to in paragraphs 2 and 3 is:
   (a) the name of the planning supervisor for the project
   (b) the name of the principal contractor for the project and
   (c) the contents of the health and safety plan or such part of it as is relevant to the construction work which any such employer or, as the case may be, which the self-employed person, is to carry out.

5 It shall be a **defence** in any proceedings for contravention of paragraph 2 or 3 for the employer of self-employed person to show that he made **all reasonable enquiries and reasonably believed**:
   (a) that he had been provided with the information mentioned in paragraph 4 or
   (b) that, by virtue of any provision in regulation 3, this regulation did not apply to the construction work.

8

Regulation 21 – exclusion of civil liability

Breach of a duty imposed by these regulations, other than those imposed by regulation 10 and regulation 16(1)(c), shall not confer a right of action in any civil proceedings.

Regulation 22 – enforcement

The enforcing authority for these regulations shall be the Health and Safety Executive.

Schedule 1: particulars to be notified to the HSE

1 Date of forwarding.

2 Exact address of the construction site.

3 Name and address of the client or clients (see Note).

4 Type of project.

5 Name and address of the planning supervisor.

6 A declaration signed by or on behalf of the planning supervisor that he has been appointed as such.

7 Name and address of the principal contractor.

8 A declaration signed by or on behalf of the principal contractor that he has been appointed as such.

9 Date planned for the start of the construction phase.

10 Planned duration of the construction phase.

11 Estimated maximum number of people at work on the construction site.

12 Planned number of contractors on the construction site.

13 Name and address of any contractor or contractors already chosen.

Note: Where a declaration has been made in accordance with regulation 4(4), item 3 above refers to the client or clients on the basis that the declaration has not yet taken effect.

Environmental pollution

Pollution of the environment has been a matter for public concern since the Industrial Revolution. As such, the term implies some form of contamination of the surrounding air, water and land which is prejudicial to the health of both workers and the general public. Numerous legal measures have been taken over the last century with a view to curbing these forms of pollution, including the various Public Health Acts, Clean Air Acts, Control of Pollution Act 1984 and, more recently, the Environmental Protection Act (EPA) 1990 (see later in this chapter).

Pollution of the environment is very broadly defined in the EPA as meaning pollution of the environment due to the release (into any environmental medium) from any process of substances which are capable of causing harm to many or any other living organisms supported by the environment. The **environment** consists of all, or any, of the following media, namely the air, water and land; and the medium of air includes the air within buildings and the air within other natural or man-made structures above or below ground.

Sources of environmental pollution

Many industries have, over the last century, been guilty of polluting the environment, such as the fuel and power industry (gasification and carbonisation plants), the mineral industry (cement, asbestos and ceramic manufacture), the chemical industry (petrochemical, pharmaceutical and pesticide manufacture), the metal industry (iron and steel manufacture) and other industries, such as paper manufacturing.

Pollution is associated with releases to air, water and land of substances prescribed under the EPA. These include:

- **Release to air** – oxides of sulphur and other sulphur compounds, oxides of nitrogen and other nitrogen compounds, oxides of carbon, organic compounds and partial oxidation products. These may take the form of aerosols, gases, particulates, dusts and mists.
- **Releases to water** – aldrin, dieldrin, mercury and its compounds, cadmium and its compounds, polychlorinated biphenyls, dichlorvos, all iso-

omers of DDT and fenitrothion. The accidental release of toxic wastes and sewage discharges to rivers, lakes or into the sea can cause deposition of poisonous sediments and the dispersal of toxins in currents.

● **Releases to land** – organic substances, organo-metallic compounds, oxidising agents, phosphorus, various pesticides and azides. Land may become contaminated as a result of crude tipping or dumping of industrial wastes, the actual burial of wastes and through leakages from plant installed on land. The contamination of the soil and groundwater follows, and various chemical reactions or microbial degradation may take place over a long period of time. In some cases, the products of these reactions will leech out through natural or man-made features of the land.

Potential hazards

Air pollution

Pollution caused by smoke, gases, fumes and dust from a variety of sources, such as chimneys, ventilation openings, the combustion of fuels, the incineration of wastes and as a result of certain processes, can affect the upper respiratory tract resulting in diseases such as bronchitis. Air pollution may also be a factor in the incidence of cancer of the lung, oesophagus and stomach.

Water pollution

Pollution of streams, ground water and other basic water sources, such as wells, implies that the polluting agents could eventually enter the public drinking water supply, unless appropriate purification measures are taken. Water distribution systems may also be a cause of contamination from the actual metal pipes, such as lead and copper pipes. Protection of the public water supply from chemical and bacterial contamination has always been one of the principal areas of public health practice. This entails the regular collection of water samples from a variety of sources and their analysis to detect the presence of these various forms of contamination.

Chemical pollution may be caused by free ammonia and ammonium salts in solution, which are indicators of decomposing organic matter, including faecal matter. Chlorine, present as sodium chloride in natural waters, is introduced by sewage. Nitrogen as nitrites suggests recent sewage pollution undergoing oxidation. Nitrogen as nitrates is an indicator of longstanding pollution from sewage. pH is also a measure of water purity, pure water being neutral with a pH of 7. Acidic waters of pH 5.5 or less may indicate the presence of lead.

The bacterial organisms most commonly used as indicators of faecal pollution are the coliform group as a whole, particularly **Escherichia coli**. High counts of E.coli suggest recent pollution. Other intestinal organisms occasionally present in water are **Clostridium perfringens**, which is regularly found in faeces, and faecal **Streptococci**.

Land pollution

Land may be polluted by a variety of industrial, commercial and domestic wastes. The contamination can arise as a result of poor standards of controlled tipping or by the indiscriminate, and often unauthorised dumping, of wastes. The by-products of these wastes can leech into underground water supplies and form pockets of gas, such as methane. Sewage pollution of land is common as a result of defective drains and sewers.

POLLUTION PREVENTION AND CONTROL STRATEGIES

These strategies are concerned with the prevention of waste discharges to air, water and land. Much will depend upon the scale and size of these discharges in terms of strategies to be applied.

The EPA brought in a new three-tier approach to pollution prevention and control. The Environmental Protection (Prescribed Processes and Substances) Regulations 1991 lists various processes and substances which are subject to control. The first tier, namely the worst pollutants to air, such as benzene, carbon monoxide and sulphur dioxide, are controlled by Her Majesty's Inspectorate of Pollution (HMIP), who have powers similar to those of the HSE. The second tier of pollutants, that is those likely to pollute water, such as trichlorobenzene and mercury, are controlled by the National Rivers Authority, established to monitor water purity under the Water Act 1989. Processes cover, for instance, the manufacture of cement, vehicle coating and those producing waste from oil burners. The third tier is dealt with by local authorities and includes deposits on land, statutory nuisances and certain aspects of air pollution.

Integrated pollution control

Part I of the EPA brought in the concept of integrated pollution control (IPC), a new system of pollution control intended to apply to the most potentially polluting or technologically complex industrial and other processes throughout England and Wales. The main objectives of IPC are:

- to prevent or minimise the release of prescribed substances and to render harmless any such substances which are released
- to develop an approach to pollution control that considers discharges from industrial processes to all media in the context of the effect on the environment as a whole.

It has the following additional aims:

- to improve the efficiency and effectiveness of HMIP
- to streamline and strengthen the regulatory system, clarifying the roles and responsibilities of HMIP, other regulatory authorities, and the firms they regulate

- to contain the burden on industry, in particular by providing a 'one stop shop' on pollution control for the potentially most seriously polluting industries

- to maintain public confidence in the regulatory system by producing a clear and transparent system that is accessible and easy to understand and clear and simple in operation

- to ensure that the system will respond flexibly, both to changing pollution abatement technology and to new knowledge on the effects of pollutants and

- to provide the means to fulfil international obligations relating to environmental protection.

The EPA (section 6) provides that no prescribed process may be operated without an authorisation from HMIP. HMIP is required either to grant an authorisation, subject to any conditions which the EPA requires or empowers it to impose, or to refuse it. HMIP must refuse the authorisation unless it considers that the applicant will be able to carry on the process in compliance with the conditions to be included in an authorisation.

In setting the conditions within an authorisation, section 7 of the EPA places HMIP under a duty to ensure that certain objectives are met. The conditions should ensure:

- that the **best available techniques not entailing excessive cost (BATNEEC)** are used to prevent or, if that is not practicable, to minimise the release of prescribed substances into the medium for which they are prescribed; and to render harmless both any prescribed substances which might cause harm if released into an environmental medium

- that releases do not cause, or contribute to, the breach of any direction given by the Secretary of State to implement European Community or international obligations relating to environmental protection, or any statutory environmental quality standards or objectives, or other statutory limits or requirements and

- that when a process is likely to involve releases into one medium (which is probably the case in many processes prescribed by IPC), the **best practicable environmental option (BPEO)** is achieved (ie the releases from the process are controlled through the use of BATNEEC so as to have the least effect on the environment as a whole).

The conditions in the authorisation must ensure that **all** these various objectives are met. If two separate objectives implied two different standards, for example, one implied a tighter limit on a particular release than another, the tighter standard would prevail. In practice this means that HMIP must, as a minimum, ensure that BATNEEC is achieved but may, in some circumstances, need to set more stringent conditions to achieve other section 7 objectives. An authorisation issued by HMIP will contain specific conditions to ensure that it fulfils the objectives contained in section 7 of the EPA. Conditions may relate to the method of operation, the training of staff, abatement techniques used to reduce the release of substances, etc. Releases are regulated by conditions in authorisations explicitly limiting the substances that can be released to the various environmental media, both in terms of their concentration in the releases and the amount of the substances released.

The EPA enables either HMIP or an operator to initiate variation of an authorisation. There are arrangements for consultations and public participation if a proposed alteration is substantial.

Registers of information

Registers of IPC information are available for inspection free of charge at HMIP regional headquarters and local authority offices.

Regulation 15 of the Environmental Protection (Applications, Appeals and Registers) Regulations 1991 provides more detail on the information that must be contained on the register, namely:

- all particulars of any application for an authorisation made to the Chief Inspector (HMIP)
- all particulars of any notice to an applicant and additional information furnished in response under paragraph 1(3) of Schedule 1 of the EPA
- all particulars of any representations made by statutory consultees, eg HSE, Minister of Agriculture, Fisheries and Food, National Rivers Authority
- all particulars of any authorisation granted by the authority
- all particulars of any variation, enforcement or prohibition notice issued by the Chief Inspector
- all particulars of any notice withdrawing a prohibition notice
- all particulars of any notification of the Chief Inspector by the holder of an authorisation in response to a requirement of a variation notice under section 10(4) of the EPA
- all particulars of any application for the variation of the conditions of an authorisation under section 11(4)(b) of the EPA
- all particulars of any revocation notice
- all particulars of any notice of appeal, the documents required for the appeal, any written notification by the Secretary of State relating to such an appeal and any report by a person appointed under section 15 accompanying any such written notification
- details of any conviction for any offence under section 23(1) of the EPA, including the name of the offender, the date of conviction, the penalty imposed and the name of the court
- all particulars of any monitoring information relating to a prescribed process obtained by the authority as a result of its own monitoring or furnished to the authority in writing by virtue of a condition of the authorisation under section 19 of the act

- a statement by the Chief Inspector, where monitoring information is omitted from the register on the grounds of commercial confidentiality, indicating whether or not there has been compliance with any relevant condition of the authorisation

- all particulars of any report published by the Chief Inspector relating to an assessment of the environmental consequences of the carrying on of a prescribed process in the locality of premises where the process is carried on and

- a copy of any direction given to the Chief Inspector by the Secretary of State under Part I of the EPA, other than a direction under section 21(2).

Information must be placed on the register as soon as possible. This is particularly important where the information is relevant to an application, etc on which the public are being given the opportunity to comment.

Further detailed information on IPC is provided in **Integrated Pollution Control: A Practical Guide**: Guidance issued by the Department of Environment and Welsh Office: Department of Environment, London.

ENVIRONMENTAL PROTECTION ACT (EPA) 1990

The EPA brought in fundamental changes to the control of pollution and the protection of the environment. It repealed in total the Alkali, &c Works Regulation Act 1906 and the Public Health (Recurring Nuisances) Act 1969, and certain sections of the well-established environmental protection legislation, such as the Public Health Acts 1936 and 1961, Control of Pollution Act 1954 and the Clean Air Act 1956. The Act covers eight specific aspects.

Part I – integrated pollution control and air pollution control by local authorities

A number of terms are of significance in the interpretation of this part of the EPA.

Environment consists of all, or any, of the following media, namely, the air, water and land; and the medium of air includes the air within buildings and the air within other natural or man-made structures above or below ground.

Pollution of the environment means pollution of the environment due to the release (into any environmental medium) from any process of substances which are capable of causing harm to man or any other living organisms supported by the environment.

Harm means harm to the health of living organisms or other interference with the ecological systems of which they form part and, in the case of man, includes offence caused to any of his senses or harm to his property; and **harmless** has a corresponding meaning.

Process means any activities carried on in Great Britain, whether on premises or by means of mobile plant, which are capable of causing pollution of the environment and **prescribed process** means a process prescribed under section 2(1).

Authorisation means an authorisation for a process (whether on premises or by means of mobile plant) granted under section 6; and a reference to the conditions of an authorisation is a reference to the conditions subject to which at any time the authorisation has effect.

A substance is **released** into any environmental medium whenever it is released directly into that medium whether it is released into it within or outside Great Britain and **release** includes:

- in relation to air, any emission of the substance into the air
- in relation to water, any entry (including any discharge) or the substance into water
- in relation to land, any deposit, keeping or disposal of the substance in or on land.

This part of the EPA identifies industrial processes which are scheduled for control either by Her Majesty's Inspectorate of Pollution (HMIP) or by local authorities (LAs). Industrial processes are split for the purposes of enforcement into a two-part schedule.

Category A processes are subject to **integrated pollution control** (IPC) by HMIP. IPC applies the principle of **best practicable environmental option** (BPEO) and Category A processes have controls applied to all waste streams. BPEO is not defined in the EPA but was considered at length by the Royal Commission on Environmental Protection, whose definition is as follows:

> 'A BPEO is the outcome of a systematic consultative and decision making procedure which emphasises the protection and conservation of the environment across land, air and water. The BPEO procedure establishes, for a given set of objectives, the option that proves the most benefit or least damage to the environment as a whole, at acceptable cost, in the long term as well as in the short term.'

IPC covers waste streams to air, water and land. The general approach is to minimise those waste streams to ensure that the BPEO for the process is applied. Authorisations and controls are applied to all emissions. (Section 7) Fundamentally, the approach hinges around a prior authorisation procedure. Authorisations for industrial processes can have stringent conditions applied and those conditions apply the concept of the use of **best available techniques not entailing excessive costs** (BATNEEC). The principal objective of BATNEEC is that of minimising pollution or predicted pollution to the environment as a whole from an industrial process, having regard to the BPEO. Section 7(2) specifies objectives to be considered in the conditions of authorisation as:

- ensuring that, in carrying out a prescribed process, the best available techniques not entailing excessive cost will be used:
  - for preventing the release of substances prescribed for any environmental medium into that medium or, where that is not practicable by such means, for reducing the release of such substances to a minimum and for rendering harmless any such substances which are so released and
  - for rendering harmless any other substances which might cause harm if released into any environmental medium
- compliance with any directions of the Secretary of State given for the implementation of any obligations in the United Kingdom under the Community treaties or international law relating to environmental protection
- compliance with any limits or requirements and achievements of any quality standards or quality objectives prescribed by the Secretary of State under any of the relevant enactments
- compliance with any requirements applicable to the grant of authorisations specified by or under a plan made by the Secretary of State.

Those processes identified as Category B industrial processes are subject to a similar prior authorisation procedure administered by the LA environmental health department for discharges to air only. Processes discharging substances to water are regulated by the National Rivers Authority's (NRA) discharge consent procedure and discharges to land are controlled by the Waste Regulation Authority (WRA) using controls detailed in Part II of the Act. Liaison between central and local government inspectorates is maintained through HMIP.

Under Part I of the EPA enforcing authorities must establish and maintain public information registers which contain details of the authorisations and conditions applied to processes.

Enforcement arrangements

Section 13 of the EPA states that where the enforcing authority is of the opinion that the person carrying on a prescribed process under an authorisation is contravening any condition of the authorisation, or is likely to contravene any such condition, the authority may serve on them an **enforcement notice**.

An enforcement notice shall:

- state that the authority is of the said opinion
- specify the matters constituting the contravention or the matters making it likely that the contravention will arise, as the case may be
- specify the steps that must be taken to remedy the contravention or to remedy the matters that make it likely that the contravention will arise, as the case may be and
- specify the period within which those steps must be taken.

Section 14 of the EPA makes provision for the service of **prohibition notices**.

If the enforcing authority is of the opinion, as respects the carrying on of a prescribed process under an authorisation, that the continuing to carry it on, or the continuing to carry it on in a particular manner, involves **an imminent risk of serious pollution of the environment** the authority shall serve a prohibition notice on the person carrying on the process.

A prohibition notice may be served whether or not the manner of carrying on the process in question contravenes a condition of the authorisation and may relate to any aspects of the process, whether regulated by the condition of the authorisation or not.

A prohibition notice shall:

- state the authority's opinion
- specify the risk involved in the process
- specify the steps that must be taken to remove it and the period in which they must be taken and
- direct that the authorisation shall, until the notice is withdrawn, wholly or to the extent specified in the notice cease to have effect to authorise the carrying on of the process

and where the direction applies to part only of the process it may impose conditions to be observed in carrying on the part which is authorised to be carried on.

Section 17 provides inspectors appointed under the EPA with considerable powers relating to premises on which a prescribed process is, or is believed to be, carried on, and to premises on which a prescribed process has been carried on, the condition of which is believed to be such as to give rise to a risk of serious pollution of the environment. Such powers include:

- power of entry at any reasonable time if there is reason to believe a prescribed process is such as to give rise to a risk of serious pollution
- to take a constable where obstruction on entry is anticipated, plus any equipment or materials
- to make such examinations and investigations as may be necessary
- to direct that a premises or any part of a premises remain undisturbed
- to take measurements and photographs and make such recordings as he considers necessary
- to take samples of articles and substances, and of air, water or land
- to cause any article or substance which has caused, or likely to cause, pollution to be dismantled or subjected to any process or test
- to take possession of and detain any above article or substance for the purpose of examination, to ensure it is not tampered with before examination and to ensure it is available for use as evidence
- to require any person to answer questions as the inspector thinks fit and to sign a declaration of truth of the answers

- to require the production of written or computerised records and to take copies of same
- to require any person to provide facilities and assistance to enable him to exercise his powers and
- any other power conferred upon him by regulations.

Part II – waste on land

The EPA imposes a duty of care on anyone who imports, carries, keeps, treats or disposes of waste. Such persons must take all reasonable steps to ensure that the waste is collected, transported, treated and disposed of by licensed operators, ie those issued with a **waste management licence**.

Public registers must be maintained by the authorities which detail licence conditions and details of enforcement actions. This part should be read in conjunction with the system for IPC that is enforced by HMIP on prescribed Category A process industries.

Part III – statutory nuisances and clean air

Section 79 deals with statutory nuisances and inspections. The following matters constitute **statutory nuisances**:

- any **premises** in such a state as to be prejudicial to health or a nuisance
- **smoke** emitted from premises so as to be prejudicial to health or a nuisance
- **fumes or gases** emitted from premises so as to be prejudicial to health or a nuisance
- any **dust, steam, smell or other effluvia** arising on industrial, trade or business premises and being prejudicial to health or a nuisance
- any **accumulation or deposit** which is prejudicial to health or a nuisance
- any **animal** kept in such a place or manner as to be prejudicial to health or a nuisance
- **noise** emitted from premises so as to be prejudicial to health or a nuisance and
- **any other matter** declared by any enactment to be a statutory nuisance.

It shall be the duty of every LA to cause its area to be inspected from time to time to detect any statutory nuisances which ought to be dealt with under section 80 (summary proceedings for statutory nuisances) and, where a complaint of a statutory nuisance is made to it by a person living within its area, to take such steps as a reasonably practicable to investigate the complaint.

Section 80 outlines the summary proceedings for statutory nuisances. Where an LA is satisfied that a statutory nuisance exists or is likely to occur or recur, in the area of the authority, the LA shall serve an **abatement notice** imposing all or any of the following requirements:

- requiring the abatement of the nuisance or prohibiting or restricting its occurrence or recurrence
- requiring the execution of such works, and the taking of such other steps, as may be necessary for any of those purposes.

and the notice shall specify the time or times within which the requirements of the notice are to be complied with.

The abatement notice shall be served:

- except in the case of the two points below, on the person responsible for the nuisance
- where the nuisance arises from any defect of a structural character, on the owner of the premises
- where the person responsible for the nuisance cannot be found or the nuisance has not yet occurred, on the owner or occupier of the premises.

A person served with an abatement notice may appeal to a magistrates' court within 21 days beginning with the date on which he was served with the notice. If a person on whom an abatement notice is served, without reasonable cause, contravenes or fails to comply with any requirement or prohibition imposed by the notice, they shall be guilty of an offence.

Failure to comply with an abatement notice can result in the defendant being subjected to a fine not exceeding level 5 on the standard scale together with a further fine of an amount equal to one-tenth of that level for each day the offence continues after conviction. A person who commits an offence on industrial, trade or business premises, however, shall be liable to a fine not exceeding £20,000. It is a defence to prove that **best practicable means** were used to prevent, or to counteract the effects of, the nuisance.

Section 81 gives the LA power, where an abatement notice has not been complied with, and whether or not it has already taken proceedings, to abate the nuisance and do whatever may be necessary in execution of that notice. Any expenses reasonably incurred may be recovered by them from the person by whose act or default the nuisance was caused or apportioned among several persons accordingly. This section also gives power to an LA, where proceedings for an offence would afford an inadequate remedy in the case of any statutory nuisance, to take proceedings in the High Court for the purpose of securing the abatement, prohibition or restriction of the nuisance, and the proceedings shall be maintainable notwithstanding the LA have suffered no damage from the nuisance.

A person who is aggrieved by the existence of a statutory nuisance need not necessarily pursue the matter through the LA. Under section 82 a magistrates' court may act on a complaint made by any person on the ground that they are aggrieved by the existence of a statutory nuisance. If the court is satisfied that the alleged nuisance exists, or that although abated it is likely to recur on the same premises, the court shall make an order for either or both of the following purposes:

- requiring the defendant to abate the nuisance (**abatement order**), within a time specified in the order, and to execute any works necessary for that purpose
- prohibiting a recurrence of the nuisance, (**prohibition order**) and requiring the defendant, within a time specified in the order, to execute any works necessary to prevent the recurrence

and may also impose on the defendant a fine not exceeding level 5 on the standard scale.

If the court is satisfied that the alleged nuisance exists and is such as, in the opinion of the court, to render premises unfit for human habitation, an order (as above) may prohibit the use of the premises for human habitation until the premises are, to the satisfaction of the court, rendered fit for that purpose.

Part IV – litter, etc

The EPA brought in new procedures with regard to the control of litter. Section 87 created the offence of 'leaving litter' and section 88 brought in fixed penalty notices for leaving litter. Section 99 also gives LAs the power to deal with abandoned shopping and luggage trolleys.

Part V – amendment to the Radioactive Substances Act 1960

Part V of the EPA makes a number of amendments to the Radioactive Substances Act 1960, (RSA) the principal amendments being:

- provision for the appointment of inspectors
- provision for a scheme of fees and charges payable for registration and authorisation under the RSA
- new powers of enforcement, ie **enforcement notices**
- withdrawal of the exemption in favour of the UK Atomic Energy Authority from certain requirements of the RSA and
- application of the RSA to the Crown.

Part VI – genetically modified organisms (GMOs)

This part has effect for the purpose of preventing or minimising any damage to the environment which may arise from the escape or release from human control of GMOs. The following definitions are important.

Organism means any acellular, unicellular or multicellular entity (in any form), other than humans or human embryos; and unless the context otherwise requires, the term also includes any article or substance consisting of biological matter. **Biological matter** means anything (other than an entity mentioned above) which consists of or includes:

- tissue or cells (including gametes or propagules) or subcellular entities, of any kind, capable of replication or of transferring genetic material or
- genes or other genetic material, in any form, which are so capable

and it is immaterial, in determining if something is or is not an organism or biological matter, whether it is the product of natural or artificial processes of reproduction and, in the case of biological matter, whether it has ever been part of a whole organism.

An organism is **genetically modified** if any of the genes or other genetic material in the organism:

- have been modified by means of an artificial technique prescribed in regulations by the Secretary of State or
- are inherited or otherwise derived, through any number of replications, from genes or other genetic material (from any source) which were so modified.

The **techniques** which may be prescribed for the above purposes include:

- any technique for the modification of any genes or other genetic material by the recombination, insertion or deletion of, or of any competent parts of, that material from its previously occurring state and
- any other technique for modifying genes or other genetic material which in the opinion of the Secretary of State would produce organisms which should for the purposes of this part be treated as having been genetically modified

but do not include techniques which involve no more than, or no more than the assistance of, naturally occurring processes of reproduction (including selective breeding techniques or in vitro fertilisation).

Section 108 of the EPA requires that no person shall import or acquire, release or market any GMOs unless, before that act:

- they carry out an assessment of the risks of damage to the environment being caused as a result of that act and
- in prescribed cases and circumstances, have given notice of intention and prescribed information to the Secretary of State.

General duties relating to the importation, acquisition, keeping, release or marketing of GMOs are detailed in section 109. Section 110 empowers the Secretary of State to serve a **prohibition notice** on any person he has reason to believe:

- is proposing to import or acquire, release or market GMOs or
- is keeping any such organisms

if they are of the opinion that doing any such act to those organisms or continuing to keep them would involve a risk of causing damage to the environment.

A system of **consents**, however, is operated through the Secretary of State whereby a person importing or acquiring, releasing or marketing GMOs may be subject to certain limitations and conditions. (Sections 111 and 112)

Similar provisions relating to enforcement, offences and the powers of a court to make orders apply as with other parts of the EPA.

Part VIII – nature conservation

This part established Nature Conservancy Councils for England, Scotland and Wales and established their functions, both generally and specifically.

Part VIII – miscellaneous

Part VIII contains a number of miscellaneous provisions. The most significant are:

- power to restrict the importation, use, supply or storage of substances or articles for the purpose of avoiding pollution, or harm to man, animals or plants
- power to restrict the importation or exportation of waste for the purpose of preventing pollution or harm to human health or for conserving facilities or resources for dealing with waste
- power to make provision for the obtaining of information about substances with potential to cause pollution or harm to human health
- provision of public registers of potentially contaminated land
- amendments of the legislation of control of hazardous substances
- increase in the maximum penalties in respect of water pollution offences
- amendments on legislation to marine deposits and the creation of public registers as to such deposits and marine incineration
- amendments of the provisions as to oil pollution offences from ships
- provisions for the control of stray dogs and
- provision as to the banning of straw, stubble and other crop residues.

ENVIRONMENT ACT 1995

Main provisions

One of the main provisions was the creation of the **Environment Agency for England and Wales**. From 1st April 1996 this brought together HM Inspectorate of Pollution, the National Rivers Authority and local waste regulation authorities. Similar arrangements were made for Scotland with the creation of the **Scottish Environment Protection Agency**. From 1st April 1996 this

brought together HM Inspectorate of Pollution, the river purification authorities and waste regulation and local air pollution control, formerly the responsibility of district and islands councils.

The Act contains detailed provisions for dealing with a range of environmental problems and issues.

Air quality

- Early legislation to establish a national strategy and framework of ambient air quality standards and targets for nine main pollutants.

- New powers for local authorities to review air quality in their districts and
  create **air quality management areas** where levels fall short of targets.

The Act provides the statutory framework for the new system. Much of the
detailed local arrangements would be made under the secondary legislation
and guidance.

Contaminated land

The 'polluter pays' principle was reinforced, but there was also recognition
that land-owners should be responsible for some aspects of the land, if the
original polluters cannot be found. No new classes of liability were created.

The measures are based on the **suitable for use** approach, the removal of
real environmental hazards without the imposition of unnecessary costs.
This approach requires remedial action only where there is **significant harm**
or pollution of controlled waters and where there are appropriate and cost
effective means available to take such action, taking into account the actual
or intended use of the site.

Pollution from abandoned mines

Statutory protection will be removed from the owners and operators of all
mines abandoned after the end of 1999. This will allow the national agencies
to deal with discharges through **consents**, as with other pollution discharges.
Failure to comply with these consents will lead to prosecution.

Mine operators will be required to give the agencies six months' notice of
their intention to abandon a mine, thus allowing steps to be taken to prevent
future mine water pollution.

National Parks Authorities (NPAs) in England and Wales

Local authority members will be drawn from parish, rather than county,
councils, and will be appointed by the Secretary of State. NPAs will be
required to foster the economic and social well-being of their local commu-
nities as well as protecting the natural beauty of the areas in their steward-
ship. Government and other public bodies must consider National Park
purposes in carrying out their functions.

Waste strategy

National waste strategies would be drawn up by the new agencies for England and Wales and for Scotland and national waste surveys would be carried out to inform these strategies. **Sustainable development** will be the cornerstone of the strategy, that is, making the best possible use of unavoidable waste and minimising the risk of pollution or harm to human health arising from waste disposal or recovery.

Producer responsibility

Regulations would be introduced to impose **producer responsibility** to increase the reuse, recovery or recycling of any product or material. The powers would be applicable to any waste stream. It is through regulations on packaging under these powers that the Government intends to fulfil its obligations to implement the recovery targets in the EC Directive on Packaging and Packaging Waste.

Minerals planning permissions

There would be an initial review and updating of old mineral permissions phased over six years. Future reviews of mineral permissions will be held every 15 years.

Water conservation

Water companies would be required to promote the efficient use of water by their customers. The Director General of Water Services will monitor this work and publish conservation performance league tables.

Water quality

The Environment Agency would have powers to require action to prevent water pollution and require polluters to clean up after pollution incidents.

Combined heat and power (CHP)

The Act amends the Electricity Act 1989 to enable CHP to compete effectively for support under the fossil fuel levy with other forms of non-fossil electricity generating schemes.

Nuisance provisions

The framework for the control of statutory nuisance contained in Part III of the Environmental Protection Act 1990 would be extended to Scotland.

NOTIFICATION OF COOLING TOWERS AND EVAPORATIVE CONDENSERS REGULATIONS 1992

These regulations require the notification to local authorities of wet cooling towers and evaporative condensers, which are components of many air-conditioning systems found in large buildings, and of industrial cooling towers.

Knowledge of the whereabouts of such equipment will be of particular help to local authorities in the investigation of outbreaks of legionnaires' disease.

Notification is by means of completion of a standard form available from the local authority. Any changes to the information contained in the form must be notified within one month. The local authority must also be informed, as soon as reasonably practicable, when equipment ceases to be operational.

The regulations came into operation on 2nd November 1992

Information required

The information required on a notification form includes:

- the name and address of the premises where the cooling towers and evaporative condensers are situated
- the number of such devices on site
- the name, address and telephone number of the person in control of the premises and
- brief information on the whereabouts in the premises of the equipment.

Bibliography and further reading

Chapter 1

British Standards Institution (1987): **BS 4478: Quality Vocabulary**; BSI, London

British Standards Institution (1987): **BS 5750: Quality Systems**; BSI, London

British Standards Institution (1974): **BS 3811: Planned Maintenance Programmes**; BSI, London

Ministry of Labour (1965): **Report of the investigation of the crane accident at Brent Cross on 20th June 1964 (Minister of Labour Cmnd 2768: 1965)**; HMSO, London

Stranks, J (1994): **Handbook of Health and Safety Practice**; Pitman Publishing

Chapter 2

British Standards Institution (1984): **BS 5304: Code of Practice: Safeguarding of Machinery**; BSI, London

Health and Safety Executive (1992): **Work Equipment: Guidance on the Provision and Use of Work Equipment Regulations 1992**; HMSO, London

Health and Safety Executive (1981): **Occasional Paper: Microprocessors in Industry: Implications in the Use of Programmable Electronic Systems**; HMSO, London

Department of Employment (1992): **Provision and Use of Work Equipment Regulations 1992**; HMSO, London

Department of Employment (1992): **Supply of Machinery (Safety) Regulations 1992**; HMSO, London

Stranks, J (1994): **Handbook of Health and Safety Practice**; Pitman Publishing

Chapter 3

Department of Employment (1994): **Control of Substances Hazardous to Health Regulations 1994**; HMSO, London

Health and Safety Commission (1994): **Approved Codes of Practice: Control of Substances Hazardous to Health, Control of Carcinogenic Substances and Control of Biological Agents**; HSE Books, Sudbury

Department of Employment (1994): **The Chemicals (Hazard Information and Packaging for Supply) Regulations 1994**; HMSO, London

Health and Safety Commission (1994): **Approved Guide to the Classification and Labelling of Substances and Preparations Dangerous for Supply: Chemicals (Hazard Information and Packaging for Supply) Regulations 1994: Guidance on Regulations**; HSE Books, Sudbury

Health and Safety Commission (1994): **Safety Data Sheets for Substances and Preparations Dangerous for Supply: Guidance on Regulation 6 of the Chemicals (Hazard Information and Packaging for Supply) Regulations 1994: Approved Code of Practice**; HSE Books

Department of Employment (1984): **Control of Industrial Major Accident Hazards Regulations 1984**; HMSO, London

Health and Safety Executive (1991): **A Guide to the Control of Industrial Major**

Accident Hazards Regulations 1984: Guidance on Regulations, HS(R)21; HSE Books, Sudbury

Department of Employment (1984): **Reporting of Injuries, Diseases and Dangerous Occurrences Regulations 1985**; HMSO, London

Department of Employment (1972): **Highly Flammable Liquids and Liquefied Petroleum Gases Regulations 1972**; HMSO, London

Stranks J (1994): **Handbook of Health and Safety Practice**; Pitman Publishing

Stranks J (1994): **Health and Safety in Practice: Health and Safety Law**; Pitman Publishing

Stranks J (1994): **Health and Safety in Practice: Occupational Health and Hygiene**; Pitman Publishing

Chapter 4

Health and Safety Executive (1987): **Lighting at Work HS(G)38**; HSE Books, Sudbury

Lyons S (1984): **Management Guide to Modern Industrial Lighting**; Butterworths, Sevenoaks

Health and Safety Executive (1992): **Workplace Health, Safety and Welfare: Approved Code of Practice: Workplace (Health, Safety and Welfare) Regulations 1992**; HSE Books, Sudbury

Health and Safety Executive (1992): **Manual Handling: Guidance on the Manual Handling Operations Regulations 1992**; HSE Books, Sudbury

Health and Safety Executive (1993): **Getting to Grips with Manual Handling**; HSE Enquiry Points, London and Sheffield

Health and Safety Executive (1982): **Transport Kills**; HSE Books, Sudbury

Health and Safety Executive (1978): **Road Transport in Factories**; HSE Books, Sudbury

Health and Safety Executive (1988): **Rider-Operated Lift Trucks – Operator Training: Approved Code of Practice and Supplementary Guidance**; HMSO, London

Health and Safety Executive (1992): **A Guide to the Lifting Plant and Equipment (Records of Test and Examination etc) Regulations 1992**; HSE Books, Sudbury

Health and Safety Executive (1989): **Approved Substance Identification Numbers, Emergency Action Codes and Classifications for Dangerous Substances Conveyed in Road Tankers and Tank Containers: The Approved List**; HSE Books, Sudbury

Health and Safety Executive (1990): **Classification and Labelling of Dangerous Substances for Conveyance by Road in Road Tankers, Tank Containers and Packages: Dangerous Substances (Conveyance by Road in Road Tankers and Tank Containers) Regulations 1981**; Approved Code of Practice; HMSO, London

Chapter 5

Health and Safety Executive (1980): **Electrical Testing: Safety in Electrical Testing HS(G)13**; HSE Books, Sudbury

Department of Employment (1989): **The Electricity at Work Regulations 1989**; HMSO, London

Health and Safety Executive (1989): **Memorandum of Guidance on the Electricity at Work Regulations 1989**; Guidance on Regulations; HMSO, London

Institution of Electrical Engineers (1989): **IEE Regulations for Electrical Installations (The Wiring Regulations)**; IEE, Hitchin, Herts

Chapter 6

Department of Employment (1989): **The Pressure Systems and Transportable Gas Containers Regulations 1989**; HMSO, London

Health and Safety Commission (1990): **Safety of Pressure Systems: Pressure Systems and Transportable Gas Containers Regulations 1989: Approved Code of Practice**; HMSO, London

Health and Safety Executive (1990): **Safety of Transportable Gas Containers: Pressure Systems and Transportable Gas Containers Regulations 1989: Approved Code of Practice**; HMSO, London

Ministry of Power (1958): **The Efficient Use of Fuel**; HMSO, London

National Vulcan Engineering Insurance Group Limited (1990): **Documentation for Written Scheme of Examination under the Pressure Systems and Transportable Gas Containers Regulations 1989**; National Vulcan Engineering Insurance Group Limited, Manchester

Stranks J (1994): **Handbook of Health and Safety Practice**; Pitman Publishing

Chapter 7

Health and Safety Executive (1992): **Assessment of Fire Hazards from Solid Materials and the Precautions Required for their Safe Storage and Use HS(G)64**; HMSO, London

Home Office (1977): **Guide to the Fire Precautions Act 1971**; HMSO, London

Home Office: **Manual of Firemanship**; HMSO, London

Stranks J (1994): **Handbook of Health and Safety Practice**; Pitman Publishing

Chapter 8

Dickie DE (1981a): **Crane Handbook**; Butterworths, London

Dickie DE (1981b): **Lifting Tackle Manual**; Butterworths, London

Health and Safety Executive (1988): **Blackspot Construction: A Study of Five Years' Fatal Accidents in the Building and Civil Engineering Industries**; HSE Books, Sudbury

Royal Society for the Prevention of Accidents (1982): **Construction Regulations Handbook**; RoSPA, Birmingham

Royal Society for the Prevention of Accidents (n.d.): **The Supervisor's Guide to the Construction Regulations**; RoSPA, Birmingham

Department of Employment (1994): **The Construction (Design and Management) Regulations 1994**; HMSO, London

Health and Safety Commission (1994): **Managing Construction for Health and Safety: Construction (Design and Management) Regulations 1994: Approved Code of Practice**; HMSO, London

Health and Safety Commission (1994): **Designing for Health and Safety in Construction: A Guide for Designers on the Construction (Design and Management) Regulations 1994**; HSE Books, Sudbury

Health and Safety Commission (1994): **A Guide to Managing Health and Safety in Construction**; HSE Books, Sudbury

Health and Safety Executive (1995): **Health and Safety in Small Construction Sites**; HSE Books, Sudbury

Chapter 9

Her Majesty's Inspectorate of Pollution (1988): **Best Practicable Means: General Principles and Practice**; HMIP, London

Health and Safety Executive (1991): **Protecting the Environment and Health and Safety**; HSE Enquiry Points, London and Sheffield

Department of Environment (1991): **Environmental Protection (Prescribed Processes and Substances) Regulations 1991**; HMSO, London

Department of Environment (1991): **Environmental Protection (Applications, Appeals and Registers) Regulations 1991**; HMSO, London

Department of Environment (1991): **Integrated Pollution Control: A Practical Guide**; Department of Environment, London

Department of Environment (1992): **Notification of Cooling Towers and Evaporative Condensers Regulations 1992**; HMSO, London

Index